Food Poisoning and Food Hygiene

Food Poisoning and Food Hygiene

Betty C. Hobbs

O.St.J., D.Sc., Ph.D., F.R.C.Path., Dip.Bact., F.R.S.H.
Formerly Director, Food Hygiene Laboratory, Central Public
Health Laboratory, London

and

Richard J. Gilbert

M.Pharm., Ph.D., M.P.S., M.R.C.Path., Dip.Bact.
Director, Food Hygiene Laboratory, Central Public Health
Laboratory, London

Fourth Edition

Edward Arnold

© Betty C. Hobbs and Richard J. Gilbert 1978

First published 1953
by Edward Arnold (Publishers) Ltd.
41 Bedford Square, London WC1B 3DQ

Second Edition 1968
Reprinted 1970
Third Edition 1974
Reprinted 1975
Fourth Edition 1978

British Library Cataloguing in Publication Data

Hobbs, Betty Constance
  Food poisoning and food hygiene. — 4th ed
  1. Food handling   2. Food poisoning
  I. Title
  614.3′1   RA601

ISBN 0-7131-4313-4

Printed in Great Britain by
T. & A. Constable Limited
Edinburgh

Preface to fourth edition

The aim of this book, as outlined in the first edition, is to bring essential facts about food poisoning and its prevention to everyone engaged in the processing of food, whether they are working in kitchens, shops, factories, or even farms. The text is composed for those who teach the principles which govern the prevention of food poisoning including medical, veterinary, and environmental health officers, supervisory staff responsible for the preparation and service of food in school, hospital, university, and industrial canteens, managerial personnel in food stores, and teachers in schools and technical colleges for catering and domestic science. It is with these disciplines in mind and to all those whose help is needed in tracing the source of infection through to the victim that this book was written and dedicated.

The facts are derived from the practical experience and knowledge gained by many workers interested in public health and hygiene during the past. Efforts to initiate preventive methods against food poisoning and food spoilage have influenced the method of presentation. The text of the fourth edition has been expanded to include more examples of outbreaks, recent statistics and notes on epidemiology and spoilage. The chapters on Kitchen Design and Equipment, Legislation and Control of Infestation have been largely rewritten; chapters 11, 12, and 13 have evolved from the original chapter 11. A short Bibliography for further reading has been included.

Revision of the Preface led to consideration of the current situation; the remarks have been transferred to the Introduction. Thus Chapter 1 includes both 'Historical perspective' and the 'Current situation'.

1978

B. C. H.
R. J. G.

Acknowledgements

The facts assembled in this book come from the experience of many workers in the field of food poisoning and food hygiene. We acknowledge them with gratitude and give thanks to our present helpers and critics.

Although much of Mr L. Kluth's contributions have been brought up-to-date by other writers, the basis of Chapters 16, 17, and 18, designed by him originally, remains the same; we remember him with gratitude and affection. We thank Mr R. J. Govett, Environmental Health and Technical Services Officer, London Borough of Brent for his earlier work on Chapter 16, and for further revisions of Chapters 17 and 18. Mr John B. Simpson, Senior Environmental Health Officer, City of Canterbury, and Mr David Ward, Principal Architect, North Yorkshire County Council made detailed revisions of Chapter 16, and the present text is largely contributed by them; we acknowledge their work with gratitude. We thank the Pest Infestation Control Laboratory, Ministry of Agriculture, Fisheries and Food, and also Mr P. L. G. Bateman, Rentokil Ltd., East Grinstead, for extensive revisions to Chapter 17. Dr Henrietta E. Schefferle revised, updated, and typed Chapter 18. Her thoroughness and care will be much appreciated by readers; we thank her for the hours spent so willingly on the task. Mrs Isobel M. Maurer and Dr J. C. Kelsey checked Chapter 15, and Mrs Maurer read the whole of the third edition for revisions; in addition Dr Kelsey contributed the section on 'Canvas and hutted camps' in Appendix B — we are grateful for their help. Mr W. Clifford's illustrations remain together with his photographs and those of Mr J. Gibson, and we thank them for this valuable material which adds interest to the book. The lecture notes in Appendix A were designed by Miss Catharine F. Scott, School Meals Organizer (retired) of the County of North Yorkshire, and the late Miss Irene J. Martin, who was Domestic Science Organizer in the County of North Yorkshire; their contribution has proved to be invaluable. The notes in their original form appeared in *Hygienic Food Handling* published by the St John

Ambulance Association. Short courses on Food Hygiene are given to those working in the School Meals Service and also to various groups of food handlers by the St John Ambulance Association together with the Association of Environmental Health Officers. We are grateful also for Miss Scott's help with information about the School Meals Service for Chapter 19.

Sir Graham Wilson, the late Professor R. Cruickshank, and the late Lt-Col. H. J. Bensted are remembered for their inspiration and help with the groundwork of the book. The immense practical work of Miss Nancy Cockman in the compilation and typing of the previous editions will always be acknowledged and our work together remembered with gratitude and thankfulness.

The following firms have submitted new photographs: Hobart Manufacturing Co. Ltd.; Clenaglass Electric Washer Ltd., Farnborough; Qantas of Sydney; Imperial Machine Co., Rickmansworth, Herts.; Crypto Peerless Ltd., Hendon Precision Engineering Co. Ltd.; J. Sainsbury Ltd; Marks & Spencer Ltd.

We are grateful to those who contributed to earlier editions.

Bowater-Scott Corporation Ltd., London; British Railways Board; Combined Laundry Group, London; Dawson Bros. Ltd., Woodford Green, Essex; Euk Catering Machinery Ltd., Oldham; Express Dairy Co. Ltd., London; The Gas Council; Hoover Ltd., Greenford, Middlesex; Mr A. C. Horne, Chief Health Inspector, Hemel Hempstead; Jeyes' Sanitary Compounds Co. Ltd., Chigwell, Essex; King Edward's Hospital Fund for London; Mac-Fisheries Ltd., London; Marks & Spencer Ltd.; Moorwood-Vulcan Ltd., Sheffield; Moreton Engineering Co. Ltd., Moreton-in-Wirral, Cheshire; The Chief Constable, York and North East Yorkshire Police; Pressarts Ltd., Leicester; Quiz Electrics Ltd., Teddington, Middlesex; J. Sainsbury Ltd., London; Staines Kitchen Equipment Co. Ltd., London; James Stott & Co. (Engineers) Ltd., Oldham; Mrs E. Vernon, Central Public Health Laboratory, Colindale, London; Waitrose, Food Group of the John Lewis Partnership; T. Wall & Sons (Ice Cream) Ltd., London.

We are grateful for the food poisoning statistics supplied by Mrs Enid Hepner, Communicable Disease Surveillance Centre, Colindale, London. We also thank our colleagues in the Food Hygiene Laboratory, Dr Diane Roberts for many helpful ideas and comments also Mrs Jean Burt and Mrs Phyllis Rose for help with checking the draft of this edition and for typing the full script of two chapters.

Miss Nancy Cockman has again been a tower of strength — typing, checking and proof-reading with much care and patience. Last but not least we would like to express our gratitude for the stimulation and help of our publisher, Edward Arnold (Publishers) Ltd., and in particular Mr P. J. Price and Miss Barbara Koster.

Contents

Part 1
Food poisoning and food-borne infection

Fig. 1 Ancient kitchen

1

Introduction

Historical perspective

Food hygiene is a subject of wide scope. It aims to study methods for the production, preparation, and presentation of food which is safe and of good keeping quality. It covers not only the proper handling of every variety of foodstuff and drink, and all the utensils and apparatus used in their preparation, service, and consumption, but also the care and treatment of foods known to be contaminated with food-poisoning bacteria which have originated from the animal host supplying the food.

Food should be nourishing and attractive. It must be visibly clean and it must also be free from noxious materials. These harmful substances may be poisonous chemicals and even chemicals harmless in small amounts but damaging in large quantities. They may enter the food accidentally during growth, cultivation, or preparation, accumulate in the food during storage in metal containers, form in the food through interaction of chemical components, or they may be concentrated from the natural components of the food. Micro-organisms or germs may be introduced directly from infected food animals, or, from workers, other foods, or the environment during the preparation of foods. Poisonous substances may be produced by the growth of bacteria and moulds in food.

This book has been written for those engaged in food handling, with the purpose of explaining simply, in so far as our knowledge permits, the nature of these various dangers, how they arise, and how some of them can be prevented.

Noxious substances in food give rise to illness called food poisoning or gastroenteritis, which is usually characterized by vomiting and/or diarrhoea, and various abdominal disturbances. Food poisoning is no new disease, it has been recognized throughout the ages. Centuries ago the laws of the Israelites contained detailed information on foods to be eaten and foods to be abhorred, as well as

3

on their methods of preparation and the cleanliness of the hands of the consumers. About 2000 BC, as recorded in the Book of Leviticus, Moses not only made many laws which protected his people against the ravages of infectious disease but also laid down rules about the washing of hands after killing animals for sacrifices and before eating. Many of these rules were based on a practical knowledge of personal hygiene and the necessity for cleanliness of those suffering from certain diseases.

Laws were given about edible animal life and concerned animals, birds, and whatever swims in the water or crawls upon the earth. Prohibited animals included swine, now known to be frequent excreters of salmonella organisms, as well as reservoirs of parasites such as *Trichinella spiralis* and *Taenia solium*, and small creatures which scurry or crawl such as mice, rats, and lizards, also well known to harbour salmonellae. Other crawling things and those that slither such as snails and snakes were forbidden. Of the water creatures only those with fins and scales could be eaten, which eliminated sea mammals, shell-fish and crustaceans. Among the prohibited birds there is a long list of those which are scavengers on land or at sea — they include the vulture and eagle, and the heron and seagull. Flying insects with four legs were forbidden but those that jump such as locusts, crickets, and grasshoppers could be eaten. The dead bodies of such creatures could defile those that touched them.

The accounts of food poisoning recorded in ancient history have generally been associated with chemical poisons — more especially with those deliberately introduced — but this is undoubtedly due to the fact that our knowledge of non-chemical, that is bacterial food poisoning, dates back no further than the latter part of the nineteenth century. Indeed the term ptomaine, i.e. alkaloid, poisoning was often used and may still be seen in the popular press to describe an outbreak of food poisoning which we know to have been caused by pathogenic or disease-producing micro-organisms or germs. The ptomaines are basic chemical substances formed by the breakdown or digestion of putrefying tissues; they were previously thought to be poisons formed in tainted foods, as food poisoning was assumed to be associated with taint. Now we know that foods heavily contaminated with food-poisoning germs may be normal in appearance, odour, and taste.

There are some naturally occurring substances in plant life, such as deadly nightshade and toadstools, which can cause illness if consumed; also, food may become contaminated during its preparation, with arsenic, zinc, copper, tin or other heavy metals, or with pesticides or disinfectants, with disastrous results. The amount of food poisoning due to these natural or chemical poisons is, however, small and it is not intended to enlarge on this subject. Nearly all our food poisoning is caused by the contamination of food by germs, the majority of which can grow actively in the food.

The study of micro-organisms including those known to cause disease is called microbiology. This term covers all aspects of the following subjects: (a) bacteriology, from the Greek word 'bactron', a rod — from the appearance of the first germs, tiny straight rods, seen through a microscope; (b) virology — viruses are among the smallest known micro-organisms; (c) mycology — the study of fungi and moulds; and (d) parasitology — organisms of different orders which parasitize man and animals. Bacteria, germs, microbes, micro-organisms, or simply organisms as they are variously called — and all these names will be used interchangeably in this book — were first seen and described in 1675 by a man who was not a professional scientist. van Leeuwenhoek was a linen draper in the town of Delft in Holland but he was also an enthusiastic maker of lenses and magnifying apparatus. It was his hobby to examine objects of nature through the lenses which he mounted together to form a primitive microscope. One day, looking through his microscope at a drop of pond water, he saw not only a number of tiny animalcules but also tiny rods, many of which moved about actively within the microscope field. He described their size as one thousand times smaller than the eye of a louse. Next he took scrapings from his own teeth and, placing them under the microscope, he saw similar objects to those he found in the water. His drawings leave no doubt that these were the first bacteria to be described, but the significance of his findings was not appreciated at the time. Indeed, it was not until Louis Pasteur, the great French chemist and bacteriologist, demonstrated the essential part that bacteria played in fermentation processes in relation to wines and beers that the scientific world understood the significance of van Leeuwenhoek's observations made nearly 200 years before.

Pasteur developed methods of growing bacteria so that a more intimate study of them could be made. After his work on fermentation he turned his attention to the silkworm plague which was threatening to ruin the silk trade, then of paramount importance in France. He showed that the disease was caused by a bacterial infection of the silkworm and he was able to suggest successful measures for its control. After this he investigated diseases of animals and man, proving beyond doubt that bacteria were a necessary cause of many diseases. Pasteur's name will be forever associated with the dreadful disease, rabies, and the method he devised for its prevention, but another aspect of his work is of particular importance in the study of food hygiene. He was able to show clearly and completely that the old theory of spontaneous generation, that is life arising from the inanimate, was false. In other words, if a particular food product was sterilized by heat, living bacteria would not appear in the food unless they came from outside, from the air, from the hands, or from some other infected material.

About the same time Robert Koch was also making great discoveries in Germany; he found that anthrax, tuberculosis, and cholera were caused by bacteria and he devised methods to grow these germs. From this time onwards the march of discovery in the field of bacteriology was rapid. From Europe, America, Japan, and other parts of the world bacteriologists were fired with enthusiasm for their new science, and soon the causative microbes of gonorrhoea, erysipelas, diphtheria, typhoid fever, dysentery, plague, gangrene, boils, tetanus, scarlet fever, and other illnesses had been found.

After thousands of years of darkness and superstition a great light was thrown on the cause of infection, and the door was opened for a vast study of the relation of bacteria to disease in animals and man. This study led to a knowledge of the way in which bacterial infections spread and, as a result, methods of prevention and of cure were found. Joseph Lister, applying the theories of Pasteur to surgery, discovered that wounds became septic by the action of bacteria. He introduced the use of antiseptics and disinfectants that would kill bacteria, and there was an immediate reduction in wound sepsis.

Before 1850 the sanitary conditions in Britain were poor. From 1840 onwards began the Great Sanitary Awakening. Edwin Chadwick belonged to a family with a strong belief in personal cleanliness — a most unusual virtue in those days — and in 1842 he was instrumental in bringing out a *Report on the Sanitary Conditions of the Labouring Population of Great Britain.* The principle that environment influenced the physical and the mental well-being of the individual was introduced and, as the connection between filth and disease was gradually understood, measures were taken to control the disposal of sewage and the purity of water supplies.

In 1854 John Snow recognized that drinking water was concerned in the spread of cholera. William Budd in 1856 concluded that typhoid fever was spread by milk or water polluted by the excretion of an infected person. Prince Albert died of typhoid fever in 1861. John Snow and William Budd were amongst the earliest epidemiologists, for at that time there were no means to grow the organisms responsible for typhoid fever and cholera. In 1874 an outbreak of typhoid fever occurred in the Swiss town of Lauren and it was traced to polluted water; the result was that water supplies and sewage systems were redesigned to eliminate this danger. The chlorination of drinking water in Britain was initiated by Alexander

Houston in 1905 during a typhoid epidemic in Lincoln, and its use has helped to abolish water-borne disease in this and other countries.

Toward the end of the nineteenth century the danger of infection by milk was discovered and in cities such as London, the heat treatment of milk by pasteurization began; this heat treatment kills many bacteria in the milk, including those that are harmful. The pasteurization of all supplies is not yet complete so that outbreaks of food poisoning and brucellosis still occur from tuberculin-tested raw milk and they will continue to do so until all milk is heat treated before distribution. The incidence of tuberculous infection in children drinking raw milk is now negligible in Great Britain, because most of the milk is pasteurized and also because the infection of cows has been almost eliminated by the destruction of animals found to be infected when subjected to the tuberculin test. A scheme for the eradication of brucellosis is in progress. A brief description of certain milk-borne and food-borne diseases is given in Chapter 8.

Acute poisoning and infection spread by food contaminated with disease-producing bacteria must have occurred from time immemorial, and they will continue to do so until we learn methods of control.

Drinking water is purified by sedimentation, filtration, and chlorination; milk is heat treated and carefully packed in clean bottles or cartons; ice-cream mix is heat treated, cooled quickly, and stored cold until frozen; liquid whole egg is heat treated (pasteurized), cooled quickly, and frozen. Some foods are preserved by heat, cold, dehydration, or chemicals before they reach the kitchen, but many of them are not. Raw foods can introduce food-poisoning organisms into kitchens and processed foods can be contaminated in the kitchen by other foods and by those preparing meals for consumption. To prevent the spread of infection by foodstuffs, therefore, we must either stop certain bacteria from entering food or, if they have entered unavoidably, make it impossible for growth to occur. When it is known that raw foods are consistently contaminated from animal or human sources, investigations should be made to find out how to produce such foods free from infection. If raw foods known to be a source of infection cannot be treated to make them safe before distribution, food hygiene education should ensure that food handlers are aware of the dangers and of the methods to reduce the risks which may lead to food poisoning.

The first description of food-poisoning bacteria, later known to be salmonella, was given by Dr Gaertner in 1888; these bacteria were isolated from the organs of a man who had died from food poisoning during an outbreak in Germany affecting 59 other persons. Similar bacteria were found in the meat served to the victims, and also throughout the carcass of beef from which the meat was cut. About the same time the so-called ptomaines, previously thought to cause food poisoning, were extracted from putrid foods and were found to be harmless if taken by mouth. These discoveries convinced many workers that the ptomaine theory of poisoning was wrong and, under the influence of Savage in the UK and Jordan in the United States, food poisoning gradually came to be associated with specific bacterial contamination.

In 1896 van Ermengem in Belgium described the organism, *Clostridium botulinum*, which is responsible for a very serious form of food poisoning known as botulism. *C. botulinum* produces in food a highly poisonous toxin affecting the nervous system and often causing death. Fortunately, botulism is rarely described in the United Kingdom, although it still occurs in other parts of the world.

In the years 1909 to 1923 many of the bacteria now known to be responsible for a large proportion of food-poisoning incidents were grouped together under the generic name *Salmonella*, in honour of Dr Salmon who isolated the first member of the group, the hog cholera bacillus, in 1885.

From 1914 onwards another group of bacteria, the staphylococci, were found to be concerned with food poisoning. Certain strains of staphylococci produce in food a poisonous substance or toxin which, if swallowed, gives rise to quick and violent reactions.

From 1945 to 1953, a fourth major causal agent of food poisoning was investigated and described, the anaerobic sporing bacillus *C. welchii* (now known as *C. perfringens*); this organism is similar to *C. botulinum* but the illness is usually mild with less disastrous results.

From time to time various common bacteria are shown to be responsible for food poisoning. They may be present in large numbers in the raw food or on surfaces or equipment, survive preparation or recontaminate the food after cooking.

The safety of food thus depends on freedom from the bacteria known to cause food poisoning and also from mass bacterial contamination usually resulting from careless storage. Clean food is free from visible dirt and bacterial spoilage; not all spoilage bacteria cause food poisoning and conversely the food-poisoning bacteria may not cause visible spoilage even when present in enormous numbers. The aim of food hygiene should be the production and service of food which is both safe and clean.

Under poor storage conditions bacteria can grow to large and dangerous numbers. Four main factors are important: (a) the initial safety of raw foods before their introduction into manufacturing establishments, shops, canteen and home kitchens; (b) the hygiene and care of those responsible for handling food during production and service; (c) the conditions under which food is stored; and (d) the general design and cleanliness of kitchens and equipment.

The incidence of food poisoning appeared to increase after World War II; outbreaks and sporadic cases are still common today even though knowledge of preventive methods has increased. Table 1 gives the recorded cases of bacterial food poisoning in England and Wales for the years 1965 to 1976. At the turn of the century food was cheap and tastes were simple. The small eating houses used for midday meals were often dingy with underground basement kitchens and inadequate washing facilities. Nevertheless, intestinal infections or intoxications from meals taken in these

Table 1 Recorded cases of bacterial food poisoning (England and Wales, 1965–76)

Year	1965	1966	1967	1968	1969	1970
Number of cases	7917	5818	7367	7103	8207	8634

Year	1971	1972	1973	1974	1975	1976
Number of cases	8079	6020	8574	8591	11 943	11 000

restaurants appeared to be rare. Mostly the meals consisted of freshly roasted or boiled meat with vegetables all freshly cooked and quickly served to relatively small groups of customers. Dessert dishes when available consisted of boiled puddings and fruit tarts.

With the increased facilities the habits of people changed; the cinema became popular, motor transport increased, and there were more attractive restaurants to meet a growing need. Immediately after World War I the popularity of large restaurants increased; they served food at reasonable prices but often pre-cooked. Made-up meat dishes and cream-filled cakes, prepared ahead of requirements and ideal for bacterial growth, became popular also. After World War II almost the whole nation participated in communal feeding, when in addition to the public restaurant, canteens were set up in factories, schools, and offices. Although the habit of communal feeding had been growing for years the nation was entirely unprepared for this enormous change-over. Canteen kitchens, often converted in a hurry, were of unsuitable design and inadequate for the number of meals required. Kitchens originally intended for serving a certain number of meals were forced to provide double or even treble that number, sometimes with limited equipment and inadequate staff. At the same time few of the people in charge of these catering establishments had any knowledge of the precautions necessary for the preparation, cooking, and serving of meals on this large scale.

Under such conditions it is not surprising that errors occurred in the bulk handling of food. Large numbers of persons were served from one canteen kitchen, and a single infected dish could affect many; whereas a similar incident in a small household would affect one or two persons only.

Another factor of importance was the growing import trade of protein foods needed to feed the increasing human and animal population. Egg products, meats, coconut, and dried feeding stuffs for animals, all now known to contain food-poisoning organisms, were brought into the country in enormous quantities. They were eaten raw, were cooked, or were used in the bulk manufacture of many foods which were purchased more and more by the busy housewife with a family to feed and a job to do.

Other problems in Britain during and after World War II included shortages of certain foods and more particularly of meat. The housewife and the canteen supervisor acquired the habit of hoarding left-overs and cooking their small cuts of meat the day before they were required in order to slice them more economically when they were cold. Some of these habits have remained and provision for cold storage is still inadequate with approximately two-thirds of British households equipped with refrigeration.

From 1960 onwards, factory farming became popular and the production of foods, poultry, and meat, particularly, increased. Convenience foods helped the army of housewives working both inside and outside their homes.

In 1939, a public health bacteriological service was instituted which supplemented the work of the public and private analysts. The number of laboratories increased, and they provided more facilities for the investigation of food-poisoning outbreaks. Also, teaching on the subject of food hygiene became popular. In 1950, for the first time, the combined recorded food-poisoning incidents from the Public Health Laboratory Service, and the Department of Health and Social Security, which receives all notifications of food poisoning from local authorities, were gathered together, so that a great deal of information on food poisoning hitherto unrecorded was brought to light. In 1955, legislation on food hygiene was passed.

What are the aims, therefore, for personal hygiene, food storage, the general design of kitchens and their equipment, and the safety of basic food ingredients? First, it must be recognized that the natural hosts of food-poisoning bacteria and viruses are the human and animal body. Second, efforts should be made to reduce the rates of excretion of salmonellae by animals and poultry by eliminating salmonellae from feeding stuffs and by care in animal husbandry. Third, essential raw food commodities known to be contaminated with salmonellae should be rendered safe before distribution or warnings given through education. Fourth, foods susceptible to bacterial growth should be cooled quickly and kept cold after being cooked; the facilities should be provided. Fifth, kitchens should be designed to provide conditions for well-ordered working, with plenty of space, good ventilation, lighting and cold storage, and with equipment in good repair, readily accessible, and easily dismantled for cleaning and disinfection. Sixth, kitchen staff should be taught the principles of hygiene in relation to themselves, the foods they handle and their surroundings and equipment.

Current situation

The evidence and belief that animals and birds, particularly those reared intensively for human consumption, frequently excrete salmonellae acquired generally from feedstuffs provided for them led to suggestions for legislation to control the spread of infection. The Zoonoses Order requires notification of salmonella excreters amongst flocks and herds; the Protein Processing Order will seek to safeguard future supplies of animal feedstuffs against the introduction and spread of salmonellae amongst livestock.

There is nothing new about the methods to prevent cross-contamination from raw to cooked foods in food preparation areas, except, perhaps, the newer designs for kitchens and equipment and more stringent methods of cleaning. The Food Hygiene Regulations seek to cover personal and environmental hygiene.

It is regrettable that the number of recorded incidents of food poisoning have not yet fallen. The episodes due to organisms of the salmonella group are still predominant, although there is a rise in the number of cases due to serotypes other than *Salmonella typhimurium.*

Remarks about *Clostridium perfringens* which appeared in the preface to the third edition are relevant today. The incidence of food poisoning caused by this organism continues to rise, and there have been serious outbreaks involving many people in hospitals. Although the reasons are obvious, it is still difficult to convince architects and food handlers that it is necessary to provide means to cool meat and poultry dishes rapidly before refrigeration. This one measure alone would reduce the number of outbreaks of *C. perfringens* food poisoning. The time and temperature of storage of foods between cooking and eating is of prime importance in all food poisoning — they can change non-infective or non-toxic numbers of organisms into clinical doses. Few cooks realize the importance of rapid cooling and cold storage, and the danger of leaving cooked food at warm temperatures. Furthermore, cooking is regarded as a sterilizing procedure, which it is not, unless steam under pressure or deep fat frying is used. The survival of spores as well as the recontamination of foods after cooking by surfaces, equipment, and hands are responsible for much food poisoning and needless suffering amongst geriatric patients in hospitals.

An International Typing Scheme for the serological identification of *C. perfringens* is near completion. The availability of antisera would serve a useful purpose all over the world, not only for the epidemiology of food poisoning but also for gas gangrene.

Much more data has appeared on *Bacillus cereus* food poisoning, another organism which survives cooking by means of spores. A serological typing scheme has been developed which is useful for the division of strains into those producing the diarrhoeal and vomiting types of illnesses; a number of serotypes have not been associated with food poisoning. In Britain, spores in rice have survived cooking and have germinated into bacilli forming toxin during growth in the rice, while it is cooled and warmed up.

Britain has remained remarkably free from botulism, it is thought due to the care of the canning and curing industries as well as care in the preservation of food by heat and cure in the home. The housewife is discouraged from preserving nonacid foods except by freezing.

The vibrios continue to be agents of infection in many parts of the world. Cholera and cholera-like illness due to the non-cholera vibrios, also infections due to *Vibrio parahaemolyticus*, are recognized not only in the East but also in European countries, Australia, and North America. The importation of *V. parahaemolyticus* and the non-cholera vibrios in frozen cooked seafoods are known to be potential sources of illness from prawn cocktail and other mixed seafood dishes.

Aeromonas hydrophila has been described as an agent of food poisoning in India and by Swedish workers in Ethiopia. This organism should not be neglected in the search for agents of infection; it needs careful identification to avoid confusion with the vibrios.

Yersinia enterocolitica and the *Campylobacter* are the subjects of much investigation as to their role in food-borne infection.

Food-borne virus infection is still difficult to elucidate, although improved techniques have allowed virus particles to be seen in stool samples from patients suffering from gastroenteritis, when bacterial agents have not been found. Epidemiological investigations are hindered by the inability to find small numbers of similar particles in foods. Poliomyelitis and viral hepatitis have been suspected, epidemiologically, to result from infected water and foods, and thus it is assumed that other human and animal-borne viruses may play a part in gastroenteritis. Much bacterial food poisoning could be prevented by limiting the growth of organisms in foods by rapid cooling and refrigeration; a virus requires living tissue for growth and thus will not multiply in foods, but it could be transmitted by food. However, when living shell-fish are swallowed, there may be large numbers of viral particles in the creatures at the time of consumption. Shell-fish growing in areas polluted by human or animal sewage may harbour the viruses infecting persons on shore.

Some serotypes of *Eschericheria coli* are associated with diarrhoea in adults, the enteropathogenicity of these strains usually requires proof, and many workers are still searching for the correct test.

The knowledge that some organisms formerly thought to be of significance in spoilage of food only can, in fact, cause food poisoning gives support to the institution of specifications or microbiological guidelines for foods. Used wisely, specifications can help to improve the microbiological condition of foods so that spoilage and health hazards are reduced or eliminated. Standards which are applied on a strictly legislative basis and which are too detailed may be impossible to implement, and therefore of little or no value as a compulsory measure. Careful legislation is necessary, however, to prevent accidental contamination of food with pesticide materials used for home and agricultural pests. Such accidents are rare in Britain but are more common in the Middle and Far East.

Information on the danger from mycotoxins, both for man and animals, is growing and more attention should be paid to the possible hazards from both natural and purposeful contamination of foods with moulds.

The food-borne parasitic infections have not been described in this book; they include amoebiasis and giardiasis, and the tapeworm infestations. Apart from instructions not to eat undercooked or raw meat, nor to drink untreated water overseas, little is known about the infective dose or the precise mode of transfer, whether from hand to food or directly from polluted water. As with the viruses, the difficulty of isolating these agents from foods hinders epidemiological research. The survival times of such microbiological systems outside the human or animal host are important also.

There is much to learn about food-borne diseases, agents, sources, spread, and mechanism of action. It will be necessary for every generation of workers to adapt the available data to fit new items in food manufacture, as well as to add fresh information to the list of microbiological agents causing food-borne infection and intoxication.

Before considering these in greater detail it may be useful to describe the shape, size, habits and requirements of those minute organisms which cause disease and poison food — the bacteria.

2

Elementary bacteriology

The size, shape and habits of bacteria

It is difficult to understand the chain of circumstances which must precede an outbreak of disease caused by contaminated food, without knowing something about the organisms responsible.

The characteristics of bacteria in relation to their source and reservoir and a knowledge of their ability to survive and grow in food are important factors in the control of both food poisoning and food spoilage. Prevention is much concerned with the destruction of bacteria and with the inhibition of growth.

Bacteria are minute, single-celled organisms of variable shape and activity. Along with the viruses, algae, fungi or moulds, and the lichens, they are classified as the lowest forms of plant life. Bacteria are everywhere in soil, water, dust, and in air. There are thousands of different types and many perform useful functions. Some turn decaying vegetable matter into manure; others, within the human or animal body, assist in the development of certain vitamins essential to health; some can be harnessed for fermentation processes such as in the production of beer or wine and the manufacture of cheese; and others are used to produce antibiotics for the cure of disease. Only a very small proportion of the total bacterial population are dangerous because they can cause disease in man and animals.

Bacteria are so small that individually they cannot be seen without a microscope. They may be as small as 1/2000 mm and clusters of a thousand or more are only just visible to the naked eye. Fifty thousand placed side by side may measure barely an inch (25 mm).* Seen under the high-powered lens of a microscope with a magnification of 500 to 1000 times (Fig. 2), the bacteria which may be spread by food are round or rod shaped and appear in one or other of the following forms according to the type of organism. Some are mobile in fluids and swim about by means of hair-like processes which arise

* Viruses are still smaller.

15

singly or in clusters from one end, both ends, or from all around the cells. Some possess capsules, outer mucinous coats, which protect them against substances which might destroy them. Capsules may be important in disease. Some can produce resting bodies called spores

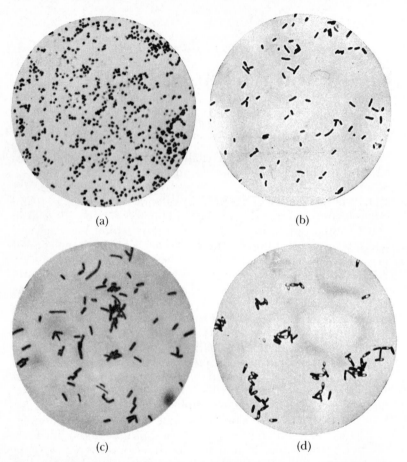

(a)   (b)

(c)   (d)

Fig. 2 Food poisoning bacteria: (a) *Staphylococcus aureus*; (b) *Salmonella*; (c) *Clostridium perfringens*; (d) *Clostridium botulinum* — showing spores

(Fig. 2d) when conditions are unfavourable for growth, and particularly when there is a lack of moisture. These spores form within the bacterial cell which afterwards gradually disintegrates leaving the spore intact. Many can withstand high temperatures for long periods and the processes required for the sterilization of canned foods are based on the time and temperature calculated to destroy the most heat-resistant spores. Sporing bacteria, when allowed to multiply in foodstuffs, may be responsible for spoilage decomposing the food with gas production. A few species, for example *Clostridium perfringens*, cause food poisoning when ingested in large numbers after multiplication in foods, particularly cooked meat dishes in which the spores have survived; *Clostridium botulinum*, the cause of botulism, produces a highly poisonous toxin while growing in food.

Although most food-poisoning bacteria cause symptoms only when eaten in large numbers after multiplication in food they do not usually alter the appearance, taste, or smell of the food. The types of bacteria which break down protein so that there is visible spoilage leading to putrefaction detectable by smell do not usually cause food poisoning, although the early onset of obvious spoilage is a safeguard against the consumption of heavily contaminated foods.

It is generally impossible by visual inspection to know whether food is dangerously contaminated with food-poisoning organisms or not. Animals infected during life may reach the market or slaughterhouse excreting small numbers of food-poisoning bacteria yet without symptoms. Even in the early stages of illness there may be no obvious signs of changes in the carcass or offal to warn the meat inspector or veterinary surgeon of the potential danger.

Growth and multiplication

Bacteria multiply by simple division into two, and under suitable conditions of environment and temperature this occurs every 20 or 30 minutes. Thus one cell could become over 2 million in 7 hours and 7000 million cells after 12 hours' continuous growth. When each cell has grown to its maximum size, a constriction appears at both sides of the centre axis, the outside membrane or envelope of the cell grows inwards and forms a division which finally splits, releasing two new twin cells (Fig. 3).

When the available nutrient has been exhausted or the waste products of growth make the environment unsuitable, for example, by the production of acid, growth ceases and the cell dies. The length of life of a bacterial cell varies according to the food or medium on or within which it is growing or resting, and also according to the type of organism. The spores produced by certain bacteria can survive in a dormant condition for long periods of time under adverse conditions but when suitable conditions of food, moisture, and temperature return they are able to germinate into actively growing bacteria again.

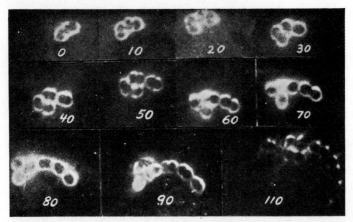

Fig. 3 Division or multiplication of bacteria. (From G. Knaysi, 1951, *Elements of Bacterial Cytology*, Comstock, Ithaca, N.Y.)

Conditions for growth and multiplication of bacteria

In the laboratory a variety of media are made to suit the growth requirements of different types of bacteria. Most of them have a meat-broth base set into a firm gel by means of agar, a substance which is extracted from seaweed. Agar has special properties; it melts at a high temperature and sets at a low temperature and it is thus more suitable for bacterial media than gelatin which melts at temperatures below those required for the growth of many bacteria. Blood, serum, milk, or other protein matter may be added for enrichment.

When bacteria are spread on the surface of agar media in a petri dish and left overnight at a suitable temperature, such as 37 °C (98·6 °F) — blood heat — they start to grow. By division of each cell into two every 15–30 minutes a small heap of bacteria is formed, consisting of millions of cells, which is called a colony. Every kind of bacterium has a typical colony form; the size, shape, colour, and consistency of these colonies on particular culture media help in identification (Fig. 4). Another method by which we can identify the different types of bacteria, as well as by their appearance under the microscope and on the surface of agar media, is to observe their activity in liquid media containing different sugars. Some bacteria ferment certain sugars with the production of acid and gas, others ferment different ones, some produce acid only, while others produce neither acid nor gas. There are chemical tests, too, which are often useful for distinguishing between different bacteria.

The individual members of bacterial groups may be divisible also by serological methods. The agglutination of organisms brought about by the altered blood serum of human beings or animals infected with the same organism may be used for this purpose.

An even finer differentiation into types is sometimes possible by means of bacteriophages, which are viruses parasitic on bacteria. The bacteria are identified according to the types of invading phage, which are specific to the bacterial host cell. Cultivated phages are inoculated on to bacterial cultures which they destroy. *Salmonella*

Fig. 4 Colonies of staphylococci

typhi, some other salmonellae, and staphylococci are typed in this way.

Many years of laboratory work have led to the development of special kinds of culture media which will enhance the growth of certain types of bacteria and depress other types. To isolate food-poisoning bacteria from foodstuffs there are media which will suppress the growth of harmless or non-pathogenic bacteria, and encourage harmful or pathogenic bacteria to grow.

Bacteria will live and multiply in many foodstuffs; sometimes the type of food and the atmospheric temperature and humidity of the kitchen provide conditions similar to those used for cultivation in the laboratory. Meats and poultry are good examples, whether raw or cooked they are excellent media for bacterial growth; pies, stews, and gravies resemble laboratory media. Milk and egg products, including custards and trifles, soft cheese and cream, are all good media for growth. Bacteria will multiply in these foods when they

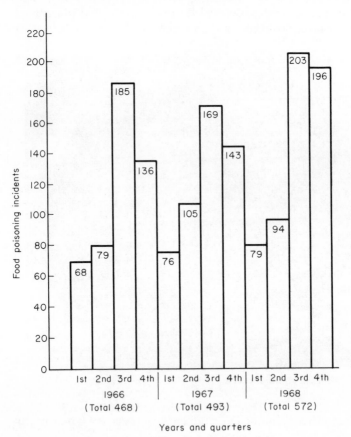

Fig. 5   Seasonal prevalence of food poisoning

are stored in the shop or kitchen without refrigeration; in the same way, they multiply in specially prepared media inoculated in the laboratory and incubated for warmth. Thus food poisoning occurs more frequently in the warmth of summer than in the winter (Fig. 5).

Most bacteria require air to live actively, but some can multiply only in the absence of oxygen; they are called <u>anaerobes</u>. Included in this group are the sporing organisms *C. perfringens* causing food poisoning, and *C. botulinum* causing botulism. *C. perfringens* flourishes under the conditions found in the centre of rolled joints of meat, in poultry carcasses, and in boiled masses of meat such as beef, cut up or minced and in stews because the oxygen is driven off by cooking. Care must be taken to destroy the spores of bacilli when meat, vegetables, and other foods are canned. Adequate heat treatment may not be given in the home, thus amateur canning or bottling of meats and vegetables is discouraged.

Pathogenic or harmful organisms grow best at the temperature of the body, which is 37 °C (98·6 °F), although the majority will multiply between 15 °C and 45 °C (59–113 °F). Except for *C. perfringens*, which grows well at temperatures up to 47 °C (117 °F) and even up to 50 °C (122 °F), the ability of most bacteria to multiply falls off rapidly above 45 °C (113 °F) and only a few groups can grow at temperatures above 50 °C (122 °F). Non-sporing cells of food-poisoning bacteria are killed at temperatures above 60 °C (140 °F), the length of time (10· to 30 minutes or more) required depending on the types of organisms (Fig. 6). For example, to make milk safe, i.e. free from harmful bacteria, it is pasteurized at 62·8 °C (145 °F) for 30 minutes, or at 71·7 °C (161 °F) for 15 seconds (Fig. 18), or at higher temperatures for an even shorter time, such as 132 °C (270 °F) for not less than 1 second as laid down in the Milk (Special Designation) Regulations 1977 for 'Ultra Heat Treated' milk. This milk must be put into sterile containers using aseptic precautions and is said to have a shelf life of several months.

Methods of heat treatment, e.g. pasteurization, can be applied to other foodstuffs such as fresh cream, imitation cream, ice-cream mix and liquid whole egg and albumen (see Chapter 5).

Boiling kills living cells, with the exception of spores, in a few seconds; however, spores may require to be boiled for 5 or more hours before they are killed. To destroy them in a shorter time, temperatures above boiling obtained by the use of steam under pressure, must be used. Figure 7 illustrates the effect of temperature on the vegetative cells of bacteria. The toxic substance produced by staphylococci in food needs boiling for 30 minutes or longer before it is destroyed, but the toxin of *C. botulinum* is destroyed more readily by heat.

Extreme cold will not kill all bacteria, but it will prevent them multiplying and for this reason foods which support bacterial growth should be stored at low temperatures. Domestic refrigerators not only delay the spoilage of foods but prevent the growth of harmful bacteria. Freezing kills a proportion of cells. Safety measures for ice-cream include both heat treatment and cold storage with rapid cooling in between.

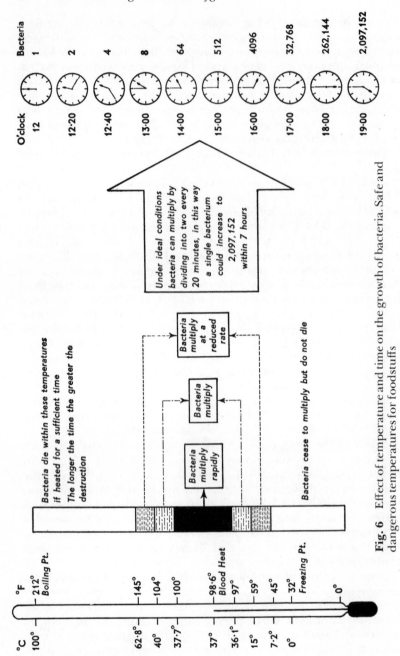

Fig. 6 Effect of temperature and time on the growth of bacteria. Safe and dangerous temperatures for foodstuffs

Bacteria cannot multiply without water. Cold cooked meats contain sufficient moisture to support growth, whereas in dehydrated products such as desiccated soup or milk powder bacteria will survive but remain dormant until there is sufficient water added to revive them.

The addition of various salts, acids, and sugar to laboratory media

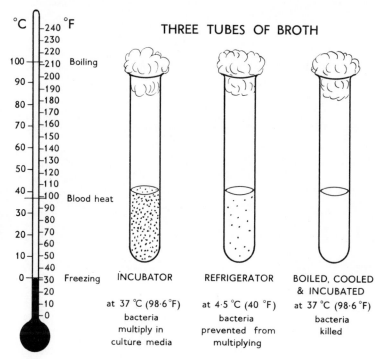

Fig. 7   The effect of temperature on bacterial cells

is carefully controlled. The presence of these substances in varying amounts in different foodstuffs exerts an effect on the ability of organisms not only to grow but to survive.

The use of these substances as preservatives and the effect of antibiotics, irradiation, and fumigation are discussed in Chapter 11. Quite simply, bacteria are single-celled living organisms which are present almost everywhere, often in large numbers. Mostly they are harmless but some cause spoilage in foods and others give rise to disease in the human and animal body. Both humans and animals may harbour disease-producing pathogenic bacteria which may be passed to foodstuffs and multiply when conditions of temperature, time, and moisture are suitable. These living bacterial cells will cease to multiply in the cold and die if they are too hot, although the structures known as spores, produced in some cells by certain bacteria, can survive long periods of boiling.

The next chapter describes the bacteria which cause food poisoning, particularly, where they live, their reservoirs, and their behaviour.

3

Bacterial and other microbial causes of food poisoning

Bacterial food poisoning is a disturbance of the gastrointestinal tract with abdominal pain and diarrhoea with or without vomiting. The onset may be less than 1 or more than 48 hours after eating contaminated food. There are at least seven groups of bacteria which are well recognized as causal agents of food poisoning:

Salmonella	*Bacillus cereus*
Staphylococcus aureus	*Vibrio parahaemolyticus*
Clostridium perfringens	*Escherichia coli*
Clostridium botulinum	other organisms

The first three groups are known to be common in many countries. Botulism from *Clostridium botulinum* is a hazard in northern countries but is rarely reported from Mediterranean and eastern areas. In Japan, food poisoning from *Vibrio parahaemolyticus* occurs frequently. *Bacillus cereus* is increasingly recognized as the causative agent of a toxin type of illness similar to that caused by staphylococcal enterotoxin; it can also produce symptoms similar to those of *Clostridium perfringens* food poisoning. Certain types of *Escherichia coli* are known to cause diarrhoea in adults, which is often referred to as traveller's diarrhoea; this organism is also a common agent of infantile enteritis. Streptococci are also occasionally incriminated in food poisoning. Other organisms, particularly the Gram-negative bacilli, are reported from time to time, but are not always proven as agents of food poisoning.

The duration of illness is mostly short, from 1 to 3 days, but patients with salmonella infection may not feel well for 7 or more days.

Clinical details, incubation periods and information about the foods eaten, how they were cooked, and the ingredients are helpful to those examining suspected material in the laboratory. When an investigation is delayed or specimens are not available, relevant and accurate information may be the only means by which the cause of an outbreak can be established.

The general characteristics of the various types of food poisoning are described in the following pages and are summarized in Table 2.

Table 2 Bacterial food poisoning: incubation period and duration of illness

Cause of food poisoning	Incubation period (hours)	Duration
Salmonella (infection)	6–36 usually 12–24	1–7 days
Staphylococcus aureus (toxin in food)	2–6	6–24 hours
Clostridium perfringens (toxin in intestine)	8–22	24–48 hours
Clostridium botulinum (toxin in food)	12–96 usually 18–36	Death in 24 hours to 8 days, or slow convalescence over 6–8 months
Vibrio parahaemolyticus (infection)	2–48 usually 12–18	2–5 days
Bacillus cereus (toxin in food)	1–16	12–24 hours
Escherichia coli (infection)	12–72	1–7 days
Streptococcus (toxin in food?)	3–22	24–48 hours

Salmonella

Organisms of the salmonella group cause food poisoning by infection; that is, by invasion of the body. They reach food directly or indirectly from animal excreta at time of slaughter, from human excreta, or water polluted by sewage; also, in the kitchen they may be transferred from raw to cooked foods by hands, surfaces, utensils, and other equipment. Illness is more likely to occur when the organisms are ingested in large numbers; a chance contamination of the food by a small number of bacilli may not be harmful. When they are allowed to multiply in the food, that is, if the lightly contaminated food stands for some hours in a warm room, then sufficient numbers of bacteria will develop to produce symptoms in the consumer.

The onset of illness occurs usually within 6 to 36 hours of eating the food, although the incubation period may be longer. The symptoms are characterized by fever, headache and general aching of the limbs, as well as by diarrhoea, and vomiting. In England and Wales there are between 20 and 40 fatal cases each year, mostly in infants, and elderly or sick people. The duration of illness, from 1 to 7 days, is longer than that caused by the toxin of the *Staphylococcus*. There are many hundreds of different types of salmonellae classified by serological methods and several types can be more finely divided by means of bacteriophage (see p. 19). The subdivisions are helpful for the investigation of outbreaks. All types can produce disease in man or animals. Organisms of the Arizona group, which may be classified with the *Salmonella*, are also described as agents of disease in man and animals.

Staphylococcus

Staphylococcal food poisoning follows the consumption of food heavily contaminated with certain types of *Staphylococcus aureus* which produce a poisonous or toxic substance in the food. The skin and nose frequently harbour staphylococci, and cooked foods such as meat and poultry intended to be eaten cold, and prepared foods such as custards, trifles and creams also, are readily contaminated by hands. Since the toxin is formed by the organism growing in food before it is eaten and not after it has entered the body, the incubation period may be as short as 2 hours but in general it is 4 to 6 hours. There is a rapid onset of symptoms characterized by severe vomiting, diarrhoea, abdominal pain, and cramps, sometimes followed by collapse. Recovery is rapid.

The typing of staphylococci both by bacteriophage and serological methods has enabled the pathogenic species to be divided into groups, some of which are more common than others in food-poisoning incidents. There are several types of enterotoxin which can be extracted from culture filtrates and foods and identified serologically. Human and animal feeding experiments have been used also. Whereas the staphylococcus itself is fairly readily destroyed by the heat of pasteurization and normal cooking procedures, the toxin is more resistant to heat: it is destroyed gradually during boiling for at least 30 minutes. It may remain active after light cooking.

Clostridium perfringens (welchii)

C. perfringens is a common organism frequently found in excreta from humans and animals, and in raw meats and poultry and other foods, including dehydrated products. It can survive heat and dehydration by means of the spores which remain dormant in food, soil, and dust. Illness occurs after eating food grossly contaminated with *C. perfringens* which has multiplied from spores which have survived cooking; they are activated to germinate by the heat. Multiplication takes place during long slow cooling and warm storage in the kitchen or canteen of cooked meat, poultry, fish, stews, pies, and gravies. The spores vary in their ability to withstand heat. Some strains of *C. perfringens* can survive hours of boiling; others only a few minutes. Some spores may survive in boiled, stewed, steamed, braised, or even roasted foods, particularly those cooked in bulk. After cooking, the spores readily germinate into bacteria which multiply rapidly under favourable conditions including temperatures up to 50 °C (122 °F); there is little growth below 15 °C (59 °F).

Symptoms occur from 8 to 22 hours after consuming the contaminated food; they include abdominal pain, diarrhoea and nausea, but rarely vomiting; they may continue for 12 to 48 hours. The symptoms result from the activities of a large dose of organisms which produce an enterotoxin in the intestine; an effective amount of toxin is not formed in the food before it is eaten.

Two of the five types of *C. perfringens*, classified according to the various toxins, other than enterotoxin, produced, are able to cause food-borne disease in man. Of these, type A is the more common agent of food poisoning, while type C causes a more serious but rare condition called enteritis necroticans. Type C was first isolated from home-canned rabbit causing illness in Germany and it has been found in pork causing similar outbreaks in New Guinea. So far it has rarely been associated with human illness in the United Kingdom. The type A strains can be further divided into many serotypes by the use of specific antisera.

Clostridium botulinum

The toxin of *C. botulinum*, another anaerobic spore-bearing bacillus, is a highly poisonous substance produced as the organism grows in food. It affects the nervous system, causing an often fatal illness. Outbreaks and cases of botulism rarely occur in Great Britain but they are reported from other countries and depend on the feeding habits of the population (p. 68). The species is divided into seven types (A to G) according to the toxin produced; four (A, B, E, and F) are known to affect man. The spores are resistant to heat, and survive boiling and higher temperatures.

The toxin is sensitive to heat, and in pure form it is destroyed by boiling. Nevertheless, it may be protected when mixed with protein and other material in food. The toxin is lethal in very small doses and gives rise to symptoms quite different from those of the organisms just described. The incubation period varies from 24 hours or less to 96 hours (usually 18–36), and the first signs of illness are lassitude, fatigue, headache, and dizziness. Diarrhoea may be present at first but later the patient is obstinately constipated. The central nervous system becomes affected and there is a disturbance of vision; later, speech becomes difficult and there is paralysis of the throat muscles. The intoxication reaches its maximum within 24 hours to 8 days and death often occurs by paralysis of the respiratory centres. If, after 8 days, the patient survives, convalescence is slow. Life may be saved by giving antitoxin as soon as possible.

Bacillus cereus

Certain members of the *Bacillus* group of organisms, and especially *B. cereus*, are increasingly reported in food-poisoning incidents. They are common aerobic sporing organisms. The spores are often found in cereals and other foods; some spores will survive cooking and subsequently germinate into bacilli which under warm storage conditions in cooked food grow and produce toxin. A wide variety of foods have been associated with outbreaks, particularly cornflour sauce in Norway, and boiled and fried rice in Britain and other countries. As with *C. perfringens*, long moist storage of warm cooked food in which spores are still alive encourages the growth of the organisms to large numbers and the consequent formation of toxin to amounts able to cause illness. Two toxins are known to cause illness.

The incubation period varies from 1 to 16 hours and the onset of symptoms may be sudden with acute vomiting and some diarrhoea; the incubation and symptoms may closely resemble those of staphylococcal enterotoxin food poisoning. They may also resemble those of *C. perfringens* food poisoning. There is a serological typing scheme for *B. cereus*. Certain serotypes appear to be more responsible for outbreaks than others.

Other aerobic spore-bearing bacilli such as *B. subtilis* have also been described as agents of food poisoning with similar characteristics to those of *B. cereus*.

Escherichia coli

Although a normal inhabitant of the intestinal flora of man and animals, many strains are enteropathogenic and give rise to acute diarrhoeal enteritis in infants. Outbreaks and sporadic cases in hospitals and maternity homes are frequently reported with fatal cases. There is a complex serotyping scheme to aid identification.

Certain serotypes cause diarrhoea in adults also, and *Esch. coli* is considered to be responsible for a proportion of incidents described as 'traveller's diarrhoea'.

Infection of infants is acquired by direct spread in maternity units and also by contaminated feeds. It is thought that symptoms in adults are initiated by large doses of enteropathogenic *Esch. coli* in foods. The organisms may enter kitchens in many raw foods and readily pass to cooked foods by the usual means of hands, surfaces, containers, and other equipment; they may be water-borne also. Human excreta may also play a part in direct spread during epidemics. The incubation period is 12 hours to 3 days and the symptoms may be those of diarrhoeal food poisoning or dysentery-like with more prolonged diarrhoea and blood and mucus in the stool. The demonstration of pathogenicity and toxigenicity is a subject for research.

There are other atypical coliform bacilli described as agents of food poisoning with symptoms resembling those of salmonellosis.

Vibrio parahaemolyticus

In Japan an organism formerly designated *Pseudomonas, Oceano-monas* and even *Pasteurella* but now *Vibrio parahaemolyticus* is reported to cause 50 per cent or more of food poisoning incidents. In the warmer weather it can be isolated from fish, shell-fish, and other seafoods and from coastal waters.

Reports of outbreaks have come from many countries, including Australia, the United States, and the United Kingdom. The organism has been isolated also from sea creatures and coastal waters of various countries, including the United Kingdom. Both raw and cooked seafoods, for example, crab, lobster, shrimps, and prawns, have been reported as vehicles of infection and it is suspected that the cooked foods were contaminated by the raw products in the kitchen or at picnics. Imports of frozen cooked sea-foods from eastern countries are frequently contaminated with vibrios including *V. parahaemolyticus*. Outbreaks of food poisoning have occurred after dinner parties and banquets including prawn cocktail in the menu.

The organism causes infection and the symptoms have been likened to those of both cholera and dysentery. The average incubation period is about 15 hours, and there is rapid onset of illness with profuse diarrhoea often leading to dehydration, vomiting, and fever. The duration of illness is usually 2 to 5 days, although the ill-effects may linger on. There are many sero-types.

Other organisms

In addition to the seven groups of food poisoning organisms already described, other bacteria are sometimes reported as causal agents of food poisoning. Certain streptococci, including those of the Lancefield Groups A and D and the viridans type, have been isolated in large numbers from incriminated foods in outbreaks of food-borne disease. It is suspected that toxins are produced causing symptoms similar to, but less acute than, those from staphylococcal enterotoxin. The Group A β-haemolytic strains have been found in foods from outbreaks of illness where symptoms included those of upper respiratory infection and gastroenteritis. The aetiology of these outbreaks is not always clear. The Gram-negative bacilli, *Proteus, Providencia, Citrobacter,* and *Pseudomonas,* have all been implicated from time to time. Usually these organisms are isolated from suspected foods but not always from the faeces of patients, so that the evidence for their role in food poisoning is scanty, although serological tests may be used to support the diagnosis.

There are three other organisms which are suspected to be agents of food-borne disease, although hitherto they have received little recognition. *Aeromonas hydrophila* causes disease amongst cold-blooded animals. Reports of outbreaks in India and Ethiopia describe the isolation of this organism from patients, including children, with diarrhoea. In the outbreak reported from Ethiopia strains of *A. hydrophila* from stool cultures were found to produce enterotoxin. It was suggested that the mechanism of the diarrhoea might be similar to that of *Vibrio parahaemolyticus* infection.

Yersinia enterocolitica has also been reported from a number of countries as an agent of enteric infection. This organism is also responsible for other symptoms of infection.

Another group of organisms which has recently been associated with gastroenteritis is the *Campylobacter.* The taxonomy of species within this group has yet to be clarified and the prevalence in man may be greater than hitherto recognized. The primary source of infection is thought to be poultry but person-to-person spread has also been demonstrated. Onset of symptoms may be sudden with abdominal cramps followed by passage of foul-smelling and often bile-stained stools. The diarrhoea, which may persist for 1 to 3 days, is sometimes preceded by a period of fever of a few hours to several days. Abdominal pain may persist after the diarrhoea has eased and symptoms may be more severe in adults than in children.

Viruses are recorded as causing outbreaks of intestinal illness of a particular pattern but the investigation of faeces from such incidents has so far given inconclusive results except that other organisms known to cause food poisoning have not been found. Viruses cannot multiply in foods, only in certain living tissues; thus if they are agents of food poisoning their spread from the hands of human carriers and from water to foodstuffs is important. Their incidence in foods grown in sewage-polluted water such as shell-fish and watercress may be relevant. There is little information about shared enteroviruses between animals and humans. The investigation of foodstuffs for viruses is carried out in some countries.

Mycotoxins

Some fungi produce toxic substances which are poisonous for man and animals. *Aspergillus flavus* growing in groundnuts and other cereals produces aflatoxin which affects turkey poults, ducklings, cattle, pigs, sheep, and trout. The induced disease in laboratory animals has given rise to hepatic changes associated with liver carcinoma. In October 1974, a large outbreak of hepatitis in India followed the consumption of chappatis and other foods made with maize flour; the maize was heavily contaminated with *Aspergillus flavus*. Of 397 persons affected, 106 died.

Toxic substances formed by *Fusarium graminarum* in corn can cause illness in pigs. More and more mould products are found to have adverse effects on animals. There is growing evidence that these toxic products can affect man also. It seems that more attention should be given to the dangers of eating mouldy foods, whether contaminated through bad practice or intentionally for flavour and texture. Fungi regularly employed for industrial purposes and in food manufacture should be carefully examined for toxic by-products. A Bibliography drawn up by the Tropical Products Institute in August 1964 (and later supplements) summarizes the literature on aflatoxin and other toxic products from fungi.

Incidence

Table 3 gives the number of cases of food poisoning due to known bacterial agents notified in England and Wales for the years 1973 to 1975.

Bacillus cereus food poisoning was rarely observed in the UK before 1973, and the figures for *Escherichia coli* episodes in 1973 are taken from the results of a particular investigation, which was an outbreak of food poisoning following a dance.

Table 4 gives the distribution of causal agents according to the place where the outbreaks occurred, and also divides the episodes into general outbreaks, family outbreaks, and sporadic cases all notified in England and Wales for the years 1973 to 1975. An 'outbreak' involves two or more related cases in persons of different

Table 3 Causal agents of bacterial food poisoning (cases recorded in England and Wales, 1973–5)*

Causal agent	1973 Number	%	1974 Number	%	1975 Number	%
Salmonella						
S. typhimurium†	2367	27·6	2036	23·7	2814	23·6
Other salmonellae‡	4504	52·5	3627	42·2	6080	50·9
Staphylococcus aureus	168	2·0	103	1·2	443	3·7
Clostridium perfringens	1311	15·3	2769	32·2	2418	20·2
Bacillus cereus	66	0·8	51	0·6	82	0·7
Bacillus spp.	—	—	—	—	4	—
Escherichia coli	141	1·6	—	—	6	0·1
Vibrio parahaemolyticus	17	0·2	5	0·1	96	0·8
Total	8574	100	8591§	100	11 943	100

* Public Health Laboratory Service figures [from Vernon (1977), *Public Health, Lond.*, **91**, 225].
† In addition, the following numbers of symptomless excreters of salmonellae were reported:

	1973	1974	1975
S. typhimurium	365	309	505
Other salmonellae	1263	956	1748

‡ Excluding *S. typhi* and *S. paratyphi* B.
§ One case of mussel poisoning was also reported.

Table 4 Causal agents of bacterial food poisoning (England and Wales, 1973–5). Outbreaks by location, family outbreaks, and sporadic cases*

	Salmonella	Clostridium perfringens	Staphylococcus aureus	Bacillus cereus	Bacillus spp.	Vibrio parahaemolyticus	Escherichia coli	All causes
General outbreaks								
Hospitals	157	44	1	—	—	—	—	202
Restaurants,† hotels, holiday camps	45	16	4	45	—	2	—	112
Farms	47	—	—	—	—	—	1	48
Reception parties	35	5	8	—	—	1	1	50
Schools	21	20	6	—	—	—	1	47
Institutions‡	28	18	—	—	1	—	1	47
Shops	23	—	4	—	—	—	—	29
Canteens	1	30	1	—	—	—	—	32
Holiday parties (UK)	5	1	1	—	—	—	—	7
Local community	16	—	—	—	—	—	—	17
Infected abroad	19	—	—	—	—	2	—	21
Other or not recorded	10	7	2	1	—	—	—	20
All general outbreaks	407	141	28	46	1	6	3	632
Family outbreaks	1278	9	22	5	—	—	—	1314
Sporadic cases	15 084	4	9	5	1	9	—	15 112

* Public Health Laboratory Service figures [from Vernon (1977) *Public Health*, Lond., **91**, 225].
† Includes 'take-away' restaurants.
‡ Includes old people's homes, hostels, halls of residence, nurseries, and children's homes.

households; a 'family outbreak' involves two or more related cases in persons of the same household; a 'sporadic case' refers to a single case unrelated to any other.

Tables 3 and 4 show that organisms of the salmonella group and particularly *Salmonella typhimurium* are responsible for the highest number of cases and outbreaks, although it should be noted that sporadic cases account for a large number of the incidents due to salmonellae. Prior to 1968, *S. typhimurium* was the predominant salmonella serotype responsible for more than 50 per cent of cases of infection; gradually, all the other serotypes (combined) began to take precedence over *S. typhimurium.*

Clostridium perfringens is the next most common agent and accounts for about one-quarter of the total number of cases.

The number of cases due to all bacterial causes and reported between the years 1969 and 1974 was 8000 to 9000, except for 1972 when the numbers dropped to 6020. In 1975 and 1976 more than 11 000 cases were reported each year, the increase was largely due to the rising incidence of salmonella food poisoning.

Over the years 1965 to 1975 cases of staphylococcal food poisoning fluctuated from approximately 100 to 900 annually; they represented a small percentage of the whole. On the other hand, cases of *C. perfringens* food poisoning recorded from 1965 to 1975 varied from 978 to 3044 annually, between approximately 12 and 35 per cent of the total number of cases recorded for all bacterial agents. *C. perfringens* food poisoning was reported mainly from outbreaks in canteens preparing food for hospitals, schools, factories, and other institutions where large numbers of people may be affected. The average number of ill persons in an outbreak was greater than in a salmonella outbreak, because many salmonella incidents are sporadic cases.

It will now be convenient to consider the reservoirs of infection and means of spread.

4

Reservoirs of infection and ways of spread

Bacteria are everywhere in the environment — in soil, water, dust, and air. Most of them are harmless but many can infect man and animals. Under certain conditions they are able to grow and multiply in the tissues of the body; some germs infect one tissue and some another. During illness it is well known that the infecting germs can be transferred from one person to another, from animal to animal, and from animal to man or man to animal, either directly or through a medium such as food. The fresh host may succumb to the disease, or he may resist it and show no symptoms although the infecting germ is harboured within his body for a variable period of time. In this way germs which are adapted to live under the conditions provided by the human or animal body maintain their existence and, when they are not actively causing disease, they may be surviving quietly in the nose, throat, or bowel of a healthy person or other living creature.

Some food poisoning is caused by the toxic products of bacteria growing actively in food and not by invasion of the body by the organism, for example staphylococcal and *B. cereus* food poisoning and botulism.

When it was first realized early in the twentieth century that bacteria were capable of causing food poisoning or food-borne disease, it was recognized that animals were the natural reservoirs of the salmonella group of intestinal organisms responsible for the majority of food poisoning cases. The original investigations led workers to diseased animals as the source of contaminated meat (eaten by those affected), but subsequent workers have shown that the human and animal body may harbour organisms of the salmonella group without showing signs of disease. Also the human nose, throat, and skin lesion are the main sources of staphylococci.

Foodstuffs of animal origin may be regarded as primary sources of food-poisoning bacteria; contamination passes from the live animal to the food during production either at home or abroad. The contaminated food as received is as much a hazard in food preparation areas as the living carrier and temporary excreter.

The human and animal reservoir

Tables 5, 6, and 7 show the reservoirs and likely paths of spread from man and animals to food for the three main groups of food-poisoning organisms which frequently reside in living creatures.

The human nose, hand and skin

The primary habitat or natural home of staphylococci are the mucous membranes of the nose, and the skin of man and animals. The left-hand side of Table 5 indicates the manner of spread of staphylococci from the human reservoir to food. We know that 30–50 per cent of non-institutional people carry staphylococci in the nose; in patients and working personnel in hospitals the nasal carriage may be as high as 60–80 per cent. Staphylococci may be isolated from the hands of 14–44 per cent of persons. There are many different types of staphylococci but they do not all produce the toxins responsible for food poisoning. Many of us touch the nose and mouth almost unconsciously, and from time to time hand-kerchiefs are used by everyone; nasal secretions are laden with bacteria, some of which may be staphylococci, and they are likely to contaminate the hands. Sometimes these organisms penetrate into the deeper layers of the skin, where they may live and multiply in the pores and hair follicles. Hands so infected may be washed and scrubbed and yet continue to harbour staphylococci. In the hot, steamy atmosphere of the kitchen the pores are open and the organisms rise to the surface of the skin in the perspiration. We can try to rid the hands of staphylococci by using antiseptic lotions, hand creams, or soaps, but there is no certain method of success although the number of organisms may be much reduced. There are preparations which are helpful in the treatment of the nasal carrier. It is better for food handlers who harbour staphylococci in the skin of their hands to avoid working with foodstuffs (such as cooked meats, milk, and egg dishes) which encourage bacterial growth.

The pus from staphylococcal skin infections such as boils, carbuncles, whitlows, and sycosis barbae (barber's rash) as well as septic cuts and burns will contain innumerable organisms, and a small speck of pus could inoculate food with millions of staphylococci.

Staphylococci like to live in cut surfaces; they thrive in the moist conditions provided by the serous fluid which is always present.

Table 5 Human reservoirs of food poisoning organisms

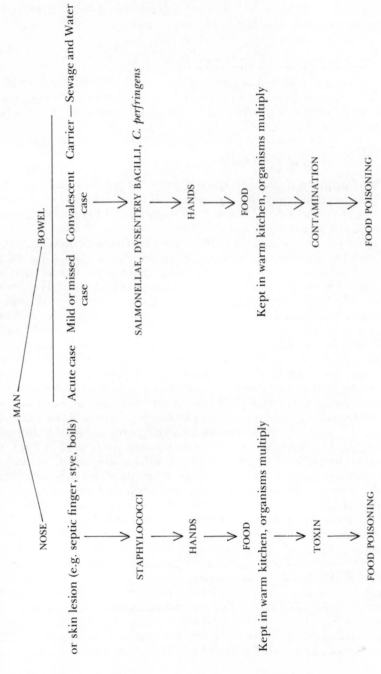

MAN

NOSE — or skin lesion (e.g. septic finger, stye, boils) → STAPHYLOCOCCI → HANDS → FOOD → Kept in warm kitchen, organisms multiply → TOXIN → FOOD POISONING

BOWEL — Acute case Mild or missed case Convalescent case Carrier — Sewage and Water → SALMONELLAE, DYSENTERY BACILLI, *C. perfringens* → HANDS → FOOD → Kept in warm kitchen, organisms multiply → CONTAMINATION → FOOD POISONING

Therefore the tiniest cut or abrasion, however clean and healthy it appears to be, may harbour large numbers of food-poisoning organisms and form a focus of infection.

There are many examples of outbreaks of staphylococcal food poisoning caused by the contamination of foods by staphylococci introduced from boils, ulcers, abrasions on the hands, and also from healthy looking hands. An infected trifle which caused acute illness among patients in a particular hospital ward was made by a chef with a varicose ulcer of the leg. The staphylococci growing profusely in the trifle were found to be of the same type as those infecting the ulcer.

The human and animal intestine

The right-hand side of Table 5 shows the chain of spread of salmonellae from the human reservoir. In any outbreak of infectious disease those who acquire the infection will react in one of four ways: a proportion will succumb to an acute illness; ambulant cases will exhibit symptoms so mild that they may be ignored or attributed to other indispositions; convalescent carriers will continue to excrete the organism after recovery from illness; and temporary carriers or symptomless excreters may harbour the infecting germ for a short time without exhibiting symptoms.

Aerosol sprays from flushed lavatory pans, soiled seats, pull chains, door handles, and taps may pass infection from person to person. The more fluid the stool the more danger from spread. Contaminated hands may pass infection to food. These intestinal organisms are readily washed from the hands by soap and water. They are not harboured in the skin like staphylococci.

Hands will also transmit bacteria from food to food. Figure 8 shows finger print cultures of colonies of bacteria from unwashed and washed hands and from hands after holding a moist scouring sponge and after touching raw chicken. It will be noted that there are moderate numbers of bacteria on a dry hand before washing but that many and various bacteria are picked up by the hands from a moist kitchen sponge and raw chicken, for example, and that immediately after being washed the hand is by no means sterile.

It is often asked how long after infection people remain carriers and continue to excrete infective organisms; this will depend on the type of organism. The excretion of *Salmonella typhi* may persist for many years, while other salmonella serotypes and dysentery bacilli are excreted for a few weeks only, rarely months, and only exceptionally for a year or more. Treatment of persistent excreters with antibiotics is not recommended because it tends to prolong the excretion and encourage resistance of the organisms.

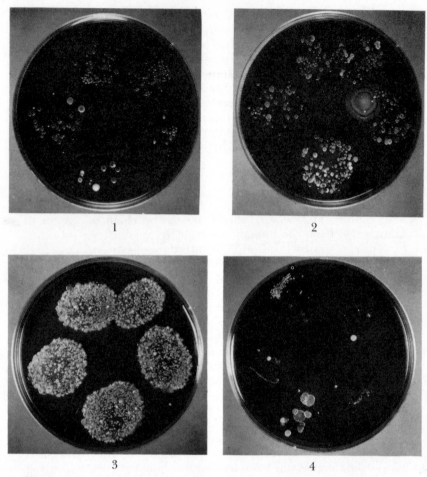

Fig. 8 Colonies of bacteria from finger prints of washed and unwashed hands.

    1 Dry hand before washing
    2 Hand after touching moist scouring sponge
    3 Hand after touching raw chicken
    4 Hand immediately after washing

The sources of *Clostridium perfringens* are likely to be both animal and human in a cycle similar to that shown in Table 6; 'animal' includes poultry, and 'meat' includes poultry meat.

Table 7 gives the names of the animals known to be occasional or persistent reservoirs of organisms of the salmonella group. Animals may suffer from salmonella infections or become transient symptomless excreters in the same way as human beings. They may become infected through eating contaminated feeding meals, grazing on contaminated pasture land, or by contact with animal, human, or bird excreters on the farm, during transport, or in the lairage of markets or slaughterhouses. It has been observed that a far higher proportion of pigs and sheep, for example, excrete salmonellae when under conditions of stress, excitement, fear, or

Table 6   Human and animal reservoirs of *Clostridium perfringens*

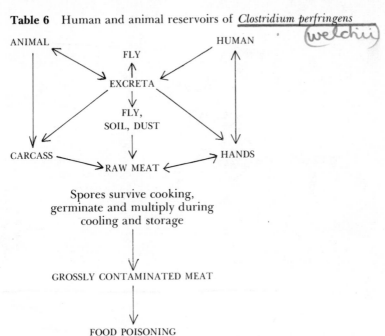

Spores survive cooking,
germinate and multiply during
cooling and storage

GROSSLY CONTAMINATED MEAT

FOOD POISONING

privation, than during normal day-to-day life on the farm. As well as animal-to-animal spread of infected excreta there may be direct soiling of food such as from cow to milk and meat, pig to meat, from poultry to the shells of eggs, and from vermin and domestic pets to all kinds of food.

Organisms from infected carcasses may be transferred to other meat in the slaughterhouse, during transport, and in the butcher's shop or factory. Widespread outbreaks of salmonella food poisoning have occurred by the distribution of contaminated raw meat and by contamination of cooked meats from the raw carcass meat. More than one thousand cases of *S. typhimurium* food poisoning with 12 deaths were reported from Scotland; the outbreak spread to England by contaminated carcasses and from minced meat originating from infected pigs (p. 97). In another large outbreak in the

Table 7 Animal reservoirs of salmonella organisms

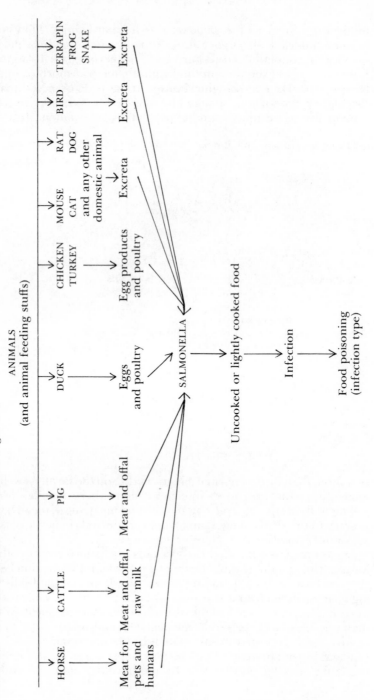

south of England, legs of pork were cooked in a factory handling large quantities of contaminated pork from infected pigs. The meat was distributed over a wide area and was eaten in the factory canteen also. An earlier outbreak investigated in 1947, illustrated the continual danger of cross-contamination from one meat to another. There were about three to four thousand cases with a few deaths. Pigs excreting salmonellae were thought to be responsible. The spread of infection from carcass to carcass in the slaughterhouse was aided by the cloths used to wipe them. The use of cloths is now forbidden in the UK (p. 271). The home-killed raw meat was distributed to butchers' shops and handled in conjunction with canned meat. The infected raw meat and the cold meats were weighed on the same balance, cut with the same knife, and handled with the same hands; there was, therefore, plenty of opportunity for the spread of infection. The contamination of the pressed beef and other cooked meats was responsible for the widespread nature of the outbreak, for these meats were eaten without further heat treatment — often after storage at a temperature favourable for bacterial multiplication. In 1960, home-killed infected veal used for manufactured products and retail sale caused a number of cases of salmonellosis in England.

The contamination rate of carcass meat will vary according to the proportion of animals excreting salmonellae and the hygiene of the meat establishment. There has been an increase in the number of calves and cattle infected with *S. typhimurium*, associated with the mass production of animals on farms using intensive rearing methods. Many strains are resistant to antibiotics which may be used liberally in feeds for prophylactic reasons to stem the intestinal infections which afflict intensively kept calves. It has now been shown that drug resistance may be passed from cell to cell and from one species of organism to another so that there is an ever-increasing danger of the spread of antibiotic-resistant salmonellae and the transfer of resistance to organisms producing other human infections. The *British Medical Journal* suggested a revision in farming practice and the use of drugs. In 1969 the Joint Committee on the use of Antibiotics in Animal Husbandry and Veterinary Medicine made the following recommendations: 'antibiotics used for treatment of humans should not be used in feeds for animals nor for prophylaxis.'

From time to time imported boneless meats have shown high rates of contamination, and when new imports are received from different countries the supplies should be monitored for uncommon serotypes of salmonellae hitherto unrecognized as agents of food poisoning in this country.

Horses have been shown to excrete salmonellae, and frozen

boneless horsemeat imported for pet food can be a major source of salmonellae. Salmonellae have been found also in a high proportion of samples of imported frozen boneless kangaroo meat. Without careful handling and cooking of the meats the organism is likely to spread in domestic kitchens so that other foods may be contaminated. Pets themselves as excreters may infect children playing with them; furthermore, the fly population alighting on infected excreta may carry the germs back into the house. In many countries horse meat is eaten by the human population; in the United Kingdom,

Table 8   *Salmonella* in raw meat (1961-5)

Raw meat and offal	Number of samples examined	Positive for salmonellae	
		Number	%
Wholesale (imported) Frozen boneless			
veal	1328	192	14·4
beef	3420	410	11·9
beef offal	102	9	8·8
mutton	1107	123	11·1
mutton offal	155	4	2·5
horse	12 406	4516	36·4
horse offal	1031	421	40·8
kangaroo	929	410	44·1
Retail (English and imported)			
butcher's shop meat	262	4	1·5
butcher's shop offal	52	0	—
pet shop meat	433	120	27·7
pet shop offal	148	25	16·9
knacker's yard meat	64	7	10·9

although mainly sold for pets, it is sometimes seen raw alongside meat and fish in retail shops, and may be dispensed with the same equipment as that used for fish or other meats. Meat from knackers' yards, condemned for human consumption but sold raw for pets, has been the source of salmonellae causing outbreaks of salmonellosis amongst families owning pets. In 1969 a new law was passed, the Meat (Sterilization) Regulations, 1969 (see p. 273), to ensure that condemned meat, whether imported or home produced, intended for animals be cooked before sale. Canned pet foods, sterilized by heat treatment during the canning process, should be safe. Table 8 gives results for the salmonella contamination of various meats. Sampling on the scale shown in the Table was not continued. It is probable that the rate of contamination decreased after improved and more frequent inspection of meat establishments.

Table 9 gives the rates of isolation of salmonellae from packets of pork sausages and samples of sausage meat from large, medium, and small manufacturers over the years 1968 to 1974. The results indicate the possibility of higher rates of isolation from manufacturers gathering in large numbers of animals from a wide area than from those dealing with small numbers of animals obtained locally. There was an average of 30 per cent isolations (435 of 1467 samples) from the various sources.

Table 9 *Salmonella* from packets of pork sausages and sausage meat from large and small manufacturers (1968–74)*

Source of samples	Number of packets examined	Positive for salmonellae† Number	%
Large manufacturer A	312	7	2·2
Large manufacturer B	854	413	48·4
Medium manufacturer C	101	4	11·0
Medium manufacturer D	100	11	11·0
Small manufacturers	100	0	0
Total	1467	435	29·7

* Roberts, D., Boag, K., Hall, M. L. M. and Shipp, C. R. (1975). The isolation of salmonellas from British pork sausages and sausage meat. *Journal of Hygiene*, **75**, 173.

† Thirty-eight different serotypes were isolated; the largest number of serotypes found in a single packet was four.

Table 10 *Salmonella* from frozen chickens (1971–6)*

Number examined†	Number positive	%	Number of different serotypes
519	175	34	16

* Results from the Food Hygiene Laboratory.

† Chickens from 13 producers.

Poultry are known to be major reservoirs of salmonella organisms. Table 10 shows that salmonellae were isolated from 175 of 519 (34 per cent) of samples of frozen chicken examined during the years 1971 to 1976; the chickens came from 13 different producers. The shells of hens' eggs may be contaminated through contact with the faeces in the cloaca, or in the nest or battery. The organisms may penetrate the shell under certain conditions of humidity and temperature. Though this may be an uncommon occurrence, one infected egg may contaminate batches of liquid egg broken out in bulk for freezing or drying. Also fragments of shell or specks of dirt may fall into the mixture; the hands of those breaking out the eggs will contaminate the equipment and the mix. Even when liquid egg is dried, organisms remain viable since the temperatures reached are not high enough or sustained for long enough to kill them. Methods of treatment to render these products free from infection will be described in Chapter 5.

The salmonella contamination of spray-dried whole egg was first discovered during the war years of 1939 to 1945 when outbreaks of salmonellosis were traced to this source. The presence of the same types of salmonellae in the faeces, mesenteric glands, and flesh of pigs was shown to be due to the consumption of dried whole egg by pigs. Some years later outbreaks of enteric fever and salmonellosis due to salmonellae, including paratyphoid bacilli, were traced to the use of Chinese frozen whole egg for cakes in bakeries preparing imitation cream cakes also (see Chapter 5). It was soon discovered that a proportion of all egg products, whole, white, or yolk, broken out in bulk for the liquid, frozen, or dried materials were contaminated with salmonellae (Table 17; see p. 63).

Although salmonellae are not commonly found in the yolk or white of hens' eggs in shell, the yolk of ducks' eggs is not infrequently infected (Tables 15 and 16; see p. 62). It seems that in the duck the oviduct, where the egg is formed, may become infected. The duck is a notorious scavenger and it is possible that in the course of the day's activities, which include swimming in a pond which may be contaminated by other birds or rats, the infected material is picked up, ingested, and transferred from the digestive tract to the oviduct. The drake may spread the infection from bird to bird.

Unlike the hen, which likes to keep dry, the duck frequently lays eggs in wet and muddy places, and the shell is more porous and more susceptible to penetration by bacteria than that of hens' eggs. Ducks' eggs are fairly frequently contaminated. They should, therefore, be used with caution and regarded as a possible source of danger even though they look and smell normal. The recommendations given for the use of ducks' eggs in cooking (see Chapter 12) should be strictly carried out.

Poultry as well as other farm animals, such as cattle and pigs, are exposed to infection from feeding meals; many of these are known to contain salmonellae which may lead to a transient carrier state or sometimes to actual disease. The rapid growth of the broiler industry for chickens, turkeys, and ducks seems to be associated with increased infection of birds and carcasses. There is likely to be a higher proportion of poultry carcasses contaminated during bulk handling than by small-scale operations. The extent of contamination may be increased by modern methods of retail cooking, storage, and packaging.

Milk-borne infection has been largely eliminated by pasteurization, but outbreaks of food poisoning due to salmonellae and staphylococcal enterotoxin still occur from raw untreated milk infected by cows or humans. Brucellosis will persist also until eradication schemes are fully implemented.

Improved methods of production of desiccated coconut have considerably reduced if not eliminated the hazard of contamination by salmonellae of human or animal origin. Furthermore, production samples are screened for salmonellae before export from certain countries, Sri Lanka for example.

Vermin and birds

Rats and mice can suffer from infection due to types of salmonellae which infect man, and they can also become symptomless excreters. It is known that a proportion of the vermin population become intestinal carriers of salmonellae, in the same way as described for other animals and for man. The organisms will be picked up on farms, in sewers and from garbage. Thus their droppings are a source of danger to food which they soil.

In the past certain vermin poisons were lethal because they contained virulent organisms of the salmonella group. The danger from the use of such material is obvious and in fact outbreaks occurred in various parts of the world owing to accidental contamination of human food with the 'poisons'; furthermore, a proportion of the animals it was intended to kill undoubtedly survived and became excreters. In Britain the sale of this material is forbidden; there are many poisons more effective for animals and harmless to human beings (Chapter 17).

Wild birds excrete salmonellae in proportion to the foods eaten by them. The scavenger type, for example sea gulls and even pigeons feeding on urban waste from tips and sewage outflows, are frequently infected; whereas salmonellae are rarely found in country birds in sparsely populated areas.

Domestic animals

In Britain approximately 1 to 2 per cent of cats and dogs were found to be excreting salmonellae without symptoms in 1956; the proportion may be much lower now because of the decreased practice of feeding raw horsemeat, which is known to be a source of salmonellae, to domestic pets; in a survey in the USA 15 per cent of dogs fed meat and bone meal (rarely free from salmonellae) were found to be excreters. In 1969, nearly 10 per cent of dogs were found to be excreting salmonellae in the Brisbane area of Australia; there were 12 serotypes which corresponded with those isolated from cases of human salmonellosis in the same area. These results suggest that food hygiene regulations which ban the presence of cats and dogs in retail food shops are justified.

The widespread distribution to farm animals of feeding meals contaminated with salmonellae may lead to transitory infection of a proportion of animals over a large area. In some circumstances when animal husbandry is good no harm may be done, but in particular instances there may be spread of infection in herds combined with poor hygiene in slaughterhouses. The distribution of contaminated carcasses for retail sale and their use for manufactured products will in some instances lead to outbreaks of food poisoning.

The sources of infection on farms are likely to be threefold:

(1) animal excreters as foci of infection;
(2) feeding stuffs;
(3) environmental factors including man, other animals, vermin, birds, and water.

It may be assumed that if the feeding stuffs were rendered safe, the importance of (1) and (3) would be reduced also. The movement of animals such as calves for breeding purposes, and pigs for mating may be a big factor in the spread of infection under present conditions.

In a survey of cattle, 21 per cent of 4496 swabs from abattoir drains were positive for salmonellae; isolations were most frequent where a high proportion of cattle were slaughtered. The same salmonella serotypes and even the same phage types of *S. typhimurium* were found in abattoirs and also in human cases of salmonellosis in the areas served by the abattoirs. These findings indicated that contaminated meat products were sold in the local shops. In 8 food poisoning incidents, 281 cases and excreters, there was convincing evidence that meat or a meat product was the vehicle of infection. In a further 23 incidents, meat-borne infection was likely. Cattle and pigs were important foci of infection and the meat from pigs, cattle, and calves was a source of infection and was responsible for both sporadic cases and outbreaks of disease.

In another investigation, salmonellae were isolated from 2 to 14 per cent of 5637 pigs in the south-west of England. The majority of serotypes were similar to those found in feeding stuffs and those causing food poisoning in the human population, such as *S. typhimurium, S. dublin, S. panama, S. livingstone, S. stanley, S. fischerkietz, S. bredeney, S. indiana, S. heidelberg, S. anatum, S. senftenberg,* and *S. montevideo.*

A comparative study made in Denmark, where there is legislation compelling treatment to free feeding stuffs from salmonellae, showed that the incidence of salmonellae in pigs was lower than in England and the majority of serotypes common in pigs in England were not found, nor were they found in the human population in Denmark.

Other ways in which infection spreads to food

In some countries flies are thought to be important in the spread of infection, particularly where horses and cattle work alongside the human population, and streets and lanes are soiled with excreta. In other countries where sanitation systems are different and transport is mechanized, the fly is for the most part controlled but there may still be direct contamination from animal sewage to food.

Where sanitation is poor and intestinal disease such as dysentery, typhoid, and paratyphoid fever are endemic, an abundance of flies is a far greater menace. There is ready access to infected excreta from cases and carriers, and they can transfer disease-producing bacteria to foodstuffs. Rivers and water courses polluted by sewage can flood wide areas of land and thus increase fly infection.

In western countries where sanitation is good there are still untidy dustbins with ill-fitting lids or no lids at all in the back premises of private houses, blocks of flats, restaurants, hotels, canteens, and other premises which prepare foodstuffs; sometimes they are placed outside kitchen windows.

The fly can feed on unwrapped waste and regurgitate its meals on to foodstuffs in the kitchen; it may also carry particles of infected material on its feet, from the waste-bin and other dirt to foods. The house-fly and the stable-fly, as well as the larger type of bluebottle and greenbottle, may transfer infection in this way. *Clostridium perfringens* has been isolated from many batches of greenbottle and bluebottle flies.

There are other insects, particularly the cockroach, which can also carry food-poisoning bacteria from place to place. An Australian article described an outbreak of salmonellosis amongst children in a hospital where flies, cockroaches, and mice were all found to be carrying the organism responsible for the infection. It was not suggested that these creatures were the original source but that they had picked up the bacteria from the contaminated environment. It was thought that contaminated wash water from ward sinks used for washing hands and infant clothing was splashed on to the surrounding floor and pipes. Cockroaches walking over these areas would pick up bacteria and convey them from place to place on their feet and bodies.

In general, however, cockroaches are less likely to harbour infection than flies because they breed in wall cracks and paper rather than refuse and manure heaps. Similarly, wasps, bees, and spiders, because of their different breeding grounds and feeding habits, are unlikely to carry harmful bacteria and, compared with flies, are less unhygienic. Ants in large numbers may be more significant.

Inanimate objects such as towels, pencils, door handles, WC equipment, crockery, and cutlery may serve as intermediate objects in the transfer of infection from person to person, or from person to food. Roller towels may be dangerous; if the hands are not washed thoroughly, dirt containing bacteria will be left on the towel to be picked up by the next person to use it. The discharge from staphylococcal infections (for example boils, barber's rash, and other septic spots present on the face, hands or arms of canteen personnel) may be left on communal towels. The spread of boils throughout a factory has been encouraged in this way. It has sometimes been suggested that a towel or other object shared by people was responsible for the passage of salmonellae from a carrier or food to a food handler.

Door handles, pull grips on chains and other WC equipment should be constructed of material which will not encourage the survival of bacteria; most metals discourage bacterial survival, and they should be used in preference to wood, rubber, or plastic.

Where practicable a pedal-operated water supply both for hand washing and for flushing toilets should be installed for hygienic reasons.

Money is frequently thought to spread infection. Coins of copper, silver or nickel commonly discourage bacterial survival, but bank-notes, newspapers and other used paper may harbour living bacteria. Care should be taken not to lick the fingers and so apply saliva and mouth organisms before picking up paper money or paper for wrapping food.

Bacteria from crockery, cutlery, and cloths may be transferred to those using them or to foodstuffs, although it is almost impossible to trace outbreaks of infection which have originated or spread in this manner. Recommended methods for washing crockery and cutlery will be given in Chapter 14.

5

The vehicle of infection

The micro-organisms responsible for food-borne illnesses may be transferred from animal hosts to foodstuffs where they may grow and multiply. The resistant spores of bacteria and moulds survive indefinitely in dust and soil and so they are present on and within many foods. Some foods, both solid and liquid, are readily contaminated and favourable for the growth of bacteria, while others are not.

Each year the same categories of food figure prominently in the statistics for bacterial food poisoning; these foods encourage the growth of bacteria whereas highly salted, sugary, and acid foods do not cause food poisoning because they are unsatisfactory media for growth of the bacterial agents.

The number of organisms in a particular food substance at any given time will depend on the nature of the foodstuff, its temperature, and the length of time it has been kept. The number or dose of organisms necessary to infect or to produce sufficient toxin to cause symptoms varies with different organisms, and also with the resistance or some other condition of the person who swallows the food.

There are only a small number of poisoning incidents each year from chemicals. Nicotinic and ascorbic acids added to raw minced meat to maintain an appearance of freshness, zinc from galvanized iron or corroded containers, copper from worn tinned containers, antimony from chipped enamel, tin from old cans of fruit are reported occasionally in poisoning incidents. There are rare accidents from pesticides and other materials used in agriculture. Poisoning from these substances occurs more often in countries without laws to control their use.

Meat and poultry

Since records for food poisoning have been kept, meat and poultry figure predominantly as food vehicles. In more than 70 per cent of

Table 11 Vehicles of infection in general and family outbreaks of bacterial food poisoning (England and Wales, 1973–5)*†‡

Vehicle of infection	Presumed causal agents							All bacterial agents	
	Salmonella	Staphylococcus aureus	Clostridium perfringens	Bacillus cereus	Bacillus subtilis	Vibrio parahaemolyticus	Escherichia coli	Number	%
Meat and poultry	76	37	117	1	1	—	2	234	70
Rice									
fried	—	—	—	27	—	—	—		
boiled	—	—	—	4	—	—	—	48	14
unspecified	—	—	—	17	—	—	—		
Milk and cream									
unpasteurized milk	30	—	—	—	—	—	1	32	10
pasteurized cream	—	—	—	1	—	—	—		
Sweets and cakes‡	1	7	2	—	—	—	—	10	3
Seafood									
prawns and scampi	—	2	—	—	—	3	—		
salmon	—	1	2	—	—	1	—	10	3
crab	—	—	—	—	—	—	—		
mackeral	—	1	—	—	—	—	—		
All foods	107	48	121	50	1	4	3	334	100

* The food responsible was established in most (80–100 per cent) of the outbreaks due to *Staphylococcus aureus, Clostridium perfringens, Bacillus cereus*, and *Vibrio parahaemolyticus*, but in only a small proportion (19 per cent of general and 2 per cent of family outbreaks) of those due to *Salmonella*.

† Public Health Laboratory Service figures [from Vernon (1977), *Public Health*, Lond., **91**, 225].

‡ Includes trifle, cream cakes, milk puddings, and custard.

incidents for which a cause was established, a meat or poultry dish was incriminated. Table 11 summarizes the food vehicle of infection of 334 general and family outbreaks of food poisoning in England and Wales between 1973 and 1975, and Table 12 classifies the meat and poultry products according to their treatment in processing and cooking.

It is clear that if freshly cooked, roasted, boiled or fried meats and poultry were invariably eaten hot, sporadic cases and outbreaks of food poisoning would be considerably reduced. The preparation of meat products and the periods of storage between preparation and eating contribute to the contamination leading to food poisoning.

In the analysis of general and family outbreaks according to food and causal agents given in Table 12, the reheated foods are predominant vehicles followed by the cold meats and poultry. The reheated meats are usually fresh meats which have been cooked some time before being required and eaten warmed up or cold. In the reheated group, except for salmonella food poisoning from poultry, *C. perfringens* is the common causal agent. The survival of the spores through cooking and subsequent outgrowth and multiplication is encouraged by storage and warming up procedures. The same applies to home- and canteen-made pies and pasties when the meat is precooked.

The cold meats are subdivided into cured and uncured meats. Both are subject to much handling and thus to contamination with staphylococci from the hands. Staphylococcal outbreaks occur mainly from cold cooked meats, including the manufactured-cured products, because staphylococci grow readily in meats with an abnormal salt content from curing solutions. The organisms usually come from food handlers involved in production or responsible for slicing and service. There are many different kinds of cold cooked meats and there is ample opportunity for contamination either during preparation or while the meats are stored in the retail shop or consumer's kitchen. Contamination may take place during manufacture, in the shop or kitchen from hands, utensils, slicing machines, and scales, and subsequent storage may encourage multiplication. Most of these products are eaten cold or merely warmed up.

The sources of the majority of salmonella serotypes which reach foods is the raw product. Poultry and comminuted meats are frequently contaminated with salmonellae before they enter the kitchen and it is not difficult to imagine the spread of infection from raw to cooked products via hands, surfaces, equipment such as chopping blocks, cutting boards and slicing machines, various utensils, and cloths. Food handlers may be victims of the foods they are preparing for the table and become sources of infection.

Table 12 Bacterial food poisoning (England and Wales, 1973–5): general and family outbreaks associated with meat and poultry*

Vehicle of infection	Presumed causal agents					All bacterial agents	
	Salmonella	Staphylococcus aureus	Clostridium perfringens	Bacillus spp.	Escherichia coli	Number	%
MEAT							
Beef							
roasted	—	—	4	—	—	4	
reheated	1	—	6	—	—	7	
stew and mince	—	1	16	—	—	17	53 22·5
steak pies (home made)	—	3	5	—	—	8	
shepherd's pies	—	—	10	—	—	10	
other and unspecified	1	2	2	1†	1	7	
Pork and ham							
roast pork	2	—	5	—	—	7	
reheated pork	—	—	6	—	—	6	
cold pork	3	—	2	—	—	5	
ham and bacon	11	6	2	—	—	19	53 22·5
canned pork and ham	—	3	—	—	—	3	
pork pies	—	2	—	—	—	2	
sausages	1	1	—	—	—	2	
other and unspecified	4	—	3	1‡	1	9	
Mutton							
roast	—	—	1	—	—	1	
reheated	—	—	9	—	—	9	11 5
mince	—	—	1	—	—	1	

Other and unspecified meat							
tongue	1	1	2	—	—	4 ⎫	
meat sauce	—	1	1	—	—	2 ⎬ 12	5
other and unspecified	3	—	3	—	—	6 ⎭	
Soup	—	1	1	—	—	2	2	1
POULTRY							
Chicken							
reheated	2	2	6	—	—	10 ⎫	
cold	12	7	5	—	—	24 ⎪	
spit-roasted	3	—	—	—	—	3 ⎬ 57	24
pies, vol-au-vent, casserole	—	1	7	—	—	8 ⎪	
other and unspecified	6	5	1	—	—	12 ⎭	
Turkey							
roast	2	—	1	—	—	3 ⎫	
reheated	8	—	9	—	—	17 ⎪	
cold	11	1	3	—	—	15 ⎬ 46	20
other and unspecified	5	—	6	—	—	11 ⎭	
Total	76	37	117	1	2	234	100

* Public Health Laboratory Service figures [from Vernon (1977), *Public Health*, **91**, 225].
† *B. subtilis.*
‡ *B. cereus.*

Table 13 Major outbreaks of *Clostridium perfringens* food poisoning
(1973–6)

Year	Type of food	Location	Number of persons affected
1973	Turkey	Factory canteen	73
	Shepherd's pie	Residential school	55
	Minced beef	Factory canteen	70
	Minced beef	Hospital	60
	Leg of lamb	School	200
1974	Savoury mince	Hospital	128
	Beef stew	Residential school	60
	Roast pork	Hotel	60
	Minced beef	Day Centre	52
	Chicken	School	50
	Stewed steak	Convalescent home	50
	Roast beef	Hospital	69
	Chicken risotto	Residential school	75
	Chicken	School	175
1975	Minced ham	Hospital	379
	Roast lamb	School	71
	Minced beef	Hospital	50
	Minced beef	Factory canteen	59
	Cottage pie	Hotel	86
	Blancmange	School	60
	Stewing steak	School	50
	Pork	Hospital	120
	Beef	School	62
	Minced beef	Hospital	57
1976	Turkey	Factory canteen	50
	Turkey	Factory canteen	210
	Bavarian cream desert	School	155
	Minced chicken	Hospital	70
	Minced liver	Hospital	85
	Minced beef	Hotel	50
	Meat pâté	Hotel	59
	Beef	School	146
	Roast mutton	School	100
	Beef	Holiday-school centre	80
	Roast beef	Factory canteen	66
	Beef	Private party	120

Meals including fresh meat and poultry eaten cold or reheated and home- or canteen-produced pies have been predominant in causing *C. perfringens* food poisoning. In large canteen kitchens meat frequently is cooked, allowed to cool slowly at atmospheric temperature and stored in a cool or cold room overnight. The following day it is served cold, warmed up, sliced in hot gravy, or made into pies, pasties, or meat puddings. This practice is dangerous for two reasons. In meats cooked at a temperature not

Table 14   Major outbreaks of staphylococcal food poisoning in England and Wales (1973–6)

Year	Type of food	Location	Number of persons affected
1973	Chicken, ham and beef	County show	35
	Chicken	Pleasure steamer	47
1974	Ham	Hotel	25
	Chicken	Wedding reception	30
	Corned beef	Canteen	30
1975	Chicken vol-au-vent	Party	30
	Chicken	Wedding reception	22
	Custard	School	129
	Chicken	School	70
	Cream cake	Party	44
	Steak and mushroom pie	Horse show	30
	Trifle	Wedding party	25
	Ham	Families	20
1976	Chicken	School	61
	Tongue	Hospital	37
	Chicken	School	133
	Ham	School	83
	Trifle	School	30
	Hard boiled egg salad	School	100
	Chicken	Old peoples outing	28

higher than 100 °C (212 °F), for example, boiled, stewed, braised, steamed, and lightly roasted meats, spores of *C. perfringens* may survive cooking and, in slowly cooling meat, germinate into actively multiplying bacterial cells able to cause food poisoning. Because heat penetrates into meat very slowly, large cuts of meat (over 2·7 kg; 6 lb) are particularly dangerous. With rolled meat the outside may become contaminated and, when folded inside, may not be heated sufficiently to destroy the contaminating organisms. Also, cooked meats and poultry carved cold may be contaminated during slicing or other manipulation carried out with the help of the fingers.

Tables 13 and 14 list recent outbreaks caused by the growth in meats of *C. perfringens* and *Staph. aureus.*

The contamination of raw meat, particularly boneless packed meat, with salmonellae has already been described in Chapter 4. The danger of cross-contamination by spread of infection from raw meats to cooked foods or to foods eaten without cooking is apparent.

The irradiation of frozen packs of boneless horsemeat with small doses of gamma-rays will successfully eliminate salmonellae. The method, as yet unsanctioned, might be considered for all packs of frozen boneless meats for human and animal consumption when the usual hygienic methods fail to prevent contamination.

Canned food

The general standard of commercial canning is high and faults in processing or structural defects leading to leakage during or after processing are rare. Foods for canning should be fresh and of good quality; they are packed and processed and sealed in airtight containers frequently lacquered to prevent interaction between the foodstuff and tinplate, which may cause discoloration. Products such as corned beef, stewed steak, and vegetables are processed at pressures calculated to give temperatures well above boiling, and known to destroy heat-resistant bacterial spores, such as those of *C. botulinum,* and these products should be sterile.

Occasionally, however, there may be small leaks in the seams of cans, or the seams may be strained during the processing and develop small pin-hole leaks which close again later. If impure water is used to cool the cans after heat treatment, organisms may be sucked through the holes, and if the food and conditions of storage are suitable the bacteria will grow and cause spoilage or perhaps food poisoning. Bacteria (for example, staphylococci) from the hands may be sucked through leaks when wet cans are transported by hand from the retort to trolleys or storage places. Cans of food stored in a moist atmosphere may rust and develop holes through which organisms may pass at any time. Spoiled or blown cans, bulged at either or both ends, rarely reach the public because they are usually discovered by the manufacturer before leaving the factory or by health inspectors during routine visits to retail shops. Yet food-poisoning organisms may grow inside cans without gas production or any obvious signs of spoilage. Thus great care is needed both with the manufacture and sealing of cans and with the processing times and temperatures required for sterility. Outbreaks of typhoid fever in England and Scotland have been caused by canned meat contaminated with typhoid bacilli from polluted cooling water. Typhoid bacilli grow well and spread in canned corned beef and they can survive in the can for at least 8 years (see Chapters 6 and 8).

Many canned meats including chopped pork, jellied veal, and tongue are not processed at such high temperatures because it is desired to preserve the maximum bulk and aesthetic qualities of appearance and palatability. Similarly, some other products such as certain soups, mushrooms, and fish are given processing times and temperatures which are borderline for safety but preserve their flavour and content. Spores of *C. botulinum* in the raw food may survive and germinate, so that toxin is later produced from the growth of the bacilli. The contents of these lightly treated cans may not be sterile and their shelf life is limited. A third category of canned meats includes the shoulders and hams of pork which are heated at 'pasteurization' temperatures only, to avoid shrinkage and loss of flavour. They are not sterile; there was a recommendation in 1955 that after the heat process there should not be more than 10 000 per g of heat resistant spores present and all vegetative cells should be killed. Good manufacturers of canned meat will ensure the lowest possible bacterial population by care in production and the preparation of meat from freshly slaughtered animals, combined with well balanced pickling solutions to inhibit growth. The maximum time and temperatures should be given to eliminate all but heat-resistant sporing organisms, which are unlikely to develop in well-cured products. All non-sterile canned meats should be labelled 'Perishable, keep in a cold place'; it is important for these products to be stored cold. International recommendations for heat treatment, salt and nitrite content are required.

Anxiety over possible hazards from nitrosamines has brought about a general desire to lower the concentration used in cures. As the suppression of growth of *C. botulinum* in cured meats depends on the interplay of various chemicals including nitrite, the risk of botulism must be considered in relation to the effect of carcinogenic agents. Suitable inhibitory substances to replace nitrite have not yet been reported.

Sterilized packs of canned meat may be kept for 5 years; cans of veal and carrots in gravy, retrieved from one of Sir Edward Parry's expeditions in search of the Northwest Passage, were wholesome after 115 years. Some canned foods should not be stored as long as 5 years, because slow chemical changes may occur; for example, the limit for milk should be 1 year, vegetables 2 years; canned fish in oil withstands 5 years' storage, but the limit for fish in tomato sauce is 1 year. A regular yearly turnover for all canned foods is advisable; therefore the date of purchase should be written on the cans.

Cans should be stored in a cool, dry place, as high temperatures may alter flavour and colour, and dampness will cause rust and may lead to perforations; badly dented cans may perforate also. Once opened, a can of meat should be kept covered and cold and the contents eaten soon. It must be remembered also that cans which show bulges at the ends are blown and should be discarded without hesitation.

The belief that foodstuffs must not remain in opened tins arose from the fear of interaction between the foodstuff, meat container, and air. Tinplate has much improved and the lacquer on the inside is an added protection. Foods may be safely stored in the opened can for a few days, particularly if refrigerated. It must be remembered, however, that foods from opened cans are susceptible to bacteria from any source and to contamination from persons handling them.

Dairy products (milk, fresh cream, cheese) and eggs

Milk

A substantial portion of urban England and Wales is now covered by directions requiring the heat treatment of all milk other than that produced under conditions enabling it to be sold as 'Untreated' formerly Tuberculin Tested. Between 1973 and 1975 there were 30 outbreaks of food poisoning from salmonella organisms consumed in unpasteurized milk. In some episodes the same phage types of S. typhimurium have been isolated from calves, cows, milk, and people; sometimes salmonellae were found in farm manure and water. Examples of outbreaks are given in Chapters 6 and 8.

The udders of cows, goats, and sheep are a source of food-poisoning staphylococci, particularly when the animals are suffering from mastitis. Staph. aureus can be isolated from most samples of raw milk, and may therefore be found in unheated or lightly heated dairy products. Nevertheless, milk-borne outbreaks of staphylococcal enterotoxin food poisoning are uncommon and they are confined to raw milk. Dehydrated milk needs care in preparation; it is considered under powdered foods on p. 73, and the danger of contamination is described. Tests for detecting traces of antibiotics in milk are statutory in some countries and in England and Wales action may be taken under the Food and Drugs Act, where a concentration of penicillin greater than 0·05 i.u. per ml is not permitted.

Fresh cream

There are few outbreaks traced to fresh cream produced in the UK, although in the USA cream seems to be a common vehicle for staphylococcal food poisoning. Cream may be prepared from raw milk, from pasteurized milk, or it may be pasteurized after separation but before bottling. A minority of creameries carry out in-bottle pasteurization. Cream may be filled into bottles and cartons at the creamery, or it may be transported in cans or churns for filling at distribution centres. A survey of the bacteriological condition of cream, sampled mostly from retail shops, indicated that there was a high degree of post-pasteurization contamination but the samples which had been heat treated again after pasteurization were almost sterile.

It has been suggested that the introduction of a grading scheme for cream similar to that for ice-cream and based on advisory tests for keeping quality would draw attention to unsuitable supplies so that methods of processing, storage in bulk, transportation, and retail storage could be improved.

Cheese

A more serious problem may arise when cheese is prepared from raw or inadequately heated milk. Commercially prepared natural cheese is made by the acidification of milk using bacterial cultures, combined with clotting by rennet. The increasing veterinary use of antibiotics for treatment of disease, including staphylococcal mastitis in cows, has resulted firstly in traces of antibiotics remaining in the milk and secondly in the development of resistance to the antibiotics by the staphylococcus. Sometimes, for this and other reasons, the starter culture fails to grow whereas the staphylococci, frequently present in raw milk, survive and multiply freely. Outbreaks of staphylococcal food poisoning have occurred in factories and hospitals through eating cheese contaminated in this way. The cheese has usually been classified as second grade because of its abnormal flavour resulting from the failure of the starter culture to grow; such cheese is imported for blending and processing and is not intended for consumption without treatment.

The pasteurization of all milk, including that from goats and sheep, whether intended for drinking or for the production of cream or cheese, greatly reduces the hazard of food poisoning from this source. In 1963 New Zealand introduced legislation to compel the pasteurization of milk for making cheese.

'Cream' cheeses have always constituted a risk when prepared from raw milk but most proprietary brands are prepared from heat-treated milk.

Eggs

The contamination of eggs by salmonellae has already been described in Chapter 4 and the results of examination of ducks' and hens' eggs (shell) are given in Tables 15 and 16. It may be seen that the isolation of salmonellae from both ducks' and hens' eggs is

Table 15   *Salmonella* from ducks' eggs (shell). Historical record (excluding *S. pullorum* and *S. gallinarum*)

Year	Country	Number examined	Number positive	Serotype
1932	England	166	7	*S. enteritidis*
1934	Germany	1500	15	*Salmonella* spp.
1936	Germany	332	19	*S. typhimurium*
1944	England	2000	0	
1945	England	16	3	*S. typhimurium*
1950–2	England	13 562	20	*S. typhimurium* *S. enteritidis*
1951–63	All countries	?	10	*S. typhimurium*
1963	All countries	?	5	*S. thompson*

Table 16   *Salmonella* from hens' eggs (shell). Historical record (excluding *S. pullorum* and *S. gallinarum*)

Year	Country	Number examined	Number positive	Serotype
1947	England	166 (dirty shells)	9 (dirty shells)	*S. thompson*
		608 (clean shells)	1 (clean shells)	*S. thompson*
1950	USA	12 (bulked)	+	*S. paratyphi* B
1950	England	'Eggs' from one hen	+	*S. typhimurium*
1952	England	3648	0	
1953	Australia	3312	0	
1956	England	350+	0	
1956	Japan	428	39	*S. give*
			26	*S. senftenberg*
1958	England	1620	0	
1959	N. Ireland	60	1	*S. anatum*
1959	Japan	717	79	*S. senftenberg*
		(eggs unable to develop)		
1959	N. Ireland	'Eggs'	+	*S. infantis* *S. albany*
1959	England	12 (bulked in groups of 4)	+ (one group of 4)	*S. thompson*
1960	N. Ireland	150	4 (shells)	*S. typhimurium*
1960	England	24 (Indian eggs)	1 (shell)	*S. enegal*

variable. The amount of infection in the parent poultry flock probably depends on the degree of contamination of the feeding stuffs and environmental factors. Nevertheless, the contamination of ducks' eggs with salmonellae is more consistent, as shown by the results of examination of melange from broken out eggs. Between 1951 and 1955 in Northern Ireland, salmonellae were isolated from 48 per cent of batches of duck egg mix compared with 2 per cent of batches of hen egg mix; the batches usually contained between 4000 and 20 000 eggs. Another group of workers in England found salmonellae in 2 of 65 samples of liquid duck egg and 6 of 1649 samples of liquid hen egg. Later the contamination of hen egg products in bulk, such as liquid, frozen, and dried whole, white, and yolk, was found to be more common and salmonellae were found in the products of many countries. Results obtained in 1961 and 1962

Table 17   *Salmonella* from egg products (1961 and 1962)

	1961			1962		
Egg products	Number examined	Number positive	%	Number examined	Number positive	%
Whole frozen	1042	165	16	327	53	16
Whole dried	898	107	12	111	25	23
White frozen	675	41	6	187	35	19
White powder	214	18	8	103	28	27
White flake	536	68	13	236	44	19
Yolk dried	57	3	5	34	14	41
Total	3422	402	11	998	199	20

are given in Table 17. By 1963 some countries were testing the practicability of pasteurization, and, of 829 samples from pasteurized whole egg from four countries, only 5 (0·6 per cent) showed salmonellae, whereas of 800 raw unpasteurized samples 136 (17 per cent) were positive for salmonellae.

The large-scale investigation of imported and home-produced egg products revealed the fact that these contaminated ingredients were sources of infection in bakeries leading to widely distributed outbreaks of paratyphoid fever and salmonella food poisoning. Outbreaks resulted from the accidental contamination of uncooked products such as imitation cream prepared in the same bowls and with the same utensils as the egg mixes used in the baked ingredients.

Bulked liquid whole egg is now made safe by pasteurization, in a manner similar to that used for milk. In England and Wales there is compulsory pasteurization of liquid whole egg at a temperature of 64·4 °C (148 °F) for $2\frac{1}{2}$ minutes; the heat treatment does not adversely affect the baking properties of the egg. Destruction of the enzyme α-amylase, present in the yolk of eggs, is used as a test for the effectiveness of heat treatment; a similar test is used for pasteurized milk when the enzyme phosphatase is destroyed by heat. Imported liquid whole egg must also conform to the α-amylase test. During the period 1971 to 1976, all 864 samples of imported frozen whole egg examined in one laboratory passed the α-amylase test. Other nations pasteurize bulked liquid egg also, but the processing times and temperatures vary. Liquid whole egg, yolk, and white should be pasteurized before being dried.

Liquid egg white coagulates at a lower temperature so that pasteurization is difficult but not impossible; a maximum temperature of 57·2 to 57·8 °C (135 to 136 °F) can be used, or higher if the egg white is stabilized in some way. Pan-dried flaked albumen may

Table 18   *Salmonella* from imported egg products (1961–75)*

Egg product	1961–70			1971–5		
	Number examined	Number positive	%	Number examined	Number positive	%
Whole dried	4289	266	5·3	695	1	0·1
Albumen						
flake and granules	2390	128	5·4	386	12	3·1
powder	2999	57	1·9	1389	16	1·1
frozen	3199	68	2·1	924	6	0·6

* Unpublished results from the Food Hygiene Laboratory.

be heated in the dry state at 54·4 °C (130 °F) for 9 to 10 days to kill salmonellae but the treatment of spray-dried albumen by heat is unsatisfactory because of its low moisture content. It is hoped that in the future both these products will be made from pasteurized liquid albumen. There is no α-amylase in egg white, therefore this particular test cannot be used as a criterion of satisfactory pasteurization of albumen. A summary of results for the isolation of salmonellae from imported dehydrated whole egg and albumen and frozen albumen for the years 1961 to 1970 and 1971 to 1975 is given in Table 18. The results indicate that there has been an improvement in the rate of contamination, but that bulk egg products can still be a source of salmonellae.

Irradiation of frozen liquid whole egg, or the white and yolk with small doses of gamma-rays will also kill salmonellae but the method is still without official sanction.

Desserts and sweets

In the sweet group, ice-cream, imitation cream, trifles, custards, and other lightly cooked and uncooked milk and egg dishes and coconut confectionery have all been responsible for outbreaks of food poisoning.

Ice-cream

The Ice-cream (Heat Treatment, etc.) Regulations of 1959, originally introduced in 1947, require ice-cream mix to be pasteurized by holding the mix either at 65·6 °C (150 °F) for at least 30 minutes, at 71·1 °C (160 °F) for at least 10 minutes, or at 79·4 °C (175 °F) for at least 15 seconds followed by cooling to 7·2 °C (45 °F) within $1\frac{1}{2}$ hours and it must not rise above this temperature until it is frozen; it must remain frozen until sold. A mix which has been held at 149 °C (300 °F) for 2 seconds and transferred aseptically into sterile, airtight containers need not be reduced in temperature until required for freezing. This mix is distributed for use in the preparation of 'soft ice-cream' which is frozen at the counter immediately prior to sale.

'Soft ice-cream' is also prepared from the pasteurized mix stored at 7·2 °C (45 °F) until required for freezing at the counter. The responsibility for the hygienic handling of such unfrozen mixtures thus passes from the specialist manufacturer to those who may not be so conscious of the need for vigorous cleansing and disinfection of the freezer and other apparatus in contact with the ice-cream.

Ice-cream prepared with a cold-mix powder evaporated and dried from a liquid mix which has received approved heat treatment need not be heated again but must be frozen within an hour of reconstitution.

Before 1947 when the regulations were made, ice-cream mix was frozen at the convenience of the manufacturer. Bacteria introduced by food handlers responsible for preparing the mix or from ingredients, multiplied during warm storage between mixing and freezing. Many outbreaks of food poisoning occurred (Chapters 6 and 8). After 1947 the hygienic quality of ice-cream was much improved in the UK and other countries with similar regulations; it is now known to be safe.

The introduction of a grading scheme based on tests for bacteriological content helped to improve the general hygiene of the ice-cream trade.

It has been demonstrated frequently that thorough cleaning and disinfection of equipment is essential for the production of a high standard of bacterial cleanliness in ice-cream. The bacteriological examination of samples taken from different points throughout the processing plant will help to indicate sources of contamination arising from faults in cleaning procedures; sources or foci of contamination may be found in the cooler, in pipes or buckets used to convey the cream from the cooler to the ageing vat, or in the vat itself, freezer, or conservator. Imperfect control of 'holder' type pasteurization may allow the survival of contaminants, from ingredients, which can multiply in imperfectly cleaned equipment. Various detergents are available for the preliminary washing process which should be followed by the application of steam, hypochlorite, or other suitable bactericidal agent.

Imitation cream

Many outbreaks of salmonellosis and paratyphoid fever have been traced to the consumption of imitation cream cakes such as chocolate éclairs, cream buns, cream layer sponges, meringues, and other confectionery including trifles garnished with cream.

The ingredients of the different types of confectionery cream vary widely. Usually they contain dried milk products emulsified with fat and a little sugar. Further nutriment is supplied from the choux pastry, sponge cakes, and other confectionery in contact with the cream, and bacterial growth is encouraged.

Some creams have a high concentration of sugar and fat so that bacteria are unable to grow in them although they may survive for many days. Egg products are rarely incorporated into imitation cream but the food-poisoning organisms which may be present in liquid or dried egg products reach the cream from utensils, vessels, surfaces, hands, and perhaps by splashes. It was assumed for many years that food-poisoning organisms originated from human excreters among food handlers responsible either for the manufacture of the cream or for its use in the bakery or kitchens. Whilst there was always the possibility of infection from human sources, the first and more potent danger was the contamination of uncooked products such as cream by the salmonellae in the egg ingredients of cake and pastry mixes. The compulsory pasteurization of bulked whole egg reduced, if not eliminated, the risk of paratyphoid fever and salmonella food poisoning from imitation cream cakes and other confectionery.

Fresh cream has largely superseded imitation cream; there are few outbreaks traced to fresh cream confectionery in the United Kingdom. Staphylococcal enterotoxin food poisoning from cream cakes is often reported in the United States of America.

Manufactured imitation cream is now pasteurized before canning and it is unusual to find a proprietary brand which is not of good bacteriological quality (low bacterial count) on delivery.

Outbreaks described in Chapter 6 illustrate the ease with which food-poisoning bacteria can spread from contaminated ingredients via mixing bowls, utensils, and other articles to cream mixes and finished products; failure to disinfect piping and Savoy bags each time they are used is another factor in the spread of contamination.

Trifles, custards and other lightly cooked milk and egg dishes

All of these foods contain milk and egg constituents and so they are suitable for the growth of micro-organisms; they are mostly eaten cold so that there is often opportunity and time for bacterial multiplication after preparation. Staphylococci from the hands may contaminate these products.

Organisms from egg products are unlikely to survive the cooking but they may be introduced with bacteria from other ingredients such as sponge cakes contaminated from surfaces, utensils, or fingers. There is no evidence for the survival of salmonellae in baked custards, custard tarts or flans, Swiss rolls, or sponges. Moreover the results of experiments indicate that with normal baking procedures angel cake, Genoese slab, Japanese biscuits, macaroons, and meringues are safe, but that when baking temperatures are allowed to fluctuate due to irregular opening of oven doors, salmonellae may survive. However, recontamination after cooking is considered to be the more serious hazard, particularly when powdered or flaked egg products are in use, because they are readily air-borne and dust-borne.

Coconut and gelatin

Desiccated coconut is frequently used to garnish and flavour cakes, trifles, and other custard dishes. Many tons, graded according to the particle size, are imported annually into the UK for industrial use in cakes and biscuits, and for making sweets; it is used also by the housewife and canteen cook for cakes, puddings, and desserts. In 1959 salmonellae including paratyphoid bacilli were isolated from 8 to 10 per cent of port samples of desiccated coconut. Cases of paratyphoid fever in children were traced to coconut confectionery and salmonellae including *S. paratyphi B* were isolated from sweetmeats and other confectionery coated with coconut. Industrial representation to the country of origin resulted in new legislation for improved hygiene which reduced the proportion of contaminated samples to negligible levels.

Salmonellae have been isolated from marshmallow as well as from uncooked coconut used as a coating. Occasional imports of gelatin used as a coagulant for marshmallow and for many other purposes have been found to contain salmonellae. Whether the organism survived the brief cooking of marshmallow or whether the cooked article became recontaminated in the whipping process was not known, but it was suspected that cooked mixtures may have been whipped in the same bowl as the cold uncooked mix. It is essential, therefore, to ensure that powdery commodities from food ingredients such as gelatin, coconut, and egg are free from contamination with organisms of the salmonella group and staphylococci. Bacterial spores will survive in small numbers and it is almost impossible to eliminate them from dehydrated products. It is assumed that spores are eaten daily without harm, but when they germinate into bacilli which grow and multiply in rehydrated and cooked dishes food poisoning may occur. The addition of liquefied gelatin to pies after cooking has been responsible for widespread outbreaks of food poisoning (see p. 100).

Fish and other seafoods

Fish eaten freshly cooked is an improbable vehicle of bacterial food poisoning. Salmonellae are unlikely to be harboured in creatures with a low body temperature and mostly caught far out at sea. Nevertheless these organisms have been isolated from fish taken from polluted river water and also from fish taken from the holds of ships washed out with polluted dock water. Contamination may take place when the fish are gutted and filleted at the quayside or in shops. Made-up dishes such as fishcakes and fish pies may be contaminated with staphylococci from the hands of those working with cooked fish, cooked potatoes, batter, and bread crumbs; there may be a build-up of contamination in equipment used for mashed potatoes, in the commercial production of fishcakes, so that a focus of infection is formed. *Clostridium perfringens* food poisoning has arisen from frozen salmon imperfectly thawed, and after boiling or steaming left in the liquor overnight to cool and then eaten cold.

Clostridium botulinum type E may be found in some fish; whether the organism is a natural inhabitant of the fish-gut is not known. However, many outbreaks of botulism in Canada, the USA, and Japan have been attributable to uncooked, or under-cooked, stale or fermented fish and also seal and whale meat. Smoked fish in open or vacuum packs, sold chilled or at ambient temperatures, and faults in canning of fish (tuna) have given rise to occasional outbreaks of botulism due to *C. botulinum* type E in various countries during recent years. (See also page 76.)

Food poisoning from *Vibrio parahaemolyticus* is common in Japan where fish and other seafoods may be infected from coastal waters. Uncooked seafoods and also recontaminated cooked fish and crab meat have been reported as vehicles of infection from other countries also.

Shell-fish

Oysters and mussels are often bred or fattened in the sewage-polluted waters of tidal estuaries, and oysters are usually consumed uncooked. From time to time cases and outbreaks of typhoid and paratyphoid fever are attributed to oysters collected from rivers receiving sewage from houses inhabited by carriers. The last outbreak of typhoid fever from this cause occurred in 1957.

There were four large stations in the United Kingdom for cleansing shell-fish — three for mussels and one for oysters. Of these only the Conway station survives; overhead expenses were great and stations cleansing mussels work only during the winter months; also, fisheries have failed. There are smaller stations for mussels from private fisheries and privately owned tanks for cleansing oysters; the water is usually purified by ultraviolet light. There are thirty or more of these small plants in the UK. They usually consist of a series of interconnected tanks; the water may be recirculated or continuously flowing from rivers or sea. The oysters are layed out on trays and remain in the tanks for 36 to 48 hours. Some of these stations may be ineffective, particularly when water is taken from highly polluted sources and the output of ultraviolet light is low. Organisms other than *Escherichia coli* and notably vibrio-type organisms can build up in the tanks and pipelines and also in the flesh of the oysters.

From 1964 onwards particular attention has been given to outbreaks of gastroenteritis of recognizable aetiology following the eating of oysters which have been cleaned in tanks of water treated with ultraviolet light. The *Esch. coli* count of samples of oysters associated with outbreaks is usually satisfactory but counts of other organisms may be high. The well-known agents of food poisoning have not been found either in the oysters or in the stools of patients. The isolation of *V. parahaemolyticus* in some coastal waters and sea creatures has suggested that vibrios may be responsible for the oyster disease.

At Conway the mussels brought by the fishermen are laid in large tanks and covered with freshly chlorinated sea-water for 48 hours. The mussels cleanse themselves by excretion and the internal contents drop through grids to the bottom of the tank. The cleansed shell-fish are bagged and collected by the fishermen (Fig. 9).

There are local laws relating to the cleansing of shell-fish. At Conway, for example, the Conway Mussel Fishery (Amendment) Order of 1948 states that any person taking mussels from the Conway River and failing 'to deposit them forthwith at the Purification Tanks' shall be guilty of an offence. On a more general scale there are over forty Closing Orders which prohibit the sale of shell-fish for food either absolutely or unless they have been treated

Fig. 9   Conway Station for cleansing shell-fish

in some way. These Orders are made under the Food and Drugs Act. They cover a large proportion of our coasts and of the areas suitable for growing shell-fish. If a fishery does not have a Closing Order there is probably no sewage pollution in the area or there is efficient treatment and the shell-fish fall regularly into the bacteriological Sanitary Grade I, that is, less than 5 *Esch. coli* per ml of body tissue in 9 or 10 mussels or in single oysters. This standard is widely accepted in the United Kingdom and in Europe.

Closing Orders refer to the gathering, distribution, etc., of shell-fish for sale for human consumption, and so they do not prevent people from gathering them for their own consumption. The law is only broken when shell-fish are sold or otherwise distributed to other people. Thus, while it is not illegal for itinerant pickers to gather mussels from any shore, they may not legally sell them if they come from a Closed Area.

There are few recorded incidents of bacterial food poisoning from mussels, since they are usually cooked by the consumer. The cockle industry is different. The cockles are collected into huts, cooked, and sometimes salted before distribution. Incidents thought to have been caused by cockles have occurred during warm weather when bacterial multiplication after cooking, during storage and retail sale in shops and on stalls, will be greatest.

Shell-fish imported from other countries should be accompanied by a certificate of bacterial purity.

Frozen cooked seafoods

Frozen cooked prawns, shrimps, and lobster tails are produced by a number of countries for international trade. They may be handled extensively after cooking and before freezing yet for most imports there have been few isolations of salmonellae from samples examined directly from the port. It must be assumed therefore that they are rarely contaminated by human excreters and that they are not a natural source of salmonellae; even raw frozen samples are rarely found to contain salmonellae.

Although staphylococci may be isolated from the hands frequently, outbreaks of staphylococcal food poisoning from seafoods are not common in the United Kingdom. *Vibrio parahaemolyticus* and other pathogenic vibrios are not infrequently isolated from samples of imported frozen cooked prawns from the East. If they are thawed in warm water some hours before they are required for a large function, there is the possibility of bacterial multiplication followed by food poisoning from prawn cocktail, or seafood salad. Microbiological guidelines for the industry and port health authorities may be of value in producing a more hygienic product.

Viable counts of less than 100 000 per g are the aim; recommendations that there should be not more than 10 per g of *Escherichia coli* and not more than 1000 per g of coagulase-positive staphylococci should be readily attainable with care in manufacture.

The responsibility of maintaining the product in a good bacteriological condition rests with the user, and the time and temperature of storage between thawing and consumption are important, as for all frozen food.

Fruit

Acid fruits, for example cooked or canned apples and plums alone or in tarts and cordials, will not allow the growth of pathogenic bacteria but the organisms may survive for indefinite periods of time. It is sometimes advisable to wash dessert fruit, such as grapes and plums which are not normally peeled before being eaten, in water containing a small amount of sodium hypochlorite so that the amount of available chlorine in solution is approximately 60 to 80 ppm (the actual dilution of the product will depend on its concentration of hypochlorite and the volume of water used for washing). Many kinds of dessert fruits are imported from countries where the rate of excretion of intestinal pathogens is high and where the fly plays a major role in the spread of infection. Washing will remove traces of pesticides also.

Vegetables

Freshly cooked vegetables may be regarded as safe unless recontaminated after cooking but it is wise to wash salad vegetables such as lettuce, tomatoes, radishes, cucumber, and watercress in water with added sodium hypochlorite (60 to 80 ppm available chlorine) for not less than 30 seconds as recommended for dessert fruit. This is particularly important in countries where crops may be flooded with human sewage containing organisms of the *Shigella* group, *Salmonella typhi* and the paratyphoid bacilli, and protozoa such as the *Entamoeba*. The cysts of *E. histolytica* require heat for destruction.

In 1959 a small outbreak of food poisoning was attributed to an excess of the alkaloid solanine in the skin of imported potatoes. Solanine poisoning is uncommon, but outbreaks have been described in other countries due to unusually high concentrations of solanine developing in the skin or green shoots of potatoes.

Pickles, sauces, and mayonnaise

Pickles, sauces, and mayonnaise made with vinegar are highly acid and they are unlikely to cause food poisoning. Certain bacteria can grow in acid foods and some of these are able to cause spoilage, but they are not dangerous for man. Dressings and sauces made without vinegar, such as Hollandaise sauce, may contain eggs, fat, and flavouring matter only. As they are suitable for bacterial growth, they should be prepared with great care and attention to hygiene and they should be eaten within 1 or, at the most, 2 hours of preparation, unless stored in the refrigerator.

Some countries like a bland mayonnaise with a pH of 5 to 7; others, such as the UK, prefer a sharp flavour and add vinegar or lemon juice until the pH is approximately 3 to 4·5 and the growth of pathogens is repressed. When mayonnaise has a neutral pH, salmonellae from eggs or staphylococci from man can grow and many outbreaks of food poisoning from this commodity have been reported. Ingredients of uncooked non-acid foods should not include ducks' eggs or unpasteurized hen egg products.

Powdered foods

Dried food substances are not sterile. Some micro-organisms and particularly spores survive dehydration, but they will not grow until water is added and the temperature is suitable.

Proprietary cake mixes and meringue powders which incorporate unpasteurized powdered egg products may contain organisms of the salmonella group. Outbreaks of salmonellosis following the use of contaminated cake mixes have been described in Canada and the USA.

Bulked egg for drying can be, but is not always, pasteurized before dehydration. There is as yet no legislation in the United Kingdom for the pasteurization of egg albumen although many supplies are in fact heat treated before being frozen or dehydrated (see p. 64).

Dried milk contaminated with salmonellae caused an interstate outbreak of salmonella food poisoning in the USA; 17 families were affected. The source of contamination was thought to be raw milk from one of 800 farms supplying the dehydration plant. Spray dried milk powder has also been the food vehicle in staphylococcal enterotoxin food poisoning. In one extensive and widespread outbreak amongst schoolchildren, growth of *Staph. aureus* occurred in the evaporated milk during storage and before the drying chamber was reached. Sludge in the balance tank, immediately before homogenization, may have encouraged the growth of residual organisms. Many children were ill shortly after school meals in which uncooked dried milk had been added to fortify the calorie content.

Milled products such as wheat and other cornflours and also rice may contain sporing organisms such as *Bacillus cereus.* Cornflour sauce and cooked rice have been vehicles of food poisoning due to this organism. This and other sporing organisms are frequent contaminants of dairy plants and may cause spoilage.

Spices, dehydrated soups, baby foods, and other convenience foods will all contain spores but they should be low in numbers.

Fats

Lard, margarine, butter, and other fats do not encourage the growth of pathogenic bacteria, and they may be disregarded as media for food-poisoning organisms. If they are contaminated during preparation with typhoid, paratyphoid, or dysentery bacilli, then small numbers, surviving for many days, may cause infection. An unusual outbreak occurred in the USA from staphylococcal enterotoxin in butter emulsified in milk.

Bread

Some people are worried about the contamination of bread, and they regard the handling of unwrapped loaves with concern. Bread is seldom if ever responsible for bacterial food poisoning; the crust forms a barrier against the invasion of bacteria and, furthermore, the substance of the loaf is far too dry to allow the growth of bacteria unless it is in contact with a moist foodstuff. Intestinal pathogens causing infection in small doses only may be transferred on sliced bread from the hands of an excreter to the victim.

It is a matter of common observation that moulds grow readily on stale bread or on bread wrapped too soon after baking. Hitherto the growth of moulds in bread has not been regarded as a hazard, but there is a growing concern about mycotoxins.

Bread which is 'ropy', from the prolific growth of aerobic spore bearers, has been described as a cause of food poisoning.

Jam and similar sweetstuffs

Among those foods which may be disregarded as vehicles of food poisoning are the preserves such as jam, and also honey and syrup; they usually contain 60 per cent or more of sugar which will not permit the survival of most bacteria. Moulds may grow on the top of jam, especially when the sugar concentration is lower than required for preservation. Mouldy jam has not been recorded as a vehicle of food poisoning, but when certain fungi grow on food substances there may be the possibility of danger from mycotoxins.

Microbiological specifications and sampling

The microbiological examination of food samples enables an assessment to be made of the safety and quality of the bulk supply. It may be used also to measure the effectiveness of hygiene measures applied in a factory, shop, canteen, or home. Nevertheless, counts of general bacterial flora in a particular sample of food are subject to variation between laboratories and workers, and they should not be used for legislative purposes. When regarded as specifications and not standards or official requirements they provide useful guidelines of good manufacturing practice. The automation of counting methods may relieve the drudgery of the work but it is unlikely to give much greater accuracy with regard to reproducibility. Most probable number counts are uniform for water only; suspensions of food and even of milk cannot be made uniform. The clumping of organisms, the adherence of food and organisms to pipettes and other glassware and the uneven distribution of organisms within a food suspension are obstacles which cannot be entirely eradicated by homogenization and dilution.

In spite of all these drawbacks, it is observed that the higher the general bacterial counts, as well as counts of organisms indicative of more serious contamination, the greater the risk of food poisoning. For example, both *Clostridium perfringens* and *Bacillus cereus* in small numbers are commonly found in foods; their presence in large numbers is a warning of the possibility of both spoilage and food poisoning. Similarly, *Staphylococcus aureus* must be present in large numbers to form sufficient toxin to initiate symptoms. It is worth recording that investigations of gut flora in relation to colon cancer draw attention to diet and the effect of consuming large numbers of certain bacteria.

As only a small number of units from the total bulk of food material are examined there must be a careful approach to sampling and to the interpretation of the results of examination.

The number of samples should reflect the risk or hazard of the particular food and more samples are required when the hazard is greater. The International Commission on Microbiological Specifications for Foods have drawn up a scheme of sampling which incorporates two-class and three-class plans. The two-class plan provides presence or absence criteria for intestinal pathogens such as salmonellae. The three-class plan is based on enumeration levels of the general flora with minimum and maximum counts, when n = the number of sample units, m = the acceptable level, and M = the rejection level. Values between m and M are undesirable but are subject to a number c which can raise the acceptance level to meet the capabilities of the food industry. With experience of results of examination of food samples from many countries, reasonable specifications can be attained in accordance with good manufacturing practice; standard methods of examination must be used.

Many food commodities can be maintained in a wholesome state by monitoring the process rather than the finished product. Legislation is more applicable to process control than to the results of microbiological tests on the finished product. When the process is a reliable heat treatment, for example, the pasteurization of milk and of liquid whole egg, the destruction of enzymes such as phosphatase in milk and α-amylase in liquid whole egg can be demonstrated by appropriate tests. Dye tests are more arbitrary, but are preferable to direct count methods with regard to economy of time, effort, and expense. The methylene blue reductase test is applicable to milk, cream, and ice-cream and a resazurin test has been described for other foods.

For many foods, quality control will still depend on the presence, absence, or enumeration of pathogens and on the quantitative estimation of the general numbers of bacteria and of indicator organisms — so-called because they are regarded as associates of the pathogenic bacteria. The general plate count is probably the most informative index of food hygiene. Persistently high counts on retail samples of cold cooked meats, for example, should lead to a thorough investigation of processing and storage methods in shops, factories, and kitchens. However, plate counts must be interpreted with caution and with agreed latitude for variable results. Automated plate counts may provide advantages, but they are unlikely to ensure uniformity.

Certain raw foods known to contain salmonellae, for example, should be monitored over a long period of time in order to assess the general rate of contamination and its significance in the kitchen.

Animal feeds should be monitored also.

Addendum — Outbreak of botulism in the UK, July 1978

Four persons were admitted to hospital suffering from severe symptoms of botulism; two of the patients died. Neurological symptoms developed about 9 hours after a meal consisting of freshly opened canned salmon from the USA, salad and fresh fruit and cream. Laboratory tests confirmed the presence of *C. botulinum* type E toxin in specimens of sera from the patients and the organism itself was isolated from a very small portion of the salmon.

6

Epidemiology and outbreaks of food poisoning

Epidemiology

Epidemiology deals with the frequency, distribution, and determinants of disease or disability in human and animal populations. Frost stated that 'epidemiology is something more than the total of the established facts. It includes their orderly arrangement into chains of inference which extend more or less beyond the bounds of direct observation. Such of these chains as are well and truly laid guide investigations to the facts of the future; those that are ill made fetter progress.'

The definitive terms used to study community disease include 'incidence', the number of new events, episodes, or outbreaks in a specified time period, for example, ten *Clostridium perfringens* food poisoning outbreaks in one month (dynamic), and 'prevalence', the number of events existing at one point in time, for example, one hundred patients with salmonella infection reported now compared with ninety last year at the same time.

The investigation of food poisoning in England and Wales is facilitated by notification under the Health Services and Public Health Act 1968. The community health physician should be informed of all suspected and actual cases and outbreaks. All communicable diseases are the dual responsibility of the NHS and local authorities. The community health specialists and the environmental health officers should seek the aid of clinicians, veterinarians, microbiologists, epidemiologists, and workers in other disciplines.

The sooner an outbreak is notified to the authorities the greater is the chance of isolating the bacterial agent from the food, stool, or vomit specimens. Retrospective investigations through the chain of infection to the source can then begin.

Data from notified incidents enable annual statistics to be collated. Incidence rates for each bacterial agent of infection or intoxication, and the food vehicle most frequently associated with food poisoning

77

due to each agent, provide valuable information for assessing the main sources and modes of spread, and faults in food preparation such as lack of cooling and cold storage facilities.

Data required from outbreaks include: (1) the clinical nature of the illness; (2) the incubation period, which is the interval between effective exposure to an agent and onset of symptoms; (3) epidemic curves amongst affected persons; (4) attack rates by age, sex, and even race, which give the incidence rate when there is a limited period of risk, and the non-attack rate; (5) the place; (6) the occasion; (7) the size of the catering concern; and (8) the climatic conditions. Many of these factors are standard criteria for the epidemiological investigation of any disease. In addition for food-borne diseases the history of the food is required, including environmental studies of the area of food production and preparation — from the farm origin, through dealers, markets, processing factories, wholesale and retail outlets, to catering establishments, including restaurants, canteens, and travel and domestic kitchens. Transport conditions for live animals and foodstuffs are also important.

Surveillance studies may be required both of nationally prepared and imported foods and animal feedstuffs to find out the proportion contaminated and to what extent. Unknown to the food handlers, intestinal pathogens from raw foods can be spread around the environment of food preparation areas and pass to cooked foods; they may temporarily become part of the flora excreted by the food handlers. It is not always sufficient to report merely the presence of a pathogenic organism in a sample of food; estimation of the approximate numbers may help to assess the potential hazard in terms of dose level for the consumer. The common spoilage organisms such as *C. perfringens, B. cereus,* and *Esch. coli* are frequently found in small numbers in both raw and cooked foods. When the numbers rise to a million or higher per gram, in cooked foods particularly, there are faults in the preparation and storage of the foods which need investigation. The significance of salmonella contamination in raw foods is usually based on the percentage rate of contamination of a large number of samples examined over a long period of time. Salmonellae in cooked foods should not be tolerated.

In order to follow the pathways of bacterial agents of disease as an aid to epidemiological studies, it is necessary to use the available methods of typing. Biochemical, serological, bacteriophage and bacteriocin methods, antibiotic sensitivity and the identity of toxins may all be used to establish characteristic patterns of reactions. Tests for pathogenicity are also required for suspected food-poisoning organisms not hitherto regarded as traditional agents of disease.

Although not strictly belonging to epidemiological studies, the behaviour or characteristics of bacterial agents in food are important factors to consider when preventive measures are devised — usually under the heading of 'food hygiene'. The temperature limits for growth, the optimum generation time (rate of multiplication), the heat resistance in relation to cooking methods and initiation of growth are all important. Also the survival and growth under different conditions of water activity (A_w), pH, salt, nitrite and other preservatives should be considered. Ease of sporulation and toxin production under different conditions are important too.

Laboratory work includes a study of stool (and vomit) specimens from the maximum number of those affected and those not affected also. Food handlers should be examined — they may be victims of the food they handle and excrete the salmonella serotypes found in raw meats and poultry; they may have initiated food contamination, which is usually so for staphylococcal food poisoning.

If the food is not available then careful food histories may help to identify the agent in terms of food preparation. For example, there were 85 cases of food poisoning in a population of 2000 students. Eighty of those affected had selected, among other items, steak and kidney pie while only five of the cases had eaten fish and chips. An epidemiological calculation of the risk of being poisoned, given that one ate steak and kidney pie is given below:

	Cases (poisoning)	Controls (remained well)	Total
Ate steak and kidney pie	80	920	1000
Ate fish and chips	5	995	1000
Total	85	1915	2000

Thus the likelihood of being poisoned, given a history of steak and kidney pie, would be $\dfrac{80\times995}{5\times920} = 17\cdot3$, quite a high probability.

However, when amongst a group of people some fall ill, the proof of food poisoning should depend on the isolation of food poisoning organisms from food common to all the patients and also from the stools of a number of patients, particularly when the nature of the outbreak suggests that salmonellae are the causal agents. It is important also to find out the foods eaten by those who remained well. It should be emphasized that not all those at risk from eating contaminated food will be ill. The character of the causal agent and its behaviour in food may indicate the reason for its growth in food and suggest the preventive measures which should be taken.

A team of workers is required to unravel the events leading to food-borne disease — medical and food microbiologists, technologists, veterinary officers and environmental health officers should work together. A suggested proforma for those receiving the first information and who are responsible for the action to be taken is given in Appendix C, page 333.

Outbreaks of food poisoning

The occurrence of bacterial food poisoning depends on a peculiar set of circumstances; the following essential factors must be present:

(1) the infecting organism (causal agent), which has reached the kitchen in foodstuffs or which is present in the food handler or in animals;
(2) the hands of the food handler or kitchen surfaces, utensils, boards, cloths and other articles of equipment soiled by contaminated foods or hands;
(3) a food suitable for bacterial growth;
(4) conditions favourable for warm storage over a period of 2 hours or more;
(5) susceptible human subjects.

The investigation and prevention of food poisoning depends on the ability to find out the details relating to each of these five factors.

The clinical symptoms and incubation period, as described in Chapter 3, will generally indicate whether the illness is due to the toxin or infection type of bacterial food poisoning.

Immediately information about food poisoning is received, the kitchen staff should be warned not to throw any foodstuffs away. The cause of many food poisoning incidents has been obscured because left-over remains of meats have been discarded before the environmental health officer has arrived.

The isolation and identification of bacteria of known pathogenic significance from the food and the patients is the key to further investigation. It may also bring to light contaminated sources of raw materials, imported or home-produced, which will require further investigation and research to make them safe.

The food vehicle is often found among prepared meats and poultry, warmed-up dishes, lightly cooked egg and milk products, and other foods which are suitable for bacterial growth and which may have been left for some hours without refrigeration.

If the suspected foodstuff is not available for examination then it may be useful to sample the ingredients, particularly raw meats and poultry which are known to be sources of salmonellae.

If the nature of the outbreak suggests that it is due to salmonellae other than *Salmonella typhi*, then enquiries should be made about all raw meat and poultry and other protein foods used in the kitchen and samples should be examined from kitchen, retail, and wholesale sources. Stools from patients and food handlers must be examined also.

If food poisoning from staphylococcal enterotoxin is suspected, stools and vomit samples from patients should be examined as well as foods, and also swabs from the nose, throat, hands, and any pustular spots or even healed lesions on food handlers. The results may reveal food handlers carrying the staphylococcus which has grown and produced enterotoxin in the food.

When *Clostridium perfringens* food poisoning is suspected, food and stools from patients must be examined. The organism is common in many foodstuffs and it is excreted in small numbers by most people, but when food poisoning occurs it will be found in large numbers in food and faeces. There is little or no significance in positive results from food handlers, and preventive measures should be directed towards obtaining better cooling and cold storage facilities.

Whatever the source of the food-poisoning bacteria, faults in preparation and storage will have led to multiplication of the organism in the cooked food (vehicle) which is the immediate cause of the outbreak. Efforts should be made, therefore, to find out not only the source but also how the organisms spread from raw to cooked foods or from persons to cooked foods in relation to methods of food preparation, and where the time lag occurred after cooking which allowed growth at temperatures convenient for the organism.

It cannot be assumed that food handlers found to be excreting the relevant organism after an outbreak are necessarily the source of infection, they may be victims through handling or eating raw materials already contaminated before entering the kitchen. Nevertheless, such victims with loose stools may help to spread infection to foods and in the environment.

Examples of typical food poisoning outbreaks are given in the next few pages. In the first, a straightforward outbreak of staphylococcal toxin food poisoning, the chain of events could easily have been broken if those responsible for the preparation of the food had understood the factors causing the contamination and had taken steps to ensure efficient cold storage.

The ham sandwich outbreak (Fig. 10)

A coach-load of people left London one summer morning on their way to the coast for a day's outing. They took with them, for their lunch, ham sandwiches cut and prepared at a public house in the home area. Before they had travelled far many had started to eat their sandwiches, and as they were nearing the coast the first victim

Ham, contaminated with cook's nasal staphylococci and stored in a broken refrigerator, made into sandwiches for a coach party.

Meanwhile cook takes some ham home.

She and husband taken to hospital that night.

Some were eaten on the way.

At the seaside several of the party taken to hospital.

Fig. 10   The ham sandwich outbreak on a trip to the seaside

LABORATORY FINDINGS
Staphylococci of the same type were isolated from ham, faeces, vomit, and from nose of cook.

COMMENTS
(1) Food handlers must not finger their noses.
(2) Food must be stored in a refrigerator below 4 °C (39·2 °F).

began to feel ill; soon other members of the party were unwell. When they arrived at the coast the illness was acute and several people were taken into the local hospitals.

News of the outbreak soon reached the medical officer of health for the area, and the coach was searched for the remains of the food; fortunately, one or two ham sandwiches were found. Specimens of stool and vomit were collected from the patients who had been taken to hospital, and these specimens were submitted to the local public health laboratory. The following day investigations were started by the medical officer of health in London. Inquiries were made at the public house where the sandwiches had been prepared; those responsible for making them were questioned about the method of preparation and the source of the ham. The bacteriologists at the coast town found large numbers of staphylococci in ham from the sandwiches retrieved from the coach, and staphylococci were found in the vomit and faeces of the patients who were in hospital. At the same time another laboratory found staphylococci in the remains of the ham taken from the public house. When the staphylococci from the three sources were compared, they were found to belong to the same type — one often associated with foodstuffs known to have caused staphylococcal enterotoxin food poisoning. The woman who prepared the sandwiches took home a small portion of the ham to share with her husband for supper; about 2 hours later they, too, became violently ill and were taken to hospital by ambulance. The strains of staphylococci isolated from these patients proved to be of the same type as that isolated from the specimens examined in the coast town and in London. The next step was to discover how these organisms had reached the meat, and why they had multiplied.

The ham was cooked at the public house; it was stored in a refrigerator and brought out day by day for the preparation of sandwiches. There were two faults: the first that the worker used her hands freely to hold the ham bone and the sliced ham, and second that the refrigerator motor failed so that conditions were warm inside the cabinet. The particular staphylococcus was resident in the nose of the worker and it would frequently be on her hands, and pass from her hands to the ham. Conditions were ideal for multiplication — warm summer weather and lack of refrigeration. Staphylococci grow well and produce toxin in many cured meats because they can tolerate salt. There were many millions per gram in the ham, and the rapid onset of violent symptoms indicated the presence of a high concentration of toxin. The organisms were isolated also from samples of faeces and vomit from the patients.

It is worth noting that the carrier herself was a victim of the toxin formed by the organisms transferred from her nose to the ham. Immunity to the powerful toxin which certain staphylococci produce during active multiplication in foodstuffs is not acquired while the organism is resident in the nose or throat. It is not easy to remove the organism; in some instances it may be possible, but in others it is better for the carrier to be transferred to other work. It may not be possible to eliminate staphylococci from the hands even after washing.

The gelatin glaze outbreak (Fig. 11)

In another widespread outbreak of food poisoning due to staphylococcal toxin, the glaze on the outside of liver sausage loaves became heavily contaminated with staphylococci of a food-poisoning type. This foodstuff was prepared on a large scale by a factory, and the meat loaves were distributed over a wide area of the country. More than 400 cases were reported in this outbreak, and there may have been many hundreds more which remained unnotified.

Large numbers of specimens of the liver sausage loaf were sent to the laboratory from various parts of the country, and each specimen told the same story. The glaze contained up to 100 million per g of staphylococci, whereas the meat part of the loaf was almost free from organisms. It was clear that the loaf had been correctly processed, that it was free from contamination, and that the glaze only had been contaminated during preparation.

The factory was visited and the methods of manufacture were watched closely. At the same time swabs were taken from the nose, hands, and any lesions or spots of all the personnel engaged in the processing, glazing, or packing. Table tops and utensils were also swabbed and samples of glaze and the constituents were taken for examination; faults in the methods of production were observed. The operative, his shirt-sleeves rolled up to the elbow, blended each ingredient by hand in a steam-jacketed container; the temperature of the mix never rose above 50 °C (122 °F) so that contaminating organisms from the hands would not be killed at any stage in the preparation.

The process of glazing took several hours; a jug was continually filled by hand from the tank and the glaze was poured over the minced liver loaves resting on grids above the tank. The bulk supply of glaze was kept in the large jacketed container while the glazing was in progress, and the small tank which supplied the well for glazing was replenished when necessary from the bulk supply, kept at approximately 34 °C (93·2 °F).

The outbreak took place during a warm spell of weather in June, when conditions were ideal for the multiplication of the contaminating staphylococci. The glaze was an excellent medium for bacterial growth, and supplies left over from one day's work were kept overnight in the refrigerator to be added to the fresh batch of glaze made the following day, thus serving as an inoculum.

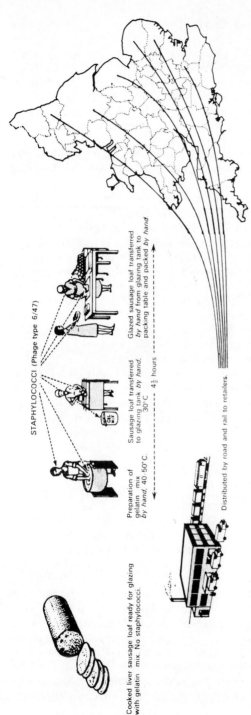

Cooked liver sausage loaf ready for glazing with gelatin mix. No staphylococci.

STAPHYLOCOCCI (Phage type 6/47)

Preparation of gelatin mix *by hand*, 40–50°C.

Sausage loaf transferred to glazing tank *by hand*. 30°C

Glazed sausage loaf transferred *by hand* from glazing tank to packing table and packed *by hand*

4½ hours

Distributed by road and rail to retailers.

Fig. 11 The contaminated glaze outbreak of food poisoning — staphylococcal enterotoxin

LESSONS LEARNT FROM OUTBREAK

(1) All contact of hands with food should be avoided.

(2) Personnel with septic fingers or other skin sepsis, acute colds, or abdominal upsets with diarrhoea, should not engage in food handling. The nose is the reservoir of staphylococci and infection may be conveyed from nose to food via the hands.

(3) Hands must be washed frequently while handling food, and particularly after visiting the WC. There should be hot running water, antiseptic soap, and plentiful supplies of clean towels, or preferably destructible paper towels or an enclosed roller towel.

(4) All cooked foods and made-up foodstuffs including fillings and glazes intended to be eaten cold should be given sufficient heat treatment to render them sterile or free from vegetative bacteria. Surplus filling and glazing material should not be stored overnight.

(5) Cooked foods, not intended for immediate consumption, should be wrapped or covered and kept at a temperature not higher than 4 °C (39·2 °F).

(6) Food containers and utensils should be well washed in hot water containing a good detergent and rinsed in water as hot as possible (not less than 80 °C). A disinfectant, e.g. hypochlorite, used separately or combined with the detergent is an advantage.

(7) Food containers and utensils, after rinsing in hot water 80–90 °C (176–194 °F), should be allowed to drain and not be dried with a cloth. Where it is essential to wipe them, paper may be used or cloths should be washed daily.

The visit to the factory took place one week after the outbreak had occurred. By this time the food-poisoning staphylococcus was fairly widespread in the glazing and packing room. It was found in the nose and on the hands of four people, and in swabs from portions of equipment and the paper used for packing the meat loaves. After outbreaks of food-borne disease the organisms responsible may become more widely dispersed in the environment than hitherto. There are many means of spreading infection including the handling of communal utensils and other equipment, and the use of communal roller towels. It is advisable to take a series of specimens from the nose, throat, and hands of suspected carriers, in order to distinguish transient from persistent carriage.

In this particular outbreak the follow-up work revealed that the employee who prepared the glaze harboured in his nose the type of staphylococcus which caused the outbreak. He was transferred to other work which did not involve the handling of susceptible foodstuffs. It was agreed that the glazing operation should be stopped temporarily and the particular area of the factory was thoroughly cleaned and disinfected.

The methods used were wrong and in order to minimize the risk of further contamination, it was recommended that the hands of the operatives should not come in open contact with the glaze during or after preparation, and that after the ingredients had been added the glaze mixture be brought to the boil. It was suggested that glazing should be carried out in a cool room and that the temperature of the glaze during this process should be maintained at approximately 60 °C (140 °F); any glaze left over after the day's work would be discarded. Thus a build-up of bacteria in the glaze would be prevented.

The lambs' tongues outbreak (Fig. 12)

An outbreak of food poisoning which occurred in a factory canteen was due to the contamination of lambs' tongues with staphylococci from the hands of two members of the kitchen staff. The frozen tongues arrived in sacks. They were allowed to thaw; they were then cooked, and laid out carefully in rows on enamel trays which stood on a table in the kitchen until the tongues were cool enough to handle. Six people stood around the table and removed the skin from each tongue, using hand and knife. The skinned tongues were again placed in rows on enamel trays and allowed to stand in the kitchen for a further period, before being refrigerated overnight. Early next morning they were taken out and sliced by one man. The slices were placed on dinner plates which were kept warm in the hotplate container until ready for lunch at midday. It was shown that, although the lower two shelves of the hot cupboard were

Frozen lambs' tongues arrived in sacks.

Boiled for 2½ hours.

Allowed to cool before handling.

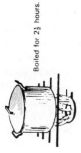

Six people helped to skin the tongues by hand. Two were found to be hand carriers of food-poisoning staphylococci.

Next morning tongues taken from refrigerator and sliced by hand. Opportunity for further contamination.

42°C
60°C
145°C

Plates of sliced tongue placed in hot-plate for one to two hours before serving. Staphylococci multiply in food on top shelf (42°C).

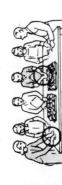

Infected tongues allowed to cool for about two hours before going into refrigerator. Staphylococci multiply.

CANTEEN
70 people ill after eating tongue. Incubation period — three hours.

2 hours   4 hours   6 hours

Staphylococci growing in tongue as seen microscopically at intervals after handling.

Fig. 12 The lambs' tongues outbreak of food poisoning — staphylococcal enterotoxin

maintained at a temperature which would kill most bacteria, the temperature of the top shelf was much lower, in fact suitable for bacterial multiplication. A few cooked tongues not used for the meal were stored in the refrigerator. They were examined at the laboratory and found to contain large numbers of staphylococci of the usual food-poisoning type.

The large factory canteen was visited a few days after the outbreak to investigate the source of the staphylococci and the reason for their multiplication.

Many people worked in the kitchen, and nose and hand swabs were taken from all of them. Table tops, floors, and other places were swabbed and samples of dust were collected.

Staphylococci were isolated from swabs of table tops and from dust even after instructions had been carried out that all surfaces should be cleaned with detergent and disinfected with hypochlorite solution. The tables were wooden and it seemed impossible to eliminate bacteria from the nooks and crannies of the irregular surface. The staphylococcus was found on the hands of two of the staff who had helped to skin the tongues; nose and hand swabs were taken at weekly intervals for several months. The organism was persistently cultured from the hands although there was no evidence that it was present in the nose. Finally, when drastic measures were used, such as exposure to ultraviolet light and the application of acriflavine to the hands, negative swabs were obtained. In the meantime, neither person was allowed to handle food known to encourage the growth of bacteria. The skinning by hand of cooked tongues while they are still warm always introduces a hazard of contamination by staphylococci. Outbreaks of staphylococcal food poisoning have occurred from large cooked tongues also. The long slow cooling of the cooked tongue followed by storage in the press provide admirable conditions for multiplication. There will be no further cooking when the tongue is eaten cold so that neither the organism nor its toxin will be destroyed. In the canning process of sterilization both the organism and its toxin are eliminated. Home processing should include a further cook after pressing.

The pressed beef outbreaks (Fig. 13)

A group of outbreaks due to staphylococcal toxin food poisoning from contaminated pressed beef are of interest because they illustrate once again the danger which may arise from much-handled cooked meat allowed to cool slowly overnight at atmospheric temperature.

During a warm summer, four outbreaks of food poisoning were

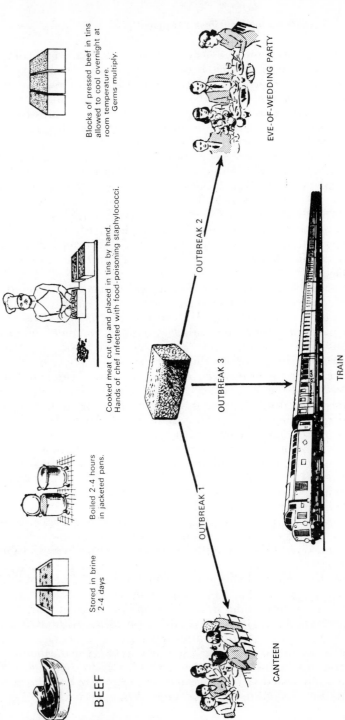

BEEF

Stored in brine 2-4 days

Boiled 2-4 hours in jacketed pans.

Cooked meat cut up and placed in tins by hand.
Hands of chef infected with food-poisoning staphylococci.

Blocks of pressed beef in tins allowed to cool overnight at room temperature.
Germs multiply.

OUTBREAK 1

OUTBREAK 3

OUTBREAK 2

CANTEEN

TRAIN

EVE-OF-WEDDING PARTY

Fig. 13 Pressed beef outbreaks of food poisoning—staphylococcal enterotoxin

reported almost simultaneously. At first, there seemed no connection between them; one had occurred on an express train speeding north, another at a wedding party held at an east coast town, another at a south coast resort, and the last in London. Specimens of food soon began to arrive at the laboratory; they included pressed beef which had been eaten by those affected in all four outbreaks. Large numbers of staphylococci of the usual food-poisoning type were isolated from many samples of pressed beef. In the meantime, the medical officer of health and health inspectors of the local authorities concerned had traced the origin of the various supplies to one particular factory. The factory was owned by a well-established and reputable firm of food manufacturers, who were astonished at the suggestion that they might have been responsible for any carelessness in production methods. Nevertheless, they co-operated willingly, genuinely anxious to find the cause of the trouble.

As usual the process of manufacture was watched from beginning to end. Samples of meat were collected at every stage of manufacture of the pressed beef, together with nose and hand swabs from all those in any way connected with its production; swabs from tables, utensils, and press cans were also taken. The laboratory results showed that the toxin-producing strain of staphylococcus was present in specimens of meat only after they had been handled in the process of filling the press cans. The chef who was responsible for this procedure was the only member of the staff who was carrying the infecting organisms on his hands. He had been doing this work for many years, and it was assumed that he had only recently become a hand carrier of a food poisoning type of staphylococcus. It may be difficult to convince carriers of potentially pathogenic bacteria of the part that they may play in the spread of infection.

The brine tank contained salt solution of the correct strength (16 to 18 per cent) and no staphylococci were found in it, nor were these organisms isolated from the samples of raw meat examined; samples of meat taken directly from the boiler were practically sterile. Only the chef's hands and the utensils used by him yielded the toxin-producing staphylococcus. His hands and nose were swabbed for many weeks; the hands were invariably positive, a few staphylococci were found in the nose on one occasion only. Many ways were tried to rid the hands of the staphylococci without success; the organisms still remained after washing.

The problem was temporarily solved by a change in the method of manufacture of the pressed beef, which was pressed into cans, hermetically sealed and heat treated. The cans were later discarded when it was desired to dispense the beef in open packs.

The ice-cream outbreaks

The Ice-Cream (Heat Treatment, etc.) Regulations introduced in 1947 stipulate that liquid ice-cream mix must be pasteurized and immediately cooled to 7·2 °C (45 °F) within 1½ hours of heat treatment. The chance contamination of ice-cream by excreters of intestinal pathogens, nasal and hand carriers of staphylococci and other nose and throat organisms capable of causing disease was far greater before the Regulations than at present. There was time for contaminating organisms to multiply in the mix before it was heated or after being heated before it was frozen, and thus outbreaks of infection and toxin poisoning occurred. In 1945, for instance, staphylococci carried in the nose and on the hands of a worker in the cook-house of an army hospital were introduced into batches of ice-cream mix after the ingredients had been cooked. The mix was allowed to cool slowly overnight and 20 to 30 hours elapsed before freezing. The staphylococci multiplied abundantly and formed enough harmful toxin to affect some 700 people. Had the mix been frozen very soon after it had been heated, as required by the present Regulations, there would have been no opportunity for the organisms to multiply, the toxin would not have been formed, and the food poisoning would not have occurred.

The typhoid outbreak at Aberystwyth described in Chapter 8 followed the contamination of ice-cream mix, several hours before freezing, by a urinary excreter of *Salmonella typhi*.

The cheese outbreaks

A family outbreak of staphylococcal toxin food poisoning followed the consumption of cheese made from goats' milk; it was the first of its kind to be reported in this country. Of six people, the five who became acutely ill 4 to 5 hours after tea had all eaten cheese made from goats' milk; the sixth, who escaped illness, had not eaten the cheese. Samples of this cheese showed the presence of many millions of staphylococci per g and the same type of staphylococcus was found in the faeces of one of the patients. This cheese was made by adding rennet to fresh goats' milk; the whey was strained through a clean muslin bag and the cheese was pressed into shape. Throat, nose, and hand swabs from those concerned in the milking and the cheese making failed to reveal staphylococci and there were no lesions on the hands of the milker or on the udders or teats of the goats. Yet from the freshly drawn milk of one goat the same type of staphylococcus was isolated, and it was assumed that multiplication of the organisms had taken place in the milk. Furthermore, extracts of the staphylococci isolated from the cheese produced violent symptoms in a human volunteer.

Some unusual outbreaks of staphylococcal food poisoning from Cheddar cheese drew attention to the fact that milk contaminated with staphylococci from the cow and insufficiently heated to kill the organisms could introduce staphylococci at the start of cheese making. If traces of penicillin or other antibiotic used in the treatment of cows suffering from staphylococcal and streptococcal diseases are present in milk, then the starter culture used for fermentation may be suppressed and the staphylococcus encouraged to grow in its place.

Such cheeses are mostly second grade and used only for processing, but they have sometimes been eaten and caused sickness. It is by no means certain that this cheese would be safe after processing. It has been recommended, therefore, that all milk intended for cheese making should be pasteurized and a law to this effect has already been passed in New Zealand. Outbreaks of staphylococcal food poisoning from unheated milk have also been reported. Although milk may come from tuberculin tested cattle it can nevertheless still be contaminated with food-poisoning organisms from the cow, milker, or equipment.

The vanilla cakes outbreak

Counts of *Staphylococcus aureus* from 18 to 200 million per g were found in vanilla cakes eaten by five families who reported sickness, abdominal pain, and in some instances diarrhoea 3 to 6 hours later. The cakes were sold from market stalls on a hot day. Staphylococci were also grown from a metal mixing bowl, an old burn on the hand of a bakery worker, and from the eczematous lesions on the right hand and elbow of another bakery worker; both were involved in the preparation of the vanilla cakes.

Other cold meat outbreaks

Many family outbreaks of staphylococcal food poisoning are caused simply by the contamination of cooked meats such as ham and similar products by the hands of food handlers in shops and homes. Then the lack of care in keeping these products cold during storage encourages multiplication of the organisms and toxin production.

The foods at wedding receptions are notorious vehicles of staphylococcal food poisoning. For example, 40 of 139 guests at a wedding developed vomiting, abdominal pain, and diarrhoea about 2 hours after a meal which included turkey and ham. Identical strains of staphylococci were isolated from turkey and ham, and from septic spots on the hand as well as from the nose of the food handler who had cut the ham and turkey the night before the reception.

At a dog show on a hot day, 30 of 120 spectators who ate cold chicken and salad for lunch developed abdominal pain, diarrhoea, and vomiting 2 to 3 hours later; 14 were admitted to hospital. The cooked chickens were left at 'tent' temperature overnight and jointed the following morning. There were 55 million staphylococci per g in a pooled sample of chicken joints.

Beef, ham, and tongue, remnants of a meal eaten in a church hall, were found to contain millions of staphylococci per g after all of 38 elderly ladies complained of symptoms; 11 were hospitalized. The meats had been handled by a number of persons including a chef, responsible for the slicing, who had recently returned to work after three weeks' absence with an injured finger and tonsillitis. There were no obvious lesions on his hands.

Cold chicken is so frequently responsible for staphylococcal food poisoning, that it is worthwhile to consider the reasons and to describe the events in the kitchen preceding such outbreaks.

Doctors at a lunch party were taken ill 2 to 4 hours after their meal of cold chicken and salad. The chicken had been cooked the day before and dismembered by hand while still warm. The portions were piled on trays and eventually placed in the refrigerator overnight. The cooling rate was slow and staphylococci from the hands of the workers were quick to grow in the warm chicken flesh. Multiplication would continue when the chicken was removed from the cold room and before service. A similar outbreak occurred on an aircraft after a meal of cold chicken prepared in the same way. The main fault was in portioning the chicken while it was still warm. The carcasses should not have been touched until cold and required for service. When food is cold the staphylococci will be slow to grow and the numbers will remain low until consumption if this is soon after the poultry carcasses have been portioned.

In many of these outbreaks the enterotoxin responsible for illness was demonstrated in growth from the staphylococci and sometimes from the food itself.

Food handlers should be aware that staphylococci are commonly present on the skin of the hands and other parts of the body; washing by ordinary means in soap and water does not remove them. Thus, care in handling cooked foods and, above all, care in prompt and persistent cold storage is essential. Small numbers of organisms are harmless but, as they grow, toxin is formed in the food and the longer the storage out of a refrigerator the larger the number of staphylococci and the greater the volume of toxin and if consumed the symptoms of illness may be more acute.

Staphylococci and salmonellae in canned food

Although canned goods should normally be regarded as safe, there have been instances in which leakage after processing has given rise to staphylococcal and salmonella food poisoning; even typhoid bacilli have multiplied in canned meat after leakage through microscopic holes.

In a series of outbreaks arising from 2·7 kg (6 lb) cans of peas it was found that the employee handling the cans after the water-cooling process had septic lesions on her hands caused by a food-poisoning strain of staphylococcus. A very occasional can was imperfect in its construction and a small pinhole in a seam would allow staphylococci from her hands to be sucked in with water while the can was still under vacuum — the pressure being lower inside than outside. The staphylococci grew inside the can and produced toxin but not gas so that the spoiled cans were not blown and there was no indication that the contents were contaminated. The degree of heat necessary to cook canned peas would be insufficient to destroy the toxin.

Similar outbreaks have been known to occur from freshly opened cans of meat, particularly corned beef, and again contaminated cooling water or contamination from the hands of employees were suspected as the source of the organism growing inside the can. A similar method of contamination may occur with organisms of the salmonella group including typhoid bacilli. The outbreak arising from *Salmonella typhi* in canned corned beef is described in Chapter 8.

Some canned meats such as ham, pork, and veal in large containers are not given sufficient heat treatment to sterilize them, in a deliberate attempt to produce a more appetizing food. The following incident illustrates the hazard which may occur.

Salmonella wien in canned ham

An unusual outbreak of salmonella infection occurred one September when 49 residents in two small adjoining towns suffered from diarrhoea and vomiting after eating portions of a large 6·3 kg (14 lb) cooked ham from a tin container. The time between ingestion and onset of symptoms varied from 4 to 5 hours, and an unusual member of the salmonella group was isolated from the actual substance of the remainder of the ham, from portions of ham recovered from purchasers, and from stools of all those who suffered from gastroenteritis.

The ham, part of a large consignment of 240 cans received from the Continent, had been preserved with salts in the usual way and pasteurized. This light heat treatment was intended, not to sterilize, but to reduce the bacterial content and to produce an appetizing product. Although sealed in a can for transport purposes, such hams cannot be compared with most canned foods which are given sufficient heat under pressure to kill all bacteria including those which are heat resistant; such sterile packs withstand storage for several years under atmospheric conditions. The manufacturers of 'pasteurized' hams do not intend the packs to be regarded as sterile, for they are usually marked '*Keep in a cool place*', and sometimes '*Perishable — Keep under refrigeration*'.

It is reasonable to suppose that the ham in question was already infected or became contaminated during preparation for packing — in fact before it was cooked — and that subsequent heat treatment failed to kill the contaminants, although leakage into the can of polluted cooling water is another possibility. The bacteriological examination of many samples of ham from pasteurized packs has shown the presence of numerous bacteria of various types. If conditions of storage are poor and the cans are stored at warm, atmospheric temperatures, many become blown and spoiled.

The role of animal and poultry excreters in human salmonellosis

The role of animal and poultry excreters of salmonellae and the spread of the organisms to carcass meat of both animals and poultry and so to the human population is illustrated in many outbreaks.

Salmonella typhimurium in calves and veal

At least 90 persons in 55 separate incidents were taken ill after eating veal. The special typing technique (phage-typing) of the *S. typhimurium* showed that supposed unrelated cases were all part of the same outbreak and that sick calves from a farm many miles away were also infected with the same organism. Calves from this and other farms in the same area were slaughtered in abattoirs providing meat for shops in the districts affected by food poisoning. Calf meat in one form or another was the probable vehicle of infection.

The examination of faecal samples taken at farms from more than a thousand calves showed that approximately 0·5 per cent of the faeces of the animals were infected. However, when faecal samples were taken from calves from the same areas, but after the animals had been herded together in collecting centres for 2 to 5 days under poor conditions, 36 per cent of faecal samples were positive for

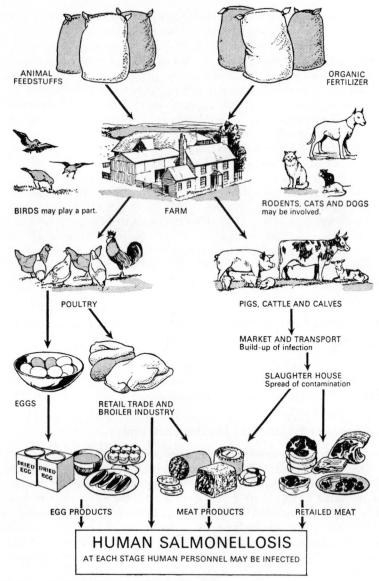

Fig. 14   Spread of salmonella contamination

PREVENTIVE MEASURES INCLUDE:

(1) Improved hygiene of production in country of origin, on farms, in markets, slaughterhouses, and in factories.

(2) Treatment of foods liable to contamination including human and animal foodstuffs by pasteurization, dry heat, irradiation, and other methods.

salmonellae and a high proportion gave the epidemic type. Thus stress and cross-infection were important factors.

Many outbreaks with a similar history have been related to pork products made from carcasses contaminated by salmonellae from the intestinal contents of the pig. Ham, sausages, faggots, and pork joints have all been implicated in outbreaks of salmonellosis, and in some instances the same types of salmonellae have been isolated from the living animals, the environment of the slaughterhouse, and carcasses, glands and offal.

Sometimes sick animals inadvertently killed in the abattoir have led to a heavy contamination of the environment; sometimes the animals have been kept many days before slaughter so that infection from a few has spread to many, encouraged by poor conditions. A similar situation arises with poultry and poultry meat.

The most likely single source of infection is the feeding stuffs, such as bone, fish and meat meals fed to the animals on the farm. The numbers of salmonellae in the meals are usually small so that the animals remain well, but some retain the organism. The rate of excretion on the farm is low because the animals are living under normal conditions but when the creatures are exposed to stress by travel, unfamiliar weather conditons, overcrowding, and fighting, the rate of excretion rises and the infection spreads.

The amount of general contamination arising because of these factors will vary according to the level of hygiene in the establishments concerned, but these hazards cannot all be removed until feeding stuffs for animals are themselves freed from salmonellae (Fig. 14).

Salmonella typhimurium phage type 32 in pigs and pork

A widespread outbreak of salmonellosis from *S. typhimurium* phage type 32 resulted in hundreds of cases of food poisoning and twelve deaths in a Scottish city. Pork meat products from many shops all over the city were vehicles of infection and the same strain was isolated from live pigs in the large local abattoir and also from the gut room and drains. *S. typhimurium* phage type 32 was also found in 4 of 10 samples of a feeding stuff ingredient produced locally for various farms. It was never fully established whether this phage type was recirculated in feeding stuffs compounded from rendered lots of infected pork or whether it had suddenly appeared from an imported ingredient. The outbreak died down, so presumably the focus of infection disappeared.

During the height of the outbreak cases occurred in England, in an area receiving pork carcasses from the Scottish abattoir. Of two hospitals, both receiving the same pork meat, one, with a bad kitchen, reported cases of salmonellosis due to the same organism. The other, with a good kitchen, remained free from cases. In the bad kitchen, lighting, surfaces, utensils, and general morale were poor; the good kitchen was a model of lightness, new equipment, cleanliness, and efficiency.

Salmonella brandenburg in pigs and sausage meat

The incidence of human cases and symptomless excreters of *S. brandenburg* increased 37 times during a period of 5 years and 18 times during a period of 1 year. Over the same period of time *S. brandenburg* was found in 12 per cent of samples of minced meat prepared for sausages by two factories. The organism was found in 12 of 24 pens in the relevant abattoir where pigs were kept for 2 days to 1 month or longer (now illegal) before slaughter. Sewer swabs were also positive. When appropriate measures were taken there were improvements in the isolation rates of *S. brandenburg* in factory products and the abattoir, and the incidence of food poisoning due to this organism dropped. Although it proved impossible to track the organism back to its source, it was assumed that one or more farms were responsible for the infected pigs. *S. brandenburg* has been isolated many times from imported meat and bone meal.

Salmonella weltevreden in a hospital

Salmonella weltevreden is known to be excreted by goats and other animals in eastern countries. Eighty-four cases of salmonellosis due to this serotype occurred over a period of 9 months amongst patients and staff in a hospital in India.

The first isolation was made from the child of a staff member. It was followed by patients admitted with gastroenteritis due to *S. weltevreden.* The organism spread within the hospital affecting patients admitted with other illnesses, doctors, and nurses. Three symptomless excreters were found amongst the food handlers in the diet kitchen which cooked goat meat daily. A few samples of raw chicken and goat meat were examined, and *S. newport* was isolated, but *S. weltevreden* was not found; however, with a mixture of different serotypes it is difficult to find a particular agent of infection.

News that gastroenteritis was occurring frequently in the town was reported from local practitioners and, therefore, it was suspected that the vehicle of infection was goat meat from infected herds. Proof from animals and goat meat at that precise time was missing. Two interesting facts were the different pattern of multiple drug-resistant strains of *S. weltevreden* isolated from the paediatric ward and also the greater spread of the organism within this ward.

Salmonella in pies

It is probable that outbreaks of salmonella food poisoning from meat pies are caused usually by contaminated meat supplies and that symptomless excreters among food handlers are victims rather than originators of infection. An outbreak from meat pies which occurred in July 1949 is described. Two hundred and six pies and 450 sausage rolls were made by a Midland firm and distributed to twelve branches. Of those who ate the pies, 29 of 11 family groups and 21 Scouts at camp in Scotland became acutely ill with food poisoning symptoms 5 to 24 hours later, while those who ate the sausage rolls were unaffected. A dog fed with the remains of a pie which gave rise to human cases likewise suffered from acute gastroenteritis. Twenty-one of the 27 members of the Scout camp were taken ill during their first night in camp. Rain which started heavily that night continued for 6 days; the latrine had been dug in a distant part of the field. For nearly 3 weeks the camp was never free of invalids; some developed high temperatures and were transferred to the local hospital and houses in the district. In 2 cases recovery was not complete until October. Organisms of the salmonella group were isolated from the stools of patients, from a symptomless excreter, and from 13 meat pies. There were both large and small pies, but the attack rate was higher among those who ate the large pies on the first day after manufacture, although by the second day the small pies were causing severe diarrhoea and the severity of illness varied with the quantity of pie eaten.

The bakery at which the pies had been made employed about 100 persons; their standard of cleanliness was high and there was good sanitary accommodation. The same consignment of meat had been used for both pies and sausage rolls; it had been minced, seasoned and mixed with 'filler'. The prepared meat was hand-filled into the pastry blocks by three persons. The pies were heated from 25 to 30 minutes at 232–246 °C (450–475 °F) and the gelatin was added after baking; sheet gelatin was soaked in water, dissolved in fresh boiling water, and cooled and filled into the pies from a jug. The pies were stored at room temperature overnight and distributed next day. It seemed that the cooking time and temperature were adequate to sterilize the sausage rolls but not the pies. The higher attack rate from the large pies eaten on the first day of manufacture indicates that the heat penetration into these pies was slower than for the small size and that therefore more bacteria survived the cooking in the large pies.

An examination of stool samples showed that one of the three pie makers was excreting salmonella organisms. She was probably a victim through eating raw meat as was her custom. Specimens of sheet gelatin, washings from the tin used for the gelatin, a mouse trapped in the bakery, and specimens from six batches of pies prepared subsequently were examined bacteriologically with negative results.

Conditions in the butcher's shop from which the meat was obtained were far from satisfactory, but the most likely source of the organism was the carcass meat used for the mince.

Salmonellae may be found in a small proportion of home-killed meat on sale in butchers' shops, and in a much larger percentage of frozen boneless meat, for both human and animal consumption (see Chapter 4, Table 8). Boneless packs of veal, beef, and mutton are used by manufacturers for pies and sausages as well as for canning. It is not surprising therefore that samples of uncooked sausages and minced meat contain salmonellae. The proportion of samples found to be positive will depend on the raw meat itself.

Food-poisoning outbreaks due to meat pies occur from time to time. It seems that they will continue to do so until steps are taken to ensure that the times and temperatures of cooking are such that the raw meat is well cooked, even though the pastry may become over-brown in consequence. The use of precooked meat in pies is not a safe alternative. Heat-resistant spores may survive the first cooking and develop into actively growing bacilli in meat left overnight; the new growth of organisms may not be destroyed by the cooking time and temperature needed merely to bake the pastry and warm through the meat. Great care should also be taken with the gelatin which is poured into the pie after it is cooked. It should be boiled and filled into the pies hot, not less than 65·6 °C (150 °F); the pies should then be cooled rapidly and maintained in the cold until required.

Years after the outbreak described above there was a similar outbreak, due to pork pies, from which the danger from gelatin is well illustrated.

In June 1976 four hospitals in a city in the Midlands reported salmonella infection in staff and patients. In one hospital, *Salmonella senftenberg* was isolated from 8 of 9 persons with diarrhoea, 16 persons without symptoms, and also from 3 of 41 food handlers tested. Within about a fortnight several further outbreaks were reported, all in the Midlands. They included cases in maternity, orthopaedic, medical, and coronary care units in one hospital; persons in another hospital in the same county; two families in an adjacent county; and persons at a maternity hospital and special care baby unit, and nurses at a medical centre in another city in the area. Sporadic infections were also reported, and by the middle of July the infection was widespread throughout the Midland region.

The suspected vehicles of infection were large pork pies prepared at one factory and used by catering establishments and hospitals in the region. Pies were examined, and *S. senftenberg* was isolated from the large 2 kg catering-size cooked pies but not from the smaller 450 g cooked pies sold directly to the public. In addition coliform counts up to 3 million per g were found in the large but not in the small pies, which suggested that heat treatment of the large pies had been insufficient. Shortly after information was received that a salmonella had been isolated from the pies, another public health laboratory discovered that pork pies from the same factory were due to be served in 18 hospitals that evening. The menus were quickly changed. It was not possible, however, to prevent an outbreak following an athletics competition attended by about 3500 school-children and teachers. Pork pies were served for lunch as wrapped slices together with other cold meats. Many people developed gastroenteritis, and the organism was isolated from several teachers and children and also from 60 cooks and food handlers who sliced the pies and prepared the packed lunches for the competition. In the following weeks, laboratories from many parts of the country reported further infections in persons who had attended the athletics meeting. In yet another outbreak, 100 persons attended a dinner at which pork pie was served, and several developed diarrhoea 24–72 hours later.

By the third week of July the isolation of *S. senftenberg* from 2 kg pork pies with and without eggs had been independently reported by five laboratories. Two of these laboratories isolated the organism from the jelly in the pies and in one instance from the machinery used for filling jelly into the pies after cooking. Some of the isolations were made only after repeated testing, and it appeared likely that only a small number of salmonellae were present in the pies initially but that the organisms multiplied during distribution and storage under less than adequate refrigeration. The jelly machine in the factory was cleaned, but the jelly became contaminated again, and production was stopped pending investigations.

After a detailed study of the raw materials, production line processes, and end products in the factory, contamination of the 2 kg pork pies but not the smaller pies was found to occur in the jellying process. The jelly was injected into the pies after cooking and the machine was contaminated with *S. senftenberg*; hence the pies were contaminated prior to wrapping and dispatch.

Molten gelatin at 80 °C was tipped into the reservoir of the jellying machine and kept molten at 59 °C by a thermostatically controlled outer casing. The molten jelly was kept circulating by an impeller driven by an electric (washing-machine type) pump. Two hoses connected to the distribution head of the machine supplied two nozzles with lances for injecting jelly into the pies. The nozzle and lance consisted of outer and inner tubes. The outer tube, which was held in the hand, was spot welded at each end of a smaller tube (which conveyed the hot molten jelly) by three crude spot welds.

The complete machine was transported to a public health laboratory, where each removable part was disconnected and cultured. In all, 34 parts were examined; *S. senftenberg* was isolated from one part only — one of the jelly injector nozzles. The gelatin accumulated between the hand grip and inner pipe which was almost impossible to clean, because of the spot-welded type of construction. Thus a culture of *S. senftenberg* was established, shedding the organisms into the pies and contaminating the reservoir of jelly when it cooled.

The small pork pies were not contaminated with salmonella because their production was separate and different; they were handled far less than the large pies, and the jellying process was automatic. The gelatin came from a different tank, it was maintained at a temperature of 100 °C, and it was injected into the pies at a temperature of 71 °C. The pipe-work in this machine was made from stainless steel, while that of the other machine used for the large pies was made locally from assorted pieces of piping.

The times of cooking for the two types of pies also differed. Small pies were put into preheated ovens and cooked for 55 minutes at 216 °C. The large pies on the other hand were put into ovens at 205 °C for about 1 hour 30 minutes, although the cooking was usually judged by appearance of the crust. Shelves in all ovens rotated in a starwheel formation, and the pies were packed with adequate air space — no more than 20 large pies in a 5·5 m × 46 cm (10 ft × 18 in.) shelf.

The firm installed a new jellying machine for the large pork pies. The parts were made of stainless steel and glass, and all parts could be removed, cleaned, and disinfected by heat. The cooking process was also improved in that the large pork pies were cooked in a preheated oven at 187 °C for 2 hours and 10 minutes — that is, 1 hour 5 minutes per kg — which did not make the pastry unacceptably brown. It was assumed that the *S. senftenberg* originated from the gelatin; the heat resistance of the strain was not established.

Milk outbreaks

Salmonella and staphylococcal outbreaks from unpasteurized milk are not uncommon. In staphylococcal outbreaks the cow's udder excretes staphylococci into the milk. Salmonellae may come from the faeces or even from the udder of the cow; polluted water, feeding stuffs, other livestock, and human excreters may be involved.

The following description of an outbreak illustrates the paths of spread of infection, when 58 of 900 people including children were infected by raw TT milk contaminated with *S. typhimurium* during October and November 1960. The dairy, run by the owner and one employee, sold 227–273 litres (50–60 gallons) per day of raw TT milk bottled on the premises but purchased from a farm nearby. The dairyman and his family lived on the premises, the employee elsewhere. Near the house the dairyman kept several hundred hens in deep litter houses.

The farmer concerned milked about 40 cattle. One cow was clinically suspect, another had been sold to the knacker's yard, and the farmer had suffered from diarrhoea a fortnight earlier. *S. typhimurium* was isolated from a milk sample taken from the dairy, from stools from three of the dairyman's family and his employee, from three members of the farmer's family and from two rectal swabs taken from the cattle — one from the sick beast. All the strains of *S. typhimurium* were of the same phage type. The milk samples from the farm were negative, and so was the water. It was assumed that the milk was contaminated in the cowshed, the milk-room, or in the bottling plant of the dairy. Cowshed dung may have been responsible and in the milk-room contamination could have been introduced by vessels or by hands contaminated by the cows. Milk at the dairy may have been infected in the bottling plant by the positive dairyman's assistant but it was suspected that the infection originated from the farm, possibly from the farmer himself. Wet weather may have helped to spread infection because the tails, legs and udders of the cattle were dirty. Other possible sources of infection were hens and grazing land.

Formal notice was served requiring heat treatment of the milk. It is stressed that no milk is safe unless pasteurized. The sale of raw milk in vending machines and for schools should be strictly forbidden.

Salmonella senftenberg in poultry

For many years a small hospital was invaded by this salmonella serotype. At one stage one-third of the hospital staff were excreting *S. senftenberg* and the number of sick people increased. The hospital was closed temporarily, thus disrupting the work and the training of nurses. Many excreters were found in the kitchen as well as amongst patients, nurses, and doctors. It was noteworthy that the staff of two departments who ate food prepared at home and not in the canteen were not found to be excreters.

Turkeys were a fairly regular feature of the diet and they came from an area some distance away, where outbreaks of salmonellosis due to *S. senftenberg* had occurred amongst the flocks. Long and arduous tracking eventually established that turkeys from infected farms were supplied to the hospital. Other hospitals were supplied also but the method of cooking was particularly light in the hospital concerned, and there were environmental faults which would have encouraged the spread of salmonellae in the kitchen. An additional factor was the proximity of a pig farm to windward of the prefabricated kitchen building. The farmer mixed his own feed and the ingredients would be contaminated with *S. senftenberg* from time to time.

Salmonella virchow in poultry

Several episodes of salmonella food poisoning, four of which involved at least 140 people, were reported in 1968. They were all associated with chicken meals and spit-roasting was a prominent feature of cooking methods.

Some investigators thought that the organism survived in the cooked birds because they were not completely thawed before cooking which may have been too rapid. Others thought that salmonellae were transferred from the raw debris left on surfaces, utensils, cloths, and hands to cooked birds after removal from the spit and during subsequent cutting-up operations. The source of the infection of the dressed poultry was live birds which are likely to have picked up infection from feed meals. The next fault was storage after cooking. Warm spit-roasted carcasses pending sale will encourage multiplication of a scanty contamination; likewise non-chilled storage in the kitchen will encourage growth. Food handlers, victims of the foods they handle, were found to be excreting *S. virchow* but the part played by their faecal excretion would be minimal or non-existent compared with their part in the mechanical spread by hands and utensils from the masses of infected raw birds to the cooked product.

As poultry are a major source of organisms of the salmonella group, so eggs and egg products may be contaminated (see Chapter 5, pages 61–64), and in some large outbreaks of food poisoning, eggs have been the source of infection.

Salmonella paratyphi B and other salmonella serotypes in cream cakes and other confectionery products

For many years outbreaks of salmonellosis and of enteric fever due to *Salmonella paratyphi B* were traced to cream cakes. It was thought that the infection was associated with imitation cream contaminated from human excreters and it took a long time to discover that the source of the contamination was imported bulked egg products; the same types of salmonellae were found in frozen whole egg mixes and in stools from patients suffering from gastroenteritis and enteric fever. The same phage types of paratyphoid bacilli were persistently found in shipments of cans of frozen egg from China and in the stools of sick patients who had consumed imitation cream products from bakeries using these imported consignments of frozen whole egg.

The imitation cream arrived from the manufacturer in cans and in excellent condition; accidental contamination of the cream with small numbers of salmonellae from egg products occurred in the bakery and conditions for growth were good when the cream was in cakes, éclairs, or buns. The egg mixes were rarely if ever a constituent of the cream but mixing bowls, surfaces, utensils, and hands served to transfer contamination.

Early in 1963 there were several outbreaks of paratyphoid fever, giving rise to 400 to 500 cases. Cream products from bakeries using Chinese whole egg were vehicles of infection in all outbreaks and the same types of paratyphoid bacilli causing the illness were isolated from shipments of the frozen whole egg. Legislation to safeguard the product by pasteurization was introduced in 1964 (Chapter 18).

The use of crystalline or pan-dried albumen heavily contaminated with salmonellae has also caused hundreds of cases of salmonellosis. In one outbreak several symptomless excreters of salmonellae who were working in the same bakery and shop were undoubtedly infected from the same source. They in turn were liable to pass on infection by contaminating the foods they handled. Contaminated powdered products may be even more dangerous than liquids from airborne spread and settling in dust on ledges and beams. In Canada there have been serious outbreaks and deaths in children due to the inclusion of contaminated dried egg in prepared cake mixes. In the United States of America contaminated whole egg used uncooked for special diets in hospitals has caused outbreaks. One December, non-acid mayonnaise prepared with contaminated egg mix made many people sick.

Ducks' eggs infected with salmonellae sometimes cause illness, although it is rare now for such incidents to occur. It is worthwhile to relate two outbreaks caused by salmonellae in dishes made with ducks' eggs.

Salmonella typhimurium in Queen's pudding

At least 136 hospital nurses, domestic staff, and patients were ill with acute food-poisoning symptoms 24 to 96 hours after they had eaten a particularly appetizing pudding in which the chief ingredients were egg yolk and milk. The yolks of 200 ducks' eggs were beaten with milk and added to breadcrumbs; the mixture was baked for 35 minutes, when it became semi-solid. The top was smeared with hot jam, covered with a layer of beaten-up white of egg mixed with a boiled saturated solution of sugar, and the pudding was returned to the oven for the top to be browned. All those who ate the pudding became ill, including the family of a member of the kitchen staff who had taken some home.

It was generally agreed that the source of infection was contaminated ducks' eggs and that the temperature used to cook the pudding had not been sufficient to kill the bacteria, which could have been present in both the mixtures, one containing yolk and the other egg white. The eggs had been collected from sixteen Essex farms, and the task of detecting the particular ducks responsible for the contaminated eggs was not practicable. Furthermore, to destroy the duck population of sixteen farms would have entailed an economic loss seemingly out of proportion to the chance occurrence of another food-poisoning outbreak on the same large scale.

The warning to cook all ducks' eggs thoroughly, for at least 10 minutes if they are boiled, and both sides if fried, or better still to use them only for well-cooked foodstuffs such as baked fruit cakes or steamed puddings, is frequently given. Lightly baked puddings, meringues, or other foods which may require little or no cooking should never be made with ducks' eggs for they constitute a potential danger to the consumer, particularly the very young, the aged, and the invalid. The hazard of cross-contamination from cake mix made with ducks' eggs to uncooked cream fillings prepared with the same equipment should also be avoided.

Salmonella typhimurium in mousse (Fig. 15)

The uncooked food vehicle, mousse, prepared with ducks' eggs, was responsible for salmonellosis in a boys' school. The eggs came from ducks that lived on a pond near the school, and the sweet was prepared the day before required.

The cooks placed the mousse overnight in a cool basement room and the following morning they tasted it before they left for a day's outing. Unfortunately, in case the sweet should be forgotten, they removed it from the cool cellar to the warm kitchen where it remained until eaten by the staff only at the evening meal. The cooks were apparently unaffected, but next day all the staff were ill and the boys remained healthy and boisterous. Once again the lesson was learnt that ducks' eggs should not be used for uncooked foods and

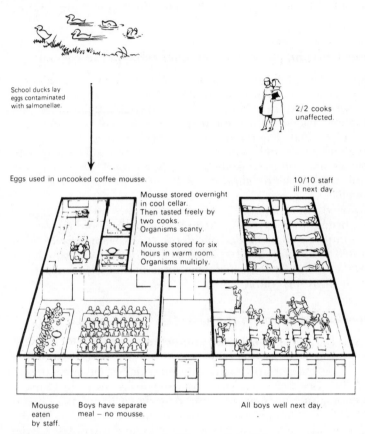

Fig. 15 The mousse outbreak. (Mousse: light dish made of beaten white of eggs. etc.)

LABORATORY FINDINGS

S. typhimurium from ducks (cloacal swabs), from ducks' eggs and from faeces of patients.

COMMENTS

(1) Ducks' eggs must not be used in uncooked or lightly cooked dishes. They may be used with safety in baked or other well-cooked food, or hard boiled (15 minutes).

(2) Foodstuffs prepared some hours before consumption should be stored in the cold.

that in any case foods suitable for bacterial growth should not be kept unrefrigerated.

Other food items such as coconut and chocolate are occasionally responsible for outbreaks of salmonella food poisoning, and of enteric fever.

Salmonella typhi, paratyphi, and other serotypes in coconut

Typhoid fever and salmonellosis were caused by contaminated desiccated coconut in Australia in 1953. The vehicle was coconut ball confectionery. Almost as soon as it was known that salmonellae and paratyphoid bacilli were present in desiccated coconut imported into the United Kingdom, there were reports of cases of paratyphoid fever and salmonellosis after eating coconut marshmallow biscuits and uncooked coconut. Some foods garnished with coconut were able to support and encourage the growth of salmonellae.

Improved conditions of production enforced by legislation in Ceylon brought about a steady drop in the proportion of contaminated samples and suspected incidents. The steam treatment of desiccated coconut to be used uncooked in or on food, which was undertaken voluntarily by many manufacturers, helped to reduce infection from this source.

Salmonella eastbourne in chocolate (USA and Canada)

Between December 1973 and mid-February 1974, 80 cases of infection due to *Salmonella eastbourne,* previously rarely isolated in the USA, were reported from twenty-three States. During a similar period 39 cases were reported from seven Provinces in Canada. Epidemiological investigation indicated that Christmas-wrapped chocolate balls manufactured by a Canadian company were the vehicles of infection; *S. eastbourne* was subsequently isolated from several samples of chocolate balls found in homes where cases occurred. These results together with those from product cultures and an investigation of the plant, formed the basis for regulatory action that most likely prevented the occurrence of many later infections from the consumption of chocolate produced for Easter.

A survey of the chocolate factory indicated that various contaminated items were produced in at least three of the moulding plants during a 6-month period. Results from environmental samples strongly suggested that contaminated cocoa beans were the source of the salmonellae; cross-contamination from raw bean dust was demonstrated by the isolation of *S. eastbourne* from roasted beans cooled by blown air.

Beyond the roaster, potential for eliminating salmonellae from the chocolate was provided by heat at 60 °C in the conches. However, salmonellae were shown to survive this process. Constant recirculation of old and new chocolate between the storage tanks and moulding plants would have prolonged the period of contamination.

Enumeration of salmonellae indicated that there was an average count of only 2·5 *S. eastbourne* per g of the chocolate samples obtained from the homes of infected persons, suggesting that a dosage of less than 1000 organisms (the number in a 1 lb bag) was sufficient to cause illness. This is one-tenth the size of the dose estimated indirectly for *S. typhimurium* in an outbreak due to contaminated imitation ice-cream and one hundred- to ten thousand-fold less than the numbers of *S. meleagridis* and *S. anatum* necessary to cause clinical symptoms in adult volunteers. Several factors may have accounted for this interesting difference, including technical difficulties in the quantitative recovery of salmonella from chocolate, the age of the patients (mostly young children) in this outbreak, possible protection of the salmonellae by fat in the chocolate against the action of the gastric acid, and perhaps greater virulence of this particular strain of *S. eastbourne* compared with that of other serotypes previously studied.

Clostridium perfringens food poisoning

Another well-defined type of food poisoning arises from the contamination, predominantly of meat and poultry dishes, with large numbers of the anaerobic sporing bacillus, *C. perfringens.* The following incidents illustrate the sequence of events which can lead to *C. perfringens* food poisoning.

School canteen outbreaks

Two outbreaks of food poisoning occurred in the same school canteen within a year of each other. On the first occasion the medical officer of health reported the occurrence of abdominal pain and diarrhoea among a large number of children in a school served by its own canteen. The kitchen was visited the day after the outbreak. The suspected meal, eaten 9 to 12 hours before the symptoms started, consisted of cold boiled salt beef, salad and boiled potatoes, followed by a steamed pudding and jam. The food was eaten without complaint and tasted good. The beef, in joints weighing about 1·8 to 2·7 kg (4 to 6 lb) each, had been delivered to the kitchen on the previous afternoon. The meat was immediately cooked for 2 hours in large boilers of the type commonly found in modern school canteens, and it was allowed to remain in the liquor all night to cool.

The following day the meat was taken from the liquor, drained, sliced, and eaten cold for lunch. A portion of this meat, left over from the meal and stored in the refrigerator, was examined at the laboratory. Several types of bacteria were found, including the sporing bacillus *C. perfringens.* It was assumed that either the spores had survived the preliminary heat treatment or that airborne contamination had occurred during cooling, and that multiplication had been vigorous overnight. The kitchen staff were warned that the procedure they had used — that of boiling the meat the day before it was required and allowing it to cool slowly overnight in the kitchen — was the most likely explanation for the outbreak. The staff appeared to understand, and agreed that it should not occur again.

Almost exactly a year later, the medical officer of health reported a similar occurrence in the same school, affecting about 200 children. In the meantime, laboratory experiments had proved that the spores of *C. perfringens,* isolated from many samples of meatstuffs suspected of causing outbreaks of diarrhoea and pain, were able to withstand a few minutes' to several hours' boiling and the story told was similar to that of many other such incidents already reported. For the greater part of the year following the warning given after the first outbreak, the staff had been careful to carry out the recommendation to cook and eat their meat on the same day; occasionally they had refrigerated overnight any meat cooked the day before it was required for a cold meal. For the past few months, however, they had lapsed into their old habits. On this occasion, rolled joints of salt beef had been boiled during the afternoon of the day before they were required. They were lifted out of the boiler on to enamel dishes, covered with cloths, and placed in the larder overnight. They were sliced and eaten cold for lunch the next day. In spite of the fact that it was mid-winter, the cooling rate inside the rolls of meat must have been very much slower than the outside and an almost pure culture of heat-resistant *C. perfringens* was found in the sample of meat examined. A similar organism was isolated from the faeces of patients (Fig. 16).

These sporing bacilli were most probably on the meat when it reached the canteen; but if the organisms had not been given the opportunity to multiply after cooking by long slow cooling and storage at atmospheric temperature, without refrigeration, food poisoning would have been prevented.

Outbreaks of *C. perfringens* food poisoning continue to occur; they follow a similar pattern. Sometimes the precooked meat or poultry is eaten cold and sometimes it is warmed up.

Soups, stews and gravies cooked in bulk and allowed to cool slowly may also encourage sporing organisms to multiply to dangerous levels. For example, gravy prepared in bulk at a central school-meals

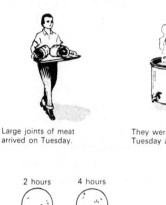
Large joints of meat arrived on Tuesday.

They were boiled on Tuesday afternoon.

There was no room in the refrigerator, so they were allowed to cool slowly overnight.

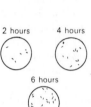
2 hours   4 hours

6 hours

During the night the heat-resistant sporing bacteria grew and multiplied.

The bacteria multiplied still more when the sliced meat was warmed with gravy on the hot plate.

300 ILL
With pain and diarrhoea after 350 children and staff had eaten meat boiled the previous day.

Fig. 16 Outbreak of *Clostridium perfringens* food poisoning in a school canteen

COMMENTS
Meat for hot dishes should be prepared, cooked and eaten the same day. When required cold, cooked meat should be cooled quickly and refrigerated. Joints should be limited to 2·72 kg (6 lb) or less.

kitchen was distributed to neighbouring schools, after it had stood in a large container in the refrigerator overnight. Several outbreaks of food poisoning occurred among children in the various schools, and the gravy was found to be heavily contaminated with sporing organisms. The amount of fluid contained in the single bowl was large and even after refrigeration overnight the temperature in the centre of the mass was such that the multiplication of micro-organisms could still occur.

Hospital outbreaks

In a series of hospital outbreaks it was found that boiled chickens in liquor were transferred to open vessels and left all night to cool; illness followed their consumption cold the following day. On the other hand, chickens which were removed from the liquor, placed on trays to cool quickly, and fed to special-diet patients did not cause illness. *C. perfringens* was found in a high proportion of dust samples from the kitchen. The organism may have been on the chickens before cooking or it may have been on the containers used for the cooked chickens. Whatever the source, the main fault was the long slow cooling which encouraged multiplication.

In another hospital outbreak minced meat was found to be the vehicle for *C. perfringens* food poisoning. Nearly 400 patients were affected and 1 died. The attack rate was high, which indicated that the food was profusely contaminated with the organism. Inadequate cooking and cooling of the cuts of meat intended for mincing the next day encouraged survival and growth of the sporing organism; the time was too short and the temperature too low to ensure destruction of the vegetative cells during the reheating stage. These are common faults which so often lead to this type of food poisoning. Another fault in this instance was the use of the same mincing machine for both raw and cooked meat with inadequate cleaning between the processes. The necessity for thorough cleaning of dual purpose mincers and mixers must be emphasized.

The recommendations after the outbreak included the usual advise to cool hot food quickly, within $1\frac{1}{2}$ hours of cooking, in a specially ventilated cold room before refrigeration; it is preferable to serve freshly cooked mince prepared from raw meat the same day. When the necessity for reheating arises, the food mass should be boiled throughout. Raw and cooked food processes should be separated and particular attention paid to cleaning methods and to instruction of the staff on safe procedures and the danger from careless practices.

More than 60 outbreaks of *C. perfringens* food poisoning in hospitals were reported in England and Wales during the period 1971–75. Crown premises are not legally bound by the regulations, so that the environmental health officer still has no right of entrance. This may well be reconsidered in view of the large number of

CL. *WELCHII* PRODUCING HEAT-RESISTANT SPORES
IS A COMMON CONTAMINANT OF MEAT AND POULTRY.

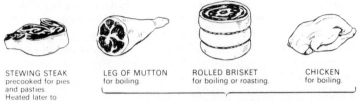

STEWING STEAK
precooked for pies
and pasties.
Heated later to
cook pastry only.

LEG OF MUTTON
for boiling.

ROLLED BRISKET
for boiling or roasting.

CHICKEN
for boiling.

Precooked some hours before required.

COMMON FAULTS IN COOKING, STORAGE AND HANDLING TECHNIQUES
ALLOW SURVIVAL OF SPORES AND MULTIPLICATION OF BACILLI.

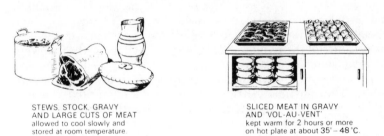

STEWS, STOCK, GRAVY
AND LARGE CUTS OF MEAT
allowed to cool slowly and
stored at room temperature.

SLICED MEAT IN GRAVY
AND 'VOL-AU-VENT'
kept warm for 2 hours or more
on hot plate at about 35° – 48°C.

SPORES transferred from raw to cooked meat during boning and slicing
by common surfaces and utensils. The human carrier may also play a part.

Fig. 17   *Clostridium perfringens* food poisoning — from meat and poultry

COMMENTS

Meat dishes should be freshly prepared and eaten hot within 1 hour of
cooking or cooled rapidly and refrigerated until required. Spores can be
killed by pressure cooking and the thorough roasting of small cuts of meat.

outbreaks of food poisoning in hospitals, for example, where the experience of an environmental health officer is useful. Figure 17 shows the meats and meat dishes which have caused *C. perfringens* food poisoning most frequently.

Meals-on-Wheels outbreak

The provision of Meals-on-Wheels to the homes of elderly people poses a problem in kitchen management. It is necessary to prepare and dish up a number of individual meals by mid-morning so that distribution can begin promptly; each van may have to make between 40 and 80 calls. There is, therefore, a temptation to serve dishes which can be prepared on the previous day.

Various faults in preparation and storage came to light during the investigation of an outbreak of *C. perfringens* food poisoning following the consumption of minced beef provided by a Meals-on-Wheels service.

The mince was purchased as 2·7 kg (6 lb) frozen packs and the contents of six packs were heated for 2 hours in chicken stock in one large pan. The pan of mince was placed in the 'vegetable' room to cool and after 5 hours was transferred to a refrigerator. The vegetable room was inadequately ventilated and when inspected the temperature of the room was 21 °C (70 °F). At 8 am on the following morning some of the mince was reheated for 20 minutes and distributed with cooked vegetables into 134 individual foil containers. The containers were placed in electrically-heated insulated cabinets which were connected to batteries in the vans. The meals were delivered between 12 noon and 2.30 pm.

It is likely that in 2 hours the heat penetration through 16·3 kg (36 lb) of frozen mince was inadequate. The mince should have been completely thawed before being cooked and placed in pans in quantities not exceeding 2·7–4·0 kg (6–9 lb) and the mix stirred to ensure even distribution of the heat. The cooling period was also inadequate in view of the volume of food involved. Where large numbers of meals are prepared a ventilated cold store, refrigerated with an extractor fan, should be supplied to aid cooling. Better still, the mince or other bulks of meat or poultry should be cooked not only on the day, but immediately before being served. In this instance, the food was apportioned in individual containers after only minimal warming; as the procedure was lengthy the meals were cold before they were packed into the heated cabinets. The cabinets were designed to maintain hot food at a temperature of 63 °C (145 °F) and certainly not to heat up lukewarm food. The highest temperature achieved (when the van was about to start on its round) was 46 °C (115 °F) and at the end of the round the temperature of the remaining food was 29 °C (85 °F). The optimum temperature for the growth of *C. perfringens* is 43–47 °C. If the mince had been reheated to 100 °C throughout and eaten freshly cooked on the same day, the outbreak would not have occurred. Dishing up should be as rapid as possible and all the meals kept hot until delivered.

Curry outbreaks

Near and Far Eastern countries specialize in curries which present a constant hazard of *C. perfringens* food poisoning. An account of a picnic will illustrate the sequence of events.

The coach started for the Bakra Dam in the Punjab, India, at 7.30 am but the chicken curry had been cooked during the night and it was observed to be present in the coach near the engine, in a large covered metal pan. The day was hot and the journey long. At 2 pm the party of 50 persons settled on the grass near the Dam for lunch. The pan of curry was warmed for 10 minutes on a kerosene stove and everyone had generous helpings of curry and rice, which were delicious.

Many hours later 3 people were obviously unwell in the coach, and early the following morning nearly everyone suffered with abdominal pain and diarrhoea. Some of the spores of *C. perfringens* in poultry and in the spices would survive cooking by boiling and the conditions were ideal for growth and multiplication.

In spite of the warning a similar trip took place the following year with the same menu and the same results. Since no one was sick after 2 hours it is assumed that *Bacillus cereus* was not growing in the rice (see p. 116), although this was another hazard.

Bacillus cereus food poisoning

Bacillus cereus is another commonly occurring organism which survives cooking by means of spores. The bacilli which arise from the germinated spores produce toxins in the food as they grow and multiply.

Cooked rice outbreaks

Fried rice containing large number of *Bacillus cereus* has been responsible for acute vomiting, sometimes followed by diarrhoea, in people eating food prepared in Chinese restaurants, and 'take-away' shops. The rapid onset of sickness, usually within 2–4 hours of eating the food, suggests that a toxin is released in the food. *B. cereus* spores readily and grows well at a wide range of temperatures. The spores can withstand near-boiling temperatures, particularly when protected by starch. In order to be ready to provide meals at a moment's notice, large quantities of rice may be boiled the day before they are required and they may be heaped in large colanders and left overnight in the kitchen. Refrigeration coagulates the rice particles. Portions are turned over in hot fat (fried) in the morning and kept warm pending sale, when they are flipped through hot fat in a final process.

Laboratory tests have shown that spores are present in many samples of uncooked rice grains and that they can survive boiling and germinate into bacilli which grow rapidly in the cooked rice. Spores are readily formed in most vegetative cells so that the second process of heating in oil still leaves spores alive to germinate and form more sporing cells which are not disturbed by the final treatment in hot fat. The effect of heat on the toxin is not known but it is possible that it withstands some of the cooking procedure.

Only a revision in the method of preparation to cut out the hours of storage between and after cooking will prevent this type of food poisoning.

More than 70 outbreaks of *B. cereus* food poisoning associated with cooked rice, usually fried rice, from Chinese restaurants and 'take-away' shops have been reported in this country since 1971 and similar episodes have been recorded in Australia, Canada, Finland, the Netherlands, and the USA. The following account of a number of incidents is typical.

A series of five small episodes of food poisoning over a period of $2\frac{1}{2}$ months affected customers consuming meals from a Chinese restaurant. Thirteen persons who ate fried rice with their meals became ill, whereas seven companions who did not eat fried rice remained well. The illness was characterized by nausea and vomiting 1–6 hours after the meal in all those affected, and diarrhoea after 2–5 hours in 8 persons. *B. cereus* was isolated in large numbers from stool specimens from the patients, from samples of fried rice, and from boiled rice ready for frying. Fried rice left by an unaffected person gave a colony count of 350 million *B. cereus* per g and the same organism was found in small numbers in samples of uncooked rice. Subsequent tests showed that the isolates of *B. cereus* from the uncooked and cooked rice, remnants of the meal, and from the stool specimens were the same serotype.

In the restaurant kitchen it was a relatively common practice to boil rice intended for frying the evening before it was required, and to allow it to dry off overnight at room temperature; thus spores which had survived the boiling process were provided with ideal conditions to germinate and multiply. The situation was made worse by the practice of adding new batches of boiled rice to the remains of old rice possibly left over from the previous day. It is interesting to note that all five incidents occurred either on Monday or Thursday.

The restaurant closed all day on Wednesday and opened for 4 hours on Sunday. One may speculate that Monday's fried rice might have been carried over from the previous Saturday, and Thursday's rice from the Tuesday.

Vibrio parahaemolyticus food poisoning

Food poisoning from *Vibrio parahaemolyticus* occurs frequently in Japan and other eastern countries where it is commonly found in sea creatures and sea food. Outbreaks due to this organism are now reported from the USA, Australia, the UK, and other countries.

Crab meat outbreaks

Passengers travelling by air from Bangkok via Dubai were taken ill as they arrived in London. Three of five who reported sick were admitted to hospital immediately; information about other cases came later. Three of the cabin crew who landed at Dubai and did not proceed to London were also ill; this established the food vehicle as part of a meal prepared in Bangkok and eaten before the aircraft reached Dubai. Samples of complete meals prepared from the same batches of food served on the flight concerned were frozen and flown to Britain. *Vibrio parahaemolyticus* was isolated from cooked crab meat in the hors d'oeuvre and the organism was of the same serotype as that isolated from stool specimens of the three hospitalized patients. Raw meat from crab claws flown from Bangkok also harboured the same serotype of *V. parahaemolyticus.*

There were two possibilities: either the organism was not killed in the process of boiling, or the cooked crab meat was recontaminated with the organism from the raw meat during extraction from the shell, and preparation and assembly of the hors d'oeuvre dish. *V. parahaemolyticus* is sensitive to heat and the greatest potential hazard with seafood is likely to be contamination after cooking either from sea water or uncooked marine products rather than inadequate cooking.

In 1973 a similar outbreak occurred among holidaymakers who had eaten crabs, caught off the south coast of England. This was the first reported outbreak of *V. parahaemolyticus* food poisoning in Britain associated with home-produced seafood. The contamination of cooked crabs by *V. parahaemolyticus* from uncooked crabs during picnics has been described in the USA outbreaks.

Once an organism has been recognized as a potential cause of trouble in food it can be found more readily the next time. The isolation of *V. parahaemolyticus* from imported frozen cooked prawns suggests the possibility of food poisoning from this product in the form of seafood cocktails prepared for banquets and parties.

V. parahaemolyticus food poisoning has been described frequently in the East, but air travel and imported foods bring East to West with rapidity. The same is true of cholera, but built-in safeguards for sewage and water control will protect the West, at least from widespread water-borne outbreaks of infection.

Escherichia coli food poisoning

Although usually a normal inhabitant of the intestine of all creatures, certain serotypes of *Esch. coli* are pathogenic in young and adult man and animals.

Outbreaks of diarrhoea have occurred in newly arrived personnel in army units in the Middle East, and also in persons attending conferences in Mexico, for example. A large outbreak in which cheese was the vehicle of infection was described in the USA.

A series of incidents occurred on a ship where cases were reported daily in small and large numbers depending partly on the atmospheric temperature. As the ship cruised through warm humid climates the reported incidents of food poisoning increased; there were probably other cases which were self-treated. During the warm days the colony counts from foods, often served from deck buffets, were high. The conditions in the galley were not good and there were heavy demands on the food service and on the food handlers. They catered for many menus, varieties of food on each menu, and, in addition, many parties. Several serotypes of *Esch. coli* were found in the foods and the epidemic type was isolated from cream prepared on the ship. Recommendations on storage and food preparation helped to reduce the incidence of illness. The organism could have originated from raw foods or from excreters, but the spread and multiplication in the foods were suspected to be the main faults. Ship-borne outbreaks of gastroenteritis, including salmonella infection and even enteric fever, are not infrequent. Galley personnel and foods come from many countries and cross-contamination takes place readily in the over-crowded pantries used for cold meats, seafoods, and salads, and in the preparation areas used for raw and cooked foods. Also foods may be kept warm for some hours pending lunch and dinner meals.

When investigating outbreaks of food poisoning suspected to be due to enteropathogenic *Esch. coli*, the results from stool specimens from patients should be compared with those from a group of healthy persons living under different conditions.

Courses on food hygiene for chefs and other galley staff as well as surgeons responsible for food safety should be instituted on a regular basis.

7

Ecology of micro-organisms in food

As regular co-inhabitants of this world, micro-organisms must not only survive but also multiply actively so that replacements are available for the frequent losses of microbial population. The spoilage organisms have less difficulty in maintaining their existence than those which depend on occupation of the human or animal body. They proliferate readily in almost any protein material or vegetable matter at a wide range of ambient temperatures. The pathogens, on the other hand, depend on the warmth and nutriment of the animal and human body for growth. If they overcome the host causing death, they must seek to invade other susceptible host tissues. At an intermediate stage foods are useful for growth when temperatures are suitable, or, when they are unsuitable, for resting phases. The characteristics of organisms in relation to the food and the living habitat, and also to survival outside both, can be the subject of an ecological study for each type of organism. Broad patterns of behaviour can be seen within the families which include the clostridia, staphylococci, salmonellae, and dysentery bacilli, aerobic sporing bacilli such as *Bacillus cereus* and the vibrios.

Clostridium

Consider the genus *Clostridium* and in particular *Clostridium perfringens*. This organism flourishes under anaerobic conditions in the lower intestinal tract and in deep wounds. In the large bowel of man and animals it spores readily and the spores will pass out with the faeces into soil or sewage systems. Water and vegetation will carry it back into the animal kingdom and into food production systems including kitchens, where it arrives in meats, vegetables, and dust. The mechanism of heat resistance enables the spores to survive normal cooking procedures. Some spores can survive an hour or more at 100 °C, others are less resistant to heat. The heat resistance is measured as the decimal reduction time for the destruction of

90 per cent of spores at a constant temperature. The heat of cooking activates the spores to germinate, possibly by damaging the spore coat.

When the slowly cooling foods (usually meat and poultry) reach a satisfactory temperature for growth (below 50 °C; 122 °F) there is rapid multiplication of the vegetative cells emerging from the spores; swallowed with food they must survive the acid conditions of the stomach and reach the intestine in sufficient number to become established. Once more inside the human or animal body they disturb the natural flora so that conditions are right for multiplication and sporulation to take place. A particularly large dose must be present in the food for the phenomenon known as diarrhoea, accompanied by cramps, to occur. Large numbers of cells and spores will be excreted in the large volume of fluid stool until the normal flora is restored.

The spores can survive indefinitely and they are resistant to environmental factors such as dehydration, heat, and cold. Another characteristic of this organism is its fast generation time under congenial conditons. Divisions occur every 10 to 12 minutes at a wide range of temperatures, the optimum being 43–47 °C (109·4–116·6 °F); the maximum temperature is about 50 °C (122 °F) and the minimum about 20 °C (68 °F). The mode of attack is not from toxin formed in the food but from toxin released in the intestine during sporulation. The organism is known to produce large numbers of spores in the intestine but not in foodstuffs. The outflow of spores as well as vegetative cells from those suffering from food poisoning will be profuse and contribute to the survival and spread of the organism. The other more lethal organism of the same family, *C. botulinum*, forms its toxin when growing in the food. It is suggested also that there may be growth and toxin production within wounds, and in the intestine of poultry infected by *C. botulinum* type C in the disease in chickens and ducks called limberneck.

The toxin which causes the fatal nerve disease of botulism is formed in food and fortunately it is sensitive to heat otherwise there would be more fatalities in those eating cooked foods. The general incidence of the organism *C. botulinum* in soil and food appears to be low, and it appears to be more common in certain areas. There are no records of the number of *C. botulinum* in the stools of the victims. The gastrointestinal phase of the illness is transient and is suspected to be due to organisms other than *C. botulinum* in the same food. The sparse incidence of the organism may be associated with the rarity of the disease compared with *C. perfringens* food poisoning and with the fact that it is not excreted profusely in the stool, in contrast to *C. perfringens*. It has been suggested that the main natural source of *C. botulinum* type C, an animal pathogen, is the carcasses of dead animals and maybe the alimentary tract of live animals. Multiplication in excreted faecal material has also been suggested. The cycle for spread and survival of *C. botulinum* type E in fish, coastal mud, and water may be the same, with man and his sewage as a contributory factor. The victim of botulism often dies as a result of the toxin which may influence the survival of the organism outside the human and animal host. Perhaps the cycle can be perpetuated with small doses of the organism in food although the system will be inefficient without the onset of clinical symptoms.

Staphylococcus

It is doubtful whether the staphylococci have an intermediate environmental phase of significance unless it be dust. Their perpetuation is not dependent on faecal excretion; it is assured in the warm damp and congenial atmosphere of the nose and throat, in the pores and hair follicles of the skin, and on the surface of skin in damp creased areas such as the perineum and axillae. It is not easy to rid the skin, or the nose, of staphylococci of any type. Measures have been suggested such as antibiotic creams for the nose; these at least can eliminate a particular type which may be giving rise to skin lesions or known to produce enterotoxin in food. Freedom from the organism may be transient but the next invader may be less harmful.

Bactericidal soaps and lotions for the skin are described but they require persistent and consistent usage to be effective. Washing the skin with soap and water usually eliminates Gram-negative bacilli, but Gram-positive cocci often remain and sometimes appear in even greater numbers. They rise to the surface of the skin from pores when the hands are soaked or rinsed in hot water; superficial layers of the skin are disturbed by scrubbing and rubbing which may even distribute the organisms over the surface.

If a moist cake of soap is passed gently over the surface of agar medium in a petri dish, organisms common to the skin of whoever is using the soap will be demonstrated by colonies growing on the plate after incubation.

Breaks in the skin surface will encourage proliferation, and septic lesions forming pus will release enormous numbers of cells which may linger on the skin indefinitely. Growth in food is a poor means of perpetuation. The enterotoxins which cause illness are produced in the food, and although there may be large numbers of cells in stool and vomit when illness is acute, there is no evidence that the numbers remain high. Approximately 30 per cent of persons have small numbers of staphylococci in stools. In staphylococcal enteritis which sometimes follows administration of antibiotics disturbing the natural flora of the intestine, staphylococci may become dominant and be excreted in large numbers; but, unlike the sporing organisms, the time of survival of the vegetative cells outside the body will be limited.

Compared with the Gram-negative and Gram-positive bacilli, staphylococci are slow in competitive growth. Although there is a high incidence of staphylococci (including *Staph. aureus*) on live poultry and on the skin of dressed poultry, there is little evidence that they are associated with food poisoning.

Phage typing has enabled the spread of staphylococci to be followed more closely, and is a useful epidemiological tool.

Salmonella

The ramifications of the various organisms of the salmonella group are far and wide, the ecology is complex, and the damage to animals as well as to man is immense.

Perhaps because the natural course of events is the surest means of survival, the salmonella cycle is important in countries where there are vast schemes for the intensive rearing of animals. The waste products and remains of animals, whether sick or healthy, are not carefully channelled into safe sewage disposal schemes or buried or burned but are processed into feeding stuffs and fertilizers and placed back in the cycle of infection.

If the methods of processing rendered them sterile or at least free from pathogens which infect both man and animals, the economy of the animal–feed–animal–food–man system would be perfect. But unless special precautions are taken the finished feed products from rendered animal products are frequently contaminated with salmonellae which are fed back to the animals. It has been demonstrated that the number of animals (or poultry) in any group found to be excreting salmonellae is dependent on contamination of the feeding stuffs used in the unit.

The animal intestine is as conducive for the survival and multiplication of salmonellae as that of man. The animal system has the added advantage of rapid spread between animals in over-crowded conditions; of the probability of survival and multiplication in rehydrated mash in troughs and lairages where trauma between animals may lead to lowered resistance to infection of the animal body; and of anxiety and stress in transport and strange surroundings and, at times, of deprivation of food and water in days before slaughter. All these factors predispose the animal to infection and will enhance excretion.

Except under war conditions and vast antisocial campaigns, humanity is rarely subjected to these circumstances and except for excretion into sewage the invading organisms may live and die with the host only.

The use of antibiotics will be more effective in man since both the type of antibiotic and the dose will be controlled more carefully. However, in animals small doses in feeds or for prophylaxis will perpetuate resistant strains of pathogens and non-pathogens and resistance factors may be active in the transfer mechanism even in the absence of antibiotics. Doses for treatment of scouring animals will, more often than not, be given without knowledge of the organism concerned and therefore of its sensitivity. The administration of antibiotics to animals should be carefully controlled and limited to treatment rather than prophylaxis. Hitherto statistical records of salmonellosis in animals have been mostly obtained from post-mortem findings from animals brought into veterinary investigation laboratories. In the Zoonoses Order 1975 the notification of salmonella excreters in farm animals is required (see p. 282).

Comparative studies have been carried out with the Danes. In Denmark, dehydrated protein feeding stuffs of animal origin are required to be salmonella-free and there is legislation for heat treatment. Pigs in Denmark have a lower rate of excretion and it is significant that *S. typhimurium* is the predominant serotype in pigs and in the population; whereas in the UK other serotypes are prominent both in animals and man, and many of these are found in foodstuffs both for man and animals. The Danes have a pathogen-free programme for poultry which relates not only to foodstuffs but also to all stages in breeding. The success of this system is shown by the freedom from salmonellae, except for an occasional batch with *S. typhimurium*, of poultry carcasses and pieces imported from Denmark and examined in the United Kingdom.

The effect of allowing animals for domestic consumption to eat salmonellae in their food is reflected in the incidence of the organism in raw products — particularly comminuted meats such as sausages and also dressed poultry. There are wide differences in the rate of contamination of meat and poultry products between enlightened manufacturers and breeders, including those responsible for slaughtering.

A partial reduction in the incidence of salmonellosis may be brought about by efforts to prevent spread of infection from raw to cooked products at the retail-consumer end of the chain; but without international co-operation of the disciplines responsible for animal care, the intestinal disease of salmonellosis will persist.

Bacillus cereus

This is another organism which is troublesome because of its ability to survive indefinitely by means of spores. It may be even more ubiquitous than the sporing clostridia, because it is an aerobic organism not dependent on an oxygen-free environment for growth, and also it forms spores freely; under good conditions for its growth spores are formed in almost every cell. The organism is a common contaminant of cereals and can cause spoilage of milk and dairy products.

Cornflour sauce, milk puddings, and rice dishes have been described as vehicles of infection for man. The survival of the spores through the cooking process, germination, proliferation, and production of toxin in food are responsible for human sickness. Harmless though they are in small numbers, the fault lies in the rise of numbers in food prepared in bulk ahead of requirements. Rice for the take-away trade is an example (p. 116).

There is no difficulty about this organism perpetuating its existence in the world; its control rests with preventing multiplication by allowing short intervals only between cooking and eating, and the full use of refrigeration.

Vibrio parahaemolyticus

The ecology of *V. parahaemolyticus* appears to be closely connected with a water–sea creature cycle; outbreaks, described frequently in Japan, are associated with the consumption of seafood both raw and cooked. There are no reports of water-borne outbreaks of *V. parahaemolyticus,* unlike those for the cholera vibrio which emphasizes the importance of polluted water supplies and sanitary incompetence in the rapid spread of cholera. When sewage becomes overloaded with *V. cholerae* the local water will be invaded by the organism and where there is no purification system it will reach the people. *V. parahaemolyticus* has also been isolated from stools of persons with cholera-like symptoms when the cholera vibrio itself has not been found.

Whereas food is a second vehicle of infection of the cholera vibrio, *V. parahaemolyticus* appears to be dependent on food for transmission to the human body; the number of organisms required to initiate symptoms may be an important factor.

In Japan food poisoning due to *V. parahaemolyticus* and the isolation of the organism from coastal waters is a summertime occurrence, and warmth and bacterial growth are correlated. Although *V. parahaemolyticus* has been isolated from coastal waters and sea creatures in England, Germany, and other countries, the numbers will be small compared with those which accumulate in the environment in epidemic periods in warm countries; infected sewage from sporadic cases and outbreaks will contribute large numbers of organisms. The sudden influx of vibrios in sewage from rare incidents such as that described on p. 117 is unlikely to pollute controlled water systems, but shell-fish could be infected from sewage outflows.

Efficient sewage and water systems will keep the threat of most water-borne diseases under control, but the use or disposal of contaminated food is another matter.

Cholera

Outbreaks of cholera in Italy (1973) and in Portugal (1974) were initiated by polluted water and shellfish harvested from this water. The vibrio was consumed in shellfish which harboured the organism; raw or poorly cooked cockles were significant in Portugal. In Portugal also, springs of water used for a brand of commercially bottled non-carbonated beverage, and the mineral water itself, were found to be vehicles of transmission of cholera.

The so-called non-cholera vibrios (NCV) are also found in choleraic and milder diarrhoeas: they have been isolated together with *V. parahaemolyticus* from frozen cooked shrimps and prawns harvested and processed in eastern countries. They are described in association with cholera. One reported outbreak from these organisms followed 6 months after an outbreak of cholera and originated from the same flight kitchen; many airline passengers were ill.

The pattern of spread is likely to be similar for all three pathogenic vibrios and is associated with excreters, sewage, water, sea and river food, and other foods contaminated in the kitchen directly from water and human sewage and from the raw foods.

Spoilage

The distinction between the terms 'spoilage' and 'pathogenic' for bacteria is sometimes difficult to maintain.

Most of the food-poisoning organisms give no indication of their presence in food by the common spoilage signs recognized by off odours and tastes, or changes in appearance such as colour, consistency, or gas production. Even when there are manifestations, such as gas production by *Clostridium perfringens*, for example, the numbers of organisms at that stage may be well beyond those initially required to invade the intestine, where they multiply or survive long enough to sporulate and release the enterotoxin.

Bacillus cereus and *Escherichia coli* are known to spoil food and to cause food poisoning also; there are other organisms such as *Pseudomonas, Proteus,* and *Citrobacter* which are well-known spoilage bacteria and sometimes suspected to be involved in food poisoning.

B. cereus is a common cause of spoilage in cream and milk, shown by the appearance of particles, hence the name 'bitty' cream or milk. When rice is the vehicle of food poisoning the numbers of *B. cereus* in the cooked rice taken from restaurants are greater than 10^6 per g and often 10^8–10^9 per g. Published figures on counts of *B. cereus* in spoiled dairy products are not available, although it has been suggested that they are much lower. The organism is common in the environment, and is fequently found in uncooked cereals such as rice and flour. It is unjustifiable to report *B. cereus* as a food-poisoning hazard when it is present in small numbers only in either raw or cooked foods. When the numbers are high (greater than 10^6 per g) in cooked foods, there is a potential danger from toxin formed in the food by the growth of the organism. This danger is due to faults, not so much in cooking, but in storage temperatures and times after cooking.

Esch. coli is commonly found in large numbers in raw foods of animal origin. Although readily destroyed by heat, it may be found in cooked foods contaminated after cooking by hands, surfaces, vessels, and utensils used for both raw and cooked foods; the organism will also be found in variable numbers in salad vegetables. *Esch. coli* indicates sewage pollution of water and unhygienic methods of food preparation; the significance of its presence in water, cooked food, and salad vegetables is often assessed by the numbers found. When enteropathogenic types of *Esch. coli* appear in the environment of food preparation and in water, there is a direct hazard of infection; again the numbers allowed to accumulate in foods ready to be eaten are important. Cross-contamination and careless storage of both cooked and uncooked foods are responsible for many outbreaks of food poisoning and hasten spoilage. Small numbers of most intestinal pathogens including salmonellae, *Staph. aureus*, the sporing organisms, *Esch. coli*, and possibly the vibrios are undoubtedly eaten without ill effect. The finding of an intestinal pathogen in food may not be immediately significant but it is an index of a potential hazard if the rules of hygiene are ignored.

Microbiological guidelines or specifications are useful to every food microbiologist and technologist, but legislative enforcement should be approached with considerable caution because of the variability in results obtained from the usual test methods. Sampling rules must be strictly enforced and a wide range of counts accepted for the desired index of good practice.

The gaps between the fields of human and animal microbiology, food microbiology, and technology need to be closed. Medical and science workers interested in food microbiology must be familiar with both fields. When outbreaks of food poisoning or serious spoilage faults occur, the examination of all samples should take place in the same laboratory where there is access to medical epidemiologists able to investigate the origin, spread, and factors for multiplication of the organisms concerned. When food and human and animal samples are separated the results of examination may not be considered together, and without the essential correlation the conclusions are likely to fall short of accuracy.

Food microbiologists ought to know the principles of epidemiology, and amongst groups of epidemiologists there should be some who are trained in laboratory methods. Tools used in medical epidemiology, such as the finer typing methods, the dissemination of information about communicable disease, and weekly, quarterly, and annual reports of data, could also be used for the microbiology of food spoilage. They would be useful for tracing sources of contamination. National and international data banks would help in the formulation of specifications for trade between countries.

8

Food-borne infection

There are many diseases spread by food which are distinguishable from the acute bacterial food poisoning described in the previous chapters. Some cause illness when small numbers of organisms are swallowed, whereas large numbers of food-poisoning bacteria are required to initiate symptoms. Thus typhoid fever, cholera, and dysentery may be water-borne and food is a vehicle of transport for the bacteria passing from source to victim and not necessarily a medium for multiplication.

Paratyphoid fever has two forms, one simulating gastroenteritis and the other enteric fever. The gastroenteritis form has similar symptoms and incubation periods to salmonellosis and is likely to require a fairly large dose of organisms, which means they need time for their multiplication in food. The enteric fever form with symptoms similar to but less severe than typhoid requires 7 to 10 days for incubation, but nothing is known about the dosage. The fact that paratyphoid fever is occasionally water borne suggests that this form may occur after the ingestion of a comparatively small dose of organisms.

Cholera is usually water borne and it spreads rapidly; it can be food borne also. Shigella can be water borne, but it appears to be more often spread from person to person and through the environment to people.

Viral agents of food- and water-borne diseases must also be infective in small doses because they cannot multiply in inanimate matter.

The virus of poliomyelitis may be isolated from faeces and sewage; it can be assumed, therefore, that it is also food and water borne. Vehicles of infection for the virus of hepatitis include water, shell-fish, and other food; investigations are hampered by an inability to grow the organism so that evidence is epidemiological.

It is suspected that certain viruses cause gastroenteritis but the difficulty of isolating viruses from faecal and food materials hinders investigations. Nevertheless the electron microscope may reveal virus particles in faeces.

In December 1976, widespread outbreaks and cases of vomiting and diarrhoea affected about 800 people who had consumed cooked cockles from one area of England. Round virus-like particles were seen in a high proportion of stool samples from patients in three of the outbreaks. The particles were similar in size, morphological features, and density to particles seen in outbreaks of winter vomiting (W agent) and other gastroenteritis cases from which the usual bacterial agents were not isolated. The particles appeared to be serologically distinctive, and differed from the Norwalk and Hawaii agents.

The incubation period for typhoid fever is 7 to 21 days; it may be less or more according to the dose and the immunity of the individual. The two forms of paratyphoid fever have already been described, the incubation periods being 24 hours or so for the one and 7 to 10 days for the other.

The enteric fevers may begin insidiously with general malaise and fever. Intestinal symptoms may or may not appear early but they are not prominent until the second and third week of fever. The incubation period for dysentery is from 2 to 4 days and acute diarrhoea may persist for several days. The virus diseases usually have long incubation periods of 10 or more days.

It is convenient to consider the water- and food-borne diseases under the headings, water, milk, ice-cream, and food.

Water

After the incident of the Broad Street pump in 1854, when sewage pollution of the district well gave rise to a large-scale outbreak of cholera and many deaths, the famous epidemiologist John Snow turned public attention to water and sanitation. Early in the twentieth century chlorination of mains water was introduced by Alexander Houston. Except for occasional incidents of typhoid fever from well water and small unchlorinated supplies in country districts there was no more trouble until the big Croydon outbreak in 1937. Then 341 persons became ill owing to the introduction into the water supply of typhoid bacilli from the urine of a symptomless excreter working on repairs to a deep well.

In 1963, holidaymakers were arriving back from Zermatt and developing typhoid fever, and many Swiss and other holidaymakers were ill because sewage had seeped into an undetected leak in the mains water pipe.

There have been instances where adults and children have imbibed contaminated river and stream waters, sometimes after falling in accidentally or with suicidal intent, and subsequently developed typhoid fever.

In one such instance the origin of *Salmonella typhi* in a stream was traced to symptomless excreters; 11 were found in a mental hospital. The sewage effluent from the hospital discharged into the stream approximately half a mile away from the point near the road where two boys had been playing and drinking the water. The patients excreting *S. typhi* were segregated into one ward, and the sewage outflow from this ward was treated with chloride of lime. The rate of excretion varied from person to person and from time to time, but continued intermittently for many years while investigations were in progress.

Water may be an indirect source of *S. typhi* when the immediate vehicle is a foodstuff. Shell-fish, oysters for example, may feed and grow in sewage-polluted water. There is a rapid circulation of water through the body of oysters and mussels, during which bacteria, including pathogenic bacteria, are filtered off. An outbreak traced to this source occurred in 1958 when oysters from the estuary of the river at West Mersea caused illness. A carrier was excreting *S. typhi* into the river.

In 1973 there was a large outbreak of cholera in coastal regions of Italy due to pollution of river water, oysters, mussels, and other seafoods. Similarly, the spread of cholera was enhanced by polluted shellfish in a widespread outbreak in Portugal. Polluted springs and non-carbonated mineral water bottled from the spring water were also vehicles of infection.

Sewage polluted water may be an indirect source of *S. typhi* in food manufacture. Untreated river water has been used for cooling heat-sterilized cans of food. Minute faults in the can structure allow water and organisms to be sucked in while the hot can is under vacuum. *S. typhi* was isolated from a small can of cream, and its suspected presence in cans of corned beef and tongue, and the resulting outbreaks of typhoid fever are described later in this chapter under Food (p. 135).

Any pathogenic organisms, including viruses living in or passing through the intestinal tract of human beings or animals, may be transmitted by untreated water polluted by sewage. The use of such water, not only in food manufacture, but also in kitchens for food preparation and the washing of vegetables, equipment, and premises, must be considered potentially dangerous. When the conditions of storage allow multiplication of the organisms in foods the hazard is even greater. Drinking water is probably grossly polluted to cause infection, unless large volumes are drunk. Infection with food or water will increase under conditions of tropical heat.

Milk

Milk is an ideal medium for bacterial growth and means of contamination are numerous. It may be already dangerously contaminated when taken from the cow. Tuberculous cattle excreting tubercle bacilli in milk used to be one of the main sources of tuberculosis in children and adults. Formerly 4000 or more new cases of tuberculosis from bovine tubercle bacilli were recorded yearly in Britain. The eradication scheme, including the tuberculin testing of cattle and the pasteurization of milk, has reduced the incidence almost to vanishing point.

Brucella abortus, the bacillus responsible for abortion in cows, may be excreted in milk and give rise to an infection known as undulant fever in those who consume contaminated raw dairy products such as milk, cream and 'cream' cheese. Farm workers in close proximity to infected cattle may also acquire the disease.

Goats and their products may be similarly infected. Undulant fever in man is not often fatal but may cause ill health over long periods of time. The disease has been eradicated from cattle in Scandinavia and the USA, and similar methods for eradication are in progress in Britain.

Infection of the udder, known as mastitis, may lead to excretion of food-poisoning staphylococci, haemolytic streptococci, or even salmonellae in the milk. The faeces of the cows infected with salmonellae may contaminate milk directly. In the intimate association between farm workers and their animals diseases are spread from one to the other, and the organisms causing infections in farmers and their helpers may spread to milk. Diphtheria bacilli from human cases and carriers may be implanted on ulcers of the teats of the cows and cause contamination of the milk in this way.

There have been widespread outbreaks of scarlet fever and tonsillitis from streptococci passing into milk from infected lesions in the udder and on the teats of cows. Occasionally, milkers with streptococcal infections have been involved. In one large outbreak pupils in two schools were infected by drinking raw milk. Haemolytic streptococci of the same type were found in the throats of 87 children with scarlet fever, the throats of the milker and his two children, and in the milk. The danger from the spread of infection by those handling cows and milk is lessened by the automatic machine method of milking. Outbreaks of dysentery, typhoid, and paratyphoid fever, and of salmonella food poisoning have been spread by milk contaminated by carriers amongst farm and dairy workers but the cow herself is also a likely source of pathogenic organisms. Widespread outbreaks of paratyphoid fever have occurred; more than 1000 people were infected in one outbreak by drinking raw milk from cows excreting *S. paratyphi B*.

Pails, milking machines, and milk bottles may be washed with water polluted with human or animal sewage. Recommended chlorine compounds are available for use on farms, and milk bottles should be rinsed, washed in detergent, and rinsed in very hot water followed by cool mains water. Chlorine is sometimes used in rinse waters also.

In spite of all the hygienic precautions which may be taken on farms, bottling depots, and dairies, the only method to safeguard milk for delivery to the consumer is by heat treatment before or after it has been bottled and capped. By this means all pathogenic organisms introduced from the cow, from subsequent contacts, or other sources will be destroyed and there will be no further danger of contamination until the bottled milk reaches the consumer's kitchen. Here the milk is subject to the hazards of household use, but with reasonable care and cold storage it may be kept safe.

There are three commercial methods for heat treatment: by pasteurization, which is usually carried out in a plant as illustrated in Fig. 18; by disinfection at a temperature of 100 °C (212 °F) or over; and by steam infiltration which necessitates aseptic filling but provides milk with a long shelf life (see Chapter 2, p. 21; Chapter 18, p. 277).

The following description of a typhoid incident illustrates some of the points mentioned.

Typhoid fever from raw milk

An extensive outbreak of milk-borne disease occurred one autumn in the adjacent towns of Christchurch, Poole, and Bournemouth. There were 518 cases among the local inhabitants and about 200 persons were infected while on holiday in the district, although the disease did not develop until they returned home; there were about 70 deaths. Men, women, and children of all ages and occupation were affected. This suggested infection by a common food of wide distribution; milk was an obvious possibility. It was soon discovered that all the primary cases had consumed raw milk from one particular dairy. Immediately, steps were taken to pasteurize the supply to kill the infecting organisms before they were able to reach more potential victims. A search for the carrier among the employees of the firm, including the 12 roundsmen, was unsuccessful. Investigations spread to the thirty-seven farms that produced the milk to be mixed and distributed by the firm under suspicion. At one farm the housewife was ill with enteric fever; she died and her son developed the disease. This farm contributed 91 litres (20 gallons) of milk each day to the mixed supply of the retailer. Yet there was another puzzling feature in that a number of people had been infected before the farmer's wife became ill.

Further inquiries revealed the fact that, some years ago, a fatal case of typhoid fever had occurred in a house adjoining the farm. The water supply was common to both houses, eight others in the

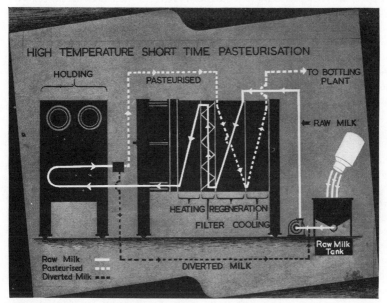

Fig. 18   Diagram of pasteurization plant (High Temperature Short Time method)

vicinity and also to the dairies. It came from a deep well situated about 91 metres (100 yards) from a small stream. This stream was liable to pollution from storm water and the sewage effluent from a large house. Typhoid bacilli were found in the effluent and their origin traced to a carrier in the house.

It was next demonstrated, by chemical means, that there was a connection between the stream water and the well. Furthermore, the farmer's cows and those of another producer, who also contributed to the same dealer's milk supply, used pasture alongside the stream. They drank from the stream, and perhaps while standing in it their udders were washed by the contaminated water. Spread of infection was considered to be water borne to the cows followed by contamination of the raw mixed milk supply consumed by the population. The milk was thought to have been contaminated with typhoid bacilli for 31 days before pasteurization was adopted.

Outbreaks of enteric fever and food poisoning due to *S. paratyphi B* in raw milk are not uncommon and the sequence of events are similar.

Ice-cream

Before the ice-cream heat-treatment regulations were introduced in 1947, ice-cream was a common vehicle for outbreaks of food poisoning and food-borne disease. The ice-cream mix was usually contaminated during preparation and it was often stored for hours or even overnight; there was opportunity for bacterial growth, which was necessary for staphylococci to produce enterotoxin, but not so necessary for the typhoid bacillus which can cause infection in smaller numbers.

Typhoid fever in Aberystwyth

The Aberystwyth outbreak illustrates the widespread and serious nature of an infectious disease initiated by a symptomless urinary excreter who, unaware of his condition, prepares and handles a commodity such as ice-cream. The vendor had been ill with typhoid fever in 1938 and was declared 'free of typhoid' on recovery.

There were approximately 210 cases, with 4 deaths in Aberystwyth. Because of warm weather and holidaymakers there was an increased demand for ice-cream and the merchant deviated from his usual practice of heating the ice-cream mix immediately before cooling and freezing it, using instead a cold mix method which required no heat treatment of the rehydrated powdered mix. There was no indication of the time between mixing and freezing in the report of the outbreak, but the atmospheric temperature was high.

Another ice-cream outbreak with paratyphoid bacilli as the causal agent occurred in Devon.

Paratyphoid fever at a holiday resort

At a North Devon holiday resort, cases of paratyphoid fever occurred occasionally from year to year amongst holidaymakers who visited the long sandy beach. As most of them had bathed at one particular end of the beach it was assumed that paratyphoid bacilli discharged into the sea from the main sewer, at a point not far from the bathers, were responsible. The bacteriologist who was in charge of the investigation was not happy with this explanation and decided to find out the true source of the organisms. He suspended cotton-wool swabs attached to suitable lengths of string at various points in the main sewer, its tributaries, and finally in the sewage waste from individual houses. When he examined these swabs in the laboratory, he found that one house only was responsible for the discharge of the infecting organisms, and that a local ice-cream manufacturer and his wife lived in the house. Specimens of stool were examined from each of them and it was revealed that, although the ice-cream manufacturer himself was clear, his wife was a carrier. Their ice-cream barrow was often seen on the bathing beach, and it is likely, therefore, that small doses of paratyphoid bacilli in ice-cream from the hands of the vendor or his wife were responsible for the outbreak of paratyphoid fever, rather than the presence of paratyphoid bacilli in the sewage which discharged into the sea.

Shigella dysentery from Pets' Corner

A child was taken by her mother to the Pets' Corner of a large general store where there were several cages of monkeys. Whilst watching them the child was eating an ice-cream cornet, and one of the monkeys put its paw through the cage to grab the cornet. The ice-cream was touched by the animal, although the child held on to it, and she licked the cornet before the mother could throw it away.

Two days later the child became ill and *Shigella flexneri* 103Z, a common type among monkeys, was isolated from a stool specimen. The same organism was found in a stool specimen from one of the monkeys at the shop. There seems little doubt that the child was infected by eating the ice-cream freshly contaminated by the monkey's paw — the habits of monkeys doubtless indicate the source of contamination of the paw. As there was no time for multiplication of the organism in the ice-cream the infecting dose was presumably confined to that directly transferred from the animal's paw.

Food

Canned meat and typhoid fever

An outbreak of typhoid fever in 1954 was traced to the consumption of canned ox-tongue, and for the first time it was postulated that the typhoid bacilli were already present within the can when it was opened.

There seemed no other explanation because those persons who had handled the tongue after removal from the can were not excreters. The Argentine establishment responsible for packing the tongue used untreated water from the river de la Plata to cool the cans after processing and typhoid bacilli of the same phage type were isolated from the river.

After this event the water was chlorinated in this establishment until 1963 when the plant broke down and again untreated water was used until in 1964 there was more trouble. Evidence pointed to a can of corned beef from the same place setting up a trail of contamination amongst cold cooked meats sold in a small supermarket in Scotland.

Under strict hygienic conditions the outbreak which ensued might have been confined to those who ate the meat from the one can assumed to be contaminated. Instead the organisms spread from meat to meat and about 400 case records indicated that for 3 weeks cold meats were bought by persons who subsequently became ill with typhoid fever. This spread and lingering of the organisms in the environment of the cold meat counter was encouraged by a number of factors. The can opener, slicing machine, pedestals for window shows, price tickets and trays for storage overnight in the refrigerator were common to all canned meats opened and sliced during the day. The slicing machine was washed each day but the use of plastic buckets for cloths, and of wooden scrubbing brushes in water without disinfectant may well have spread the organism without destroying it. With closure of the cold meat counter and finally of the shop itself the cases ceased to occur.

In 1963 three outbreaks of typhoid fever were all connected with canned meat from another establishment, where the cooling water was not chlorinated. One outbreak occurred after eating canned corned beef sold from a small butcher's shop with a chill cabinet. The number of cases almost coincided with the number of portions of corned beef from one pack. The sale of corned beef was stopped. The other two outbreaks occurred from canned corned beef sold by supermarkets, both with a high standard of hygiene and plentiful use of refrigerators.

As a result of these five outbreaks a careful search was made through the records of earlier outbreaks of typhoid fever. Many were said to have occurred due to cold meats bought at provision stores or butchers' shops; in every instance it had been assumed that the meat was contaminated after removal from the can. Since no symptomless excreters were found, it is probable that trace leakage of cooling water through seams had occurred during the cooling of the cans after heat processing.

Typhoid bacilli neither produce gas nor spoil the meat even though they grow abundantly in corned beef under both aerobic and anaerobic conditions. As their presence is not necessarily manifested in the blowing of contaminated cans, chlorination of water for the cooling process at canning factories should be strictly enforced.

Mutton pie and shigella dysentery

At least 248 of 600 pupils in a school were ill about 12 hours after a meal which included a pie made with mutton. After preparation, the pie was stored in a defective refrigerator, and it was warmed up before being served. Organisms of the dysentery group (*Shigella sonnei*) were isolated from the remains of the pie, from 130 pupils, and from 4 of 20 food handlers in the school kitchen.

Blancmange and shigella dysentery

About 100 children were ill 24 to 36 hours after a meal which included blancmange prepared the day before and stored in a cool kitchen until served. The children were in two schools and only those who ate the blancmange were ill. Organisms of the dysentery group (*Shigella sonnei*) were isolated from the stools of 29 children and all of 6 kitchen staff. Unfortunately, the remains of the blancmange were not available for examination, but packets of blancmange powder in the kitchen were examined; *Sh. sonnei* was not isolated. It was postulated that the blancmange was contaminated by a food handler during preparation.

The pease pudding outbreak of dysentery

It was customary in a certain little provisions store to prepare pease pudding one day each week. On a certain occasion several people in the vicinity of the shop were taken ill with dysentery, and inquiry revealed that they had all eaten pease pudding prepared at the little shop. Suspicions were confirmed when remains of the pudding collected from the shop were shown to contain dysentery bacilli. It was some time before the investigators were able to find out how the organisms reached the pudding. Gradually the story was pieced together. On the day that the pudding was made two visitors came to the shop, a nursemaid and a little girl 3 to 4 years of age. The nurse was friendly with a girl in the kitchen and, as usual, she went into the kitchen to talk, taking the child with her. While the two girls chatted together the child grew bored and wandered round the kitchen. Suddenly she noticed the pease pudding on the table and, deciding that it looked good to eat, she seized a handful and crammed it into her mouth. The hole in the pudding and the evidence on the child's face were vividly remembered by both the nurse and her friend. The child had recently recovered from an attack of diarrhoea which had been caused by the same dysentery bacillus as that responsible for the outbreak. The organisms were still present in her stools and must, on that occasion, have been present on her hands also, and by this means the bacilli were transferred to the pudding.

The thorough investigation of an outbreak of food poisoning may involve, therefore, not only a knowledge of the habits and illnesses of those actually employed as food handlers, but of their visitors also.

Part 2
Food hygiene in the prevention of food poisoning

9

Introduction

The previous chapters have described the bacterial causes of food poisoning, characteristics of the agents responsible, the sources or reservoirs of these germs and the conditions which encourage them to grow and reach numbers that are dangerous to the health of those who eat them.

Food hygiene may be defined as the sanitary science which aims to produce food which is safe for the consumer and of good keeping quality. It covers a wide field and includes the rearing, feeding, marketing and slaughter of animals as well as the sanitation procedures designed to prevent bacteria of human origin reaching foodstuffs. The veterinary and manufacturing aspects are beyond the scope of this book and although mentioned they are not considered in detail. With an acceptance of the fact that raw materials may contain food poisoning organisms, what can the food handler do to prevent food poisoning?

Some of the means by which foodstuffs can be protected from gross contamination will be obvious, but others may not be quite so clear. The immediate application of methods to raise standards of hygiene are sometimes thought to be impracticable, yet they should be discussed in the light of plans for future establishments designed for the preparation and service of food and for the training of food handlers.

There are two salient features which are important.

(1) *The separation of raw and cooked foods* in the general work flow of the large kitchen; this includes the necessity for different areas, workers, equipment, and utensils for raw ingredients and for the cooked products. Food handlers in small kitchens can only take note of the necessity for care in cleansing hands, equipment, and utensils in between work with raw and cooked foods. This injunction is necessary for shops also.

(2) *The care of foods after cooking* by almost any method; it is essential

141

to cool quickly and refrigerate all foods which are not to be eaten hot and freshly cooked.

If these two measures alone were understood and taken into earnest consideration there would be little food poisoning today. Other points which are better known may be listed as follows:

(1) Care of the hands by washing is usually applied to measures to be taken after using the WC but hands should be washed carefully between work jobs and after touching raw foods.

(2) Care not to touch cooked foods with the bare hands because the washing of hands cannot be an assurance against the removal of staphylococci.

(3) The removal from work with susceptible foods of any worker with septic lesions anywhere on the body. Clean, non-suppurative abrasions should be covered with a waterproof dressing.

(4) The elimination of flies, rats, mice, and other pests from food establishments.

(5) Careful instructions for cleaning the environment, equipment, food and drink containers, and utensils. Recommendations for good detergents, for cleaning and for boiling and very hot water for disinfection; chemical disinfectants may be necessary in some instances. The substitution of disposable paper for cloths, which otherwise should be boiled daily along with mop heads used for cleaning.

The words 'food hygiene' are usually associated with personal cleanliness which is often linked with the care of the hands. Normal washing procedures will not free the hands of all bacteria; staphylococci and similar organisms will remain in pores and crevices in the skin. The mass of bacteria and food-poisoning germs picked up from raw meat and poultry can largely be washed from the hands although normal skin flora will remain. Thus care is needed not to handle cooked foods and particularly meats, poultry, custards, and creams without utensils, or without disposable gloves. Yet, however carefully the food handler washes bacteria from the hands, raw products will spread them in the environment so that two more important preventive measures are:

(6) Cleanliness of all the surfaces and equipment used for cooked foods.

(7) Rapid cooling and cold storage of foods not intended to be eaten immediately on arrival or after cooking.

Thus, not only should cooked foodstuffs be protected against direct contamination by human, animal, or insect vectors of bacteria but also against indirect contamination from raw foods and articles, and surfaces used for preparation. The conditions of storage should ensure that foods can be kept at temperatures which will inhibit the growth and multiplication of bacteria. Cool and cold stores should be readily accessible to preparation areas. Most people will not be infected clinically by small numbers of food-poisoning bacteria but when millions develop in food, resistance to infection may be overcome and sufficient toxin formed in food or intestine to cause symptoms.

All those who work with food should be made aware of the ever present yet unseen danger of contamination, and taught how to store foods which encourage bacterial multiplication so that growth is suppressed. They require knowledge of the cooking times and temperatures known to kill bacterial cells, and an awareness of the survival of some spores and toxins in spite of cooking procedures that give palatable food.

The precautions needed for the care of food after cooking with regard to methods of cooling, and storage when the food is required cold and for reheating, where this is essential, must be taught in detail with strong emphasis on the ease with which bacteria from hands, surfaces, equipment, and utensils can reach food after cooking. It cannot be stated too often that the design of factories, shops, and kitchens should be such that raw and cooked food materials are well separated and all surfaces, implements, and vessels used for foods are designed and constructed so that cleaning is easy.

The following chapters describe in more detail the measures which will lessen the risk of food poisoning; these factors have been recognized while studying the spread of infection both in the field of outbreaks and in the laboratory.

There are other factors, sometimes magnified in the public mind, which may be relatively unimportant in themselves and which may serve merely as an indication that the conditions in a particular establishment are not all that may be desired. The presence of lipstick on a cup is not necessarily a sign that dangerous germs must be present also, but that the washing-up has not been carried out with due care and attention. Varnish on the nails of a waitress or kitchen employee is not in itself a harbour for bacteria, but perhaps an indication that the hands will not be washed or the nails scrubbed as often as required, for fear of damaging the cosmetic effect. The flakes of whitewash which may fall from the ceiling into food during its preparation may not constitute an immediate danger, but indicate that the general care of the kitchen is poor. The much-handled unwrapped loaf will not give rise to food poisoning or even food-borne infection except in quite unusual circumstances, yet it indicates a lack of care and respect for the food which others have to eat.

There are many such examples which arouse feelings of apprehension in the minds of people and which perhaps divert attention from more serious lapses in personal habits such as fingering the nose and mouth with hands used for the preparation of foods, failure to wash the hands between and after jobs, which include work with raw foodstuffs, as well as the after-care of cooked foods cut up for the table or to be cooled and stored.

The remaining chapters on prevention are concerned with the food handler, the food itself, the environment and equipment of food premises, and the parts which can be played by education and legislation.

10

Personal hygiene of the food handler

There is a chain of events which links the human or animal carrier or temporary excreter of food-poisoning bacteria to the food and subsequently encourages the organisms to multiply in the food before it reaches the victim. Every food producer and food handler has a part to play in the application of hygienic practices so that the links in this chain of infection may be broken.

Care of the hands

The passage of bacteria from one food to another on the hands of the food handler is an important means of spread with the hands providing a way of transport. There are personal skin bacteria which cling to the skin surface and persist in hair follicles, pores, crevices, and lesions caused by breaks in the skin. It is extremely difficult and perhaps impossible to remove these organisms by normal hand washing methods. When *Staphylococcus aureus* joins the population of the skin flora, there is danger from the contamination of food by those who finger foods in the course of preparation (see Fig. 8).

Merely eating a few hundreds, or even thousands, of staphylococcal cells newly planted on cooked food will be harmless. The number of organisms must increase to many millions per g of food during unchilled storage for sufficient toxin to be formed in the food to give symptoms of sickness.

Organisms habitually found in the bowel and which may pass through porous toilet paper, or be picked up from raw meat and poultry, can be washed more readily from the hands than those of the inherent skin flora. Experiments with salmonellae implanted on fingers and allowed to dry have indicated that there is a steady reduction in numbers but that there are usually a few survivors after 3 hours; when the original number was small they disappeared more rapidly. In these experiments a good hand wash removed these organisms.

The hands should be washed with plenty of soap and warm water and preferably rinsed in running water. Nails should be kept short, unvarnished, and scrupulously clean. Nail brushes should be made of plastic with Nylon bristles which may be disinfected periodically, preferably by heat or in a hypochlorite solution; a nail file should be available. Intestinal as well as skin and nose food-poisoning bacteria have been isolated from swabs rubbed under the nails.

Soap dispensed from a fixed container in a liquid or finely flaked or powdered form has advantages over soap tablets. When passed from hand to hand soap may accumulate a scum and curd thereby trapping bacteria which can remain on the surface. Tablets should be kept in a dry dish or suspended from a bracket by means of a small magnet. While liquid soap may have advantages, it can be a breeding ground for bacteria unless it contains an effective disinfectant and care is taken to wash the container and disinfect it in hot water when it is re-filled. The practice of topping-up liquid soaps and other watery solutions may encourage bacterial growth in spite of the presence of a chemical disinfectant (see p. 217). Soaps containing bactericidal substances are available in liquid or tablet form. The exclusive and prolonged use of antiseptic soaps may reduce the bacterial flora of the hands, and the repeated use of bactericidal liquid soap has been shown to reduce the distribution of hand contaminants.

Investigations on the bacterial flora of hands before and after washing with soap and water, alone or supplemented by antiseptic treatment, on a short-term basis showed that soap and water were effective in reducing or removing coliform organisms acquired from foods. The resident population of staphylococci, although reduced, may still be found on the hands after washing; they lodge in the hair follicles and cracks of the skin and may come to the surface after scrubbing in hot water. It is difficult to alter the resident flora of the hands, thus washed hands do not necessarily mean safe hands. Foods which readily support the growth of staphylococci, for example, cooked meats, cured and uncured, creams, and cooked sea foods, should not be touched with the fingers.

Food handlers touch equipment and utensils as well as foodstuffs, and pass on micro-organisms as well as acquiring them; therefore, care should be taken with the handling of equipment used in the preparation of food. Many food manufacturing establishments now dispense creams and lotions containing bactericidal substances for use after hand washing, in an effort to reduce the numbers of bacteria passing from hand to food when procedures cannot be performed by machine. Plain barrier creams decrease the sensitivity of hands to the effect of some food substances which have been known to produce dermatitis in certain people; they also keep the hands soft and supple so that roughness and cracks which may harbour bacteria are prevented. Barrier creams may contain a disinfectant in order to prevent growth of bacteria in the cream.

Tests have indicated that the use of rubber gloves is not necessarily an improvement bacteriologically over the use of bare hands unless the gloves retain a smooth unbroken surface and are washed frequently. They should be washed inside as well as outside to prevent soiling the hands by wearing gloves after continual use. The use of gloves is recommended, however, for procedures involving frozen foods and also when there is prolonged immersion of the hands in hot water containing detergents; in such instances protection of the skin is advisable. Thin disposable gloves are available for light work with foods, such as the assembly of salads and open sandwiches; they should not be worn for too long. Care should be taken to avoid irritating substances, unnecessary contact with dirt, chapping, or contact with very hot water.

Disposable paper towels are probably the most satisfactory means for drying the hands (Figs 19 and 20). Alternatively, cloth towels issued individually for each person's use and regularly laundered are acceptable. The continuous roller towel system which provides a portion of clean towel for each person is far better than the communal roller towel. The use of communal towels should be discontinued; they have been known to transfer infection from one person to another. It is almost impossible, even in the smallest establishment, to ensure that the hands are dried on a previously unsoiled portion of a roller towel, except by making extravagant demands on the laundering services. Electric hot-air dryers are pleasant to use, but they require more time (Fig. 21).

As already stressed, the skin of the hands must be kept not only clean but soft and healthy. A simple and inexpensive hand lotion may be made from gum tragacanth and glycerin in the proportion of one part of tragacanth to two parts of glycerin in water with the addition of a few drops each of the oils of lemon and lavender; there are also commercially produced hand creams which are both effective and economical.

Cuts, burns, and other raw surfaces however small and healthy looking can harbour staphylococci; there is a compulsory measure imposed by the Food Hygiene (General) Regulations, 1970, that in the kitchen all lesions must be covered. Waterproof dressings are essential to prevent the passage of bacteria outwards in the serous fluid or inwards from fluids in the environment. When a lesion is obviously infected as shown by inflammation and pus formation, whether it be on the hand or on any other part of the body, the person concerned should not handle foods. Even when the lesion

Figs. 19 and 20   Paper towels and head-dresses

has healed it should be remembered that the infecting staphylococci may still linger in the skin of the hands and that they may be difficult to eliminate. Skin disease from some other cause may be colonized by staphylococci so that care should be taken with skin conditions such as dermatitis from foods. The resident population of staphylococci, although reduced, may still be found on the hands after washing; they lodge in the hair follicles and cracks of the skin

Fig. 21 Hot-air dryer

and may come to the surface after scrubbing in hot water. It is difficult to alter the resident flora of the hands.

It is important, therefore, to remember that foods should not be touched with the bare hands more than is absolutely necessary. There is far too much handling of susceptible foodstuffs not only in kitchens but also in the retail shop and factory. It should be possible to have implements to carry out the work of the fingers, particularly with meat and confectionery that are not to be cooked subsequently. It may be slower to use tongs rather than fingers to serve cream cakes and sandwiches and to manoeuvre sliced meat from a machine, but the extra time given may be a factor in the prevention of food poisoning (Figs. 22 and 23).

Fig 22   Pastry tongs

Fig. 23   Hygienic method of slicing meat

Habits

There are certain bad habits which should be avoided by the food handler. The unguarded cough or sneeze can disperse from the nose, mouth, or throat numbers of bacteria suspended in droplets of moisture. These droplets serve to pass infection directly from one person to another; they may also contaminate foodstuffs.

The habit of licking the fingers to pick up paper or to turn over the pages of a book is a bad one at any time but particularly so when the paper, contaminated with saliva, is used for wrapping food.

Fig. 24 Habits to avoid — fingering the nose while preparing sandwiches

Nose picking or fingering the nose (Fig. 24) may leave staphylococci or other harmful organisms on the fingers. Clean handkerchiefs are almost free from bacteria, but dirty ones may harbour many millions; paper handkerchiefs provide a more hygienic substitute for cloth. The disposal of paper handkerchiefs should not create a problem; they may be flushed individually down the water closet or burned in a sanitary incinerator, or collected in a pedal-operated bin kept for the purpose and subsequently incinerated.

The hair should be clean and kept tidy by means of a cap, net or head-scarf (Figs 19 and 20); hair and dandruff can spread staphylococci from lesions on the scalp. The use of tobacco in any form is prohibited under the Food Hygiene Regulations so that smoking while on duty must be avoided. Smoke and ash from a cigarette are harmless but many smokers contaminate their fingers with saliva while taking the cigarette from their lips or when removing loose pieces of tobacco from the mouth. Other habits, such as chewing gum and taking snuff, which may result in the contamination of the fingers and environment should also be discouraged.

It is the practice in many self-service restaurants to clean table-tops with a moist cloth, when the crockery has been cleared away. The water used for rinsing the cloths should contain a suitable quantity of hypochlorite, or a quaternary ammonium compound, or other bactericidal substance, and the cloths themselves should be boiled and dried overnight or steeped in hypochlorite. For preference, paper should be used. Forks, spoons, cups, and glasses should be handled correctly by keeping the fingers from those parts which are touched by food and the mouth. Cutlery kept in a communal box should be supplied wrapped in a paper napkin.

Intestinal excreters

Intestinal bacteria are more likely to spread from the fluid stools excreted by those with diarrhoea than from the well-formed stools of the normal person. Aerosol sprays when the WC is flushed and general toilet cleanliness are more difficult with fluid excreta. Those with diarrhoea should not work in the kitchen, whatever job they are doing. Clearance from intestinal pathogens is required for food handlers under the Food Hygiene Regulations. The treatment of healthy excreters with antibiotics is not recommended because it may prolong the period of excretion.

The spread of intestinal pathogens, such as salmonellae in hospital wards, may be particularly troublesome. Nurses taking bedpans from bed to bed, the disposal of extreta in sluice rooms not far away from the ward followed by the dispensation of meals in the same area by nurses and patients raise peculiar difficulties in control.

Clothes, illnesses, and education

Protective clothing should be light coloured and changed frequently. Modern drip-dry fabrics ease the work of daily laundering. The provision of shower-baths in changing rooms will encourage a high standard of personal cleanliness. All large establishments should be provided with adequate changing rooms, rest rooms, and provision for storing clothes and other personal belongings. Illnesses, however mild, should be reported at once to the medical department and those which are likely to give rise to the spread of bacteria known to cause food poisoning or sepsis are required to be notified to the medical officer of health. Most large shops, stores, and factories possess a well equipped medical department including a surgery and waiting room. Small shops and kitchens should possess a first-aid box, and keep at least one member of the staff up to date in first-aid treatment.

Education on good standards of health and hygiene for all those working with food should be provided by the community health doctors, environmental health officers, welfare nurses, and other responsible persons, and regular talks should be encouraged.

11

Storage and preservation

Ways in which the food handler can help to prevent food poisoning have been discussed in the previous chapter. Yet without facilities to aid rapid cooling and to store foods under cold conditions, bacteria will multiply to dangerous levels and there may be an accumulation of toxic substances.

Storage

Cold storage

Cold affects micro-organisms in different ways depending on its intensity. As the temperature falls, bacterial activity declines; therefore foods which support bacterial growth should be stored at low temperatures to prolong their life and maintain safety. When foods are 'chilled' or stored at temperatures near but above freezing point some bacteria will grow slowly, but in the frozen or solid state many micro-organisms will be killed directly in the process of freezing; the remainder will not multiply and the numbers tend gradually to diminish. Hence freezing preserves foods for a long time, while chilling merely delays spoilage.

Chilled storage

In the refrigeration trade the term 'chilling' is used to cover any reduction in the normal temperature of the article concerned. For example, the ripening of tropical fruits is delayed during transit by storage at a temperature not far below that of the atmosphere, whereas the decomposition of imported meat is delayed by storage at −3 to 1 °C (26·6 to 33·8 °F) on the ship.

Some foods cannot be chilled at too low a temperature because there may be harmful changes; for instance, the inside flesh of apples turns brown if chilled below 3·5 °C (38·3 °F) and the resistance of some fruits to moulds may be destroyed by chilling, so that the rate of spoilage by moulds is increased.

With regard to pathogenic organisms some strains of salmonellae will grow at 10 °C (50 °F) but not at 5 °C (41 °F). *Staphylococcus aureus* will not grow below about 10 °C (50 °F); between 15 and 20 °C (59 to 68 °F) there is growth and toxin production. The sporing anaerobic organism *Clostridium perfringens* will not grow at temperatures much below 15 to 20 °C (59 to 68 °F), and no growth was observed in 6 days at 6·5 °C (43·7 °F). Most species of *C. botulinum* will grow very slowly at 10 °C (50 °F) and in some instances toxins may be formed at this temperature; in general, there is no growth or toxin formation at 5 °C (41 °F), although some strains of types B (non-proteolytic), E, and F can grow and produce toxin at 3·5 °C (38·3 °F).

Many other bacteria are able to increase slowly at chill temperatures, and under prolonged domestic refrigeration at 4 to 5 °C (39·2 to 41·0 °F) they will gradually spoil foods. Milk, for example, will develop off-flavours and off-odours from the growth of bacteria better adapted to the cold than those which grow and sour the milk at normal temperatures.

Foods of good bacteriological quality may be kept in a satisfactory condition at 4 °C for 3 to 4 days.

Deep freeze storage

The freezing of foodstuffs at approximately −18 °C (0 °F) kills many organisms, and the rate of death of the remainder will depend partly on the temperature of storage. Of the food-poisoning organisms, those of the salmonella group are said to be killed most rapidly on freezing. They disappear in 1 month, and staphylococci in 5 months, from strawberries kept at −18 °C (0 °F). Yet salmonellae have been isolated after years of frozen storage in whole egg products and meat. The spores of *C. perfringens* and *C. botulinum* are not affected by freezing and the poisonous toxin of *C. botulinum* has considerable resistance to alternate freezing and thawing at a temperature as low as −50 °C (−58 °F). Staphylococcal enterotoxin has been shown to withstand a temperature of −18 °C (0 °F) for several months.

Moulds and yeasts endure freezing conditions better than bacteria, thus refrigerators should be kept thoroughly cleaned and free from fungal and yeast growth.

When highly contaminated foodstuffs are kept frozen it is believed that changes may occur in the food owing to the slow activity of surviving organisms over a long period of time. Thus there may be slow spoilage during storage in the frozen state, although far less, of course, than that which would occur in the unfrozen food. Chemical changes in enzyme structures may also take place. Freezing will not restore the freshness of a food already highly contaminated or spoiled by bacterial action. When a frozen food is thawed those bacteria which have survived will recommence growth and decomposition, so that the keeping time of the food is limited and it must not be left at room temperature too long before being eaten, nor should it be refrozen. Manufacturers take great care in the preparation of frozen foods and most of them print instructions on the packet for their correct use. A temporary period of thawing due to power cuts or failure of the cabinet mechanism or even during shopping does not necessarily mean that the partially thawed food should be discarded. Discretion must be used depending on the length of time, rise in temperature, and general condition of the food. When the central core is still frozen the outside will still be cold enough to stop most bacteria from growing. Frozen food should be eaten as the manufacturer intends, freshly thawed from the original frozen state. Subsequent thawing and freezing will lead to quality deterioration as well as bacterial hazard.

Cold storage accommodation

There should be ample cold storage space conveniently available in every kitchen. Where the size of the canteen justifies the extra expense there should be a walk-in cold room with metal shelves and, in addition, one or more household refrigerators, so that foods with strong odours, such as fish, may be kept separate from other foods. Between the cold room and the kitchen there should be a well defined air space to prevent the hot air from the kitchen reaching the cold room. The temperatures of all domestic refrigerators and cold rooms should be checked regularly by thermometers placed in positions where they can be read easily. Cold rooms and domestic refrigerators are usually maintained at temperatures from 1 to 4 °C (33·8 to 39·2 °F).

The life of food in the refrigerator is limited and the longer it remains there the shorter its life on removal. The results of experiments on the storage life at 0 °C of meat with different initial numbers of bacteria indicated that meat of good bacteriological quality before refrigeration would keep for many days whereas poor quality meat had a short storage life. When the initial count of bacteria was low the appearance of slime on refrigerated meat was delayed for 18 days; when counts were high before refrigeration, slime appeared in 8 days. Conditions for the temporary storage of various foodstuffs are recommended by the Ministry of Agriculture, Fisheries and Food (p. 175); similar recommendations are given in the United States of America (Fig. 25).

Refrigerators should be defrosted regularly, automatically or according to the manufacturer's instructions. They should not be over-crowded, so that air circulation may be good; it is advisable to check the contents at the time of defrosting and aged foods should be thrown away. Space in the refrigerator ought to be available for cooked and uncooked foods which are perishable because they are susceptible to bacterial attack, such as meat, poultry, egg and dairy products, and fish. Tinfoil, greaseproof paper, or polythene wrapped around foods will prevent loss of moisture and the spread of flavours to other foods. Many foodstuffs commonly stored in a

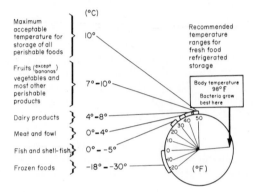

Fig. 25 Cold storage for foods

refrigerator do not encourage bacterial growth and they can with safety be kept for a few days in a cool room on a slate or stone slab; for example, fats, such as lard, margarine, and butter, hard cheese, unopened canned goods, cured bacon, and shell eggs. Milk can be stored in the cool room during the winter, but in the summer it should be refrigerated whether in bottles or churns. Receptacles containing milk should be covered and the outside cleaned before they are placed in the refrigerator, cold room, or larder.

At the time of defrosting, walls and shelves should be washed with soap or detergent and warm water and carefully dried before the food is replaced. If refrigerators are switched off at holiday times they must be emptied and carefully dried to prevent mould growth.

Domestic refrigerators are intended to keep food cold, and not to cool hot food which may damage the cooling coils and cause moisture to condense on adjacent cold foods; this may encourage the growth of slime bacteria and moulds. Cooked foods should, therefore, be cooled rapidly and placed in the refrigerator within $1\frac{1}{2}$ hours of cooking. An exception might be made for placing hot food in a walk-in type of cold room.

The penetration of heat into large joints and the loss of heat after cooking are slow, so that cuts of meat should be limited in size to 2·7 kg (6 lb) unless special precautions are taken for cooling in a chilled atmosphere with a good circulation of air.

The provision of proper facilities for the thawing, cooking, cooling, and storage of large turkey carcasses is essential. Many outbreaks of salmonella and *Clostridium perfringens* food poisoning from turkey meat have arisen because of basic faults in preparation and storage.

Cooling rates

The rapid cooling of bulks of cooked food intended to be eaten hours or even days later presents difficulties. The results of experiments to estimate the cooling rate of large cuts of meat showed that immediate storage in a well ventilated cold room was the most effective method; 2·3 kg (5 lb) cuts of meat lost approximately 60° of heat, cooling from 70 to 10 °C (158 to 50 °F) in 1½ to 2 hours. In homes and small catering establishments when cool rooms may not be available hot meat should be left in a cool and draughty place for not longer than 1½ hours before refrigeration. Even so storage of large cuts of meat cooked by boiling or by other methods not requiring temperatures above 100 °C should be discouraged.

Some food factories cool by wind-tunnels measuring about 1·5 by 0·9 by 24·4 metres long (5 by 3 by 80 feet) provided with iron rails, and while the food on metal trays passes through it is subjected to the wind from a fan 1·5 to 2 metres (60 to 80 inches) in diameter; cupboards with descending cold air-streams are also used. For large establishments compelled to cool masses of food required for frozen or chilled meals a mechanism should be provided to keep a cooling room at 10 °C (50 °F). Some new kitchens for school canteens include this facility; it is hoped that in time accommodation for efficient cooling will be provided in all kitchens cooking for large numbers of people. For small establishments a simple circulating fan installed in a well ventilated cooling room or larder situated on the north side of the building will provide a satisfactory system. A cabinet with shelves and containing a fan and air filter has been designed for quick cooling. Shallow rather than deep containers provide a larger cooling area for stews, gravies, and other liquid foods prepared in bulk. Household refrigerators could be adapted to provide space for shallow trays stacked one above the other for the cold storage of liquids.

Improvised cooling

Older houses and flats possess a cool cupboard or larder fitted with slate or stone slabs and with a ventilator protected against flies. Where the air flow is limited a small fan would be helpful. Foods should be covered, but all materials must allow an exchange of air otherwise there will be an increase in humidity, which will encourage mould and bacterial growth. Where space for cool storage is not available a box, louvered to allow a free flow of air but protected from rain, should be hung on a north wall or, at least, out of the sun.

There are various improvised methods for keeping food cool in the home. Porous earthenware vessels cooled with water help to keep foods such as milk and butter cold by evaporation. Muslin covering a bottle of milk or other container may be kept damp by dipping the four corners in cold water held in an outer receptacle; the container should be placed in a draught and out of the sun. A small louvered cupboard standing in water contained in a large basin or bath may be used for more bulky foods. Milk delivered after a family leaves for work should be placed in an insulated box, such as a polystyrene container, kept by the door in the shade.

Frozen packs of food allowed to thaw should be cooked and eaten within a short time; a vacuum flask will keep frozen foods solid for an extra day and delay the growth of bacteria for 3 to 4 days. The polystyrene container designed particularly to keep ice-cream solid is effective over a shorter period of time than the vacuum flask but it will delay the growth of bacteria for at least 24 hours. Frozen meals for elderly incapacitated folk living alone may be stored in either of these containers for 2 to 3 days after delivery.

In the UK the summer temperatures vary between 18 and 20 °C (64 and 69 °F) with occasional heatwaves with temperatures up to 32 °C (90 °F). Winter temperatures are usually 1 to 5 °C (35 to 41 °F) with occasional cold spells, and warm days when temperatures of 10 °C (50 °F) may be recorded. Kitchen and shop temperatures will be considerably higher.

The incidence of food poisoning is highest in the summer, but cases and outbreaks occur throughout the year. *Clostridium perfringens* grows rapidly in food left to cool in the warmth of kitchens, and outbreaks due to this organism occur in any season. Adequate cold storage facilities in homes, shops, and canteens would reduce the incidence of food poisoning; there is no other method which can effectively replace cold storage as a preventive measure.

The education of food handlers in matters of food hygiene should include instruction in the correct use of refrigerators and cold rooms. In particular they must be taught that the cleanliness and safety of a refrigerated foodstuff are dependent on the extent of bacterial contamination before refrigeration as well as on the temperature of refrigeration; also that extreme cold merely delays the growth and multiplication of bacteria, which immediately renew their activity when the food is transferred to a warm room.

Suggested conditions for the temporary storage of foodstuffs

Perishable foods

Certain perishable foods should be kept in a refrigerator maintained at a temperature of 0 to 4·4 °C (32 to 40 °F). These foods include meat, rabbits, game, poultry, fish, shell eggs, milk cream, fats, butter, lard, and margarine. Fish, however, should be kept separately if possible as it readily taints other foods.

Fats, butter, lard, and margarine may be kept in a cool room, but if the temperature rises they should be transferred to a refrigerator.

Frosted foods and frozen liquid egg should be kept frozen until required; a temperature of −20·6 °C (−5 °F) is suitable.

Fruit and vegetables should be kept in a cool and well ventilated place protected from frost. Sacks of root vegetables should stand on duck boards to allow the circulation of air. Vegetables should be prepared in a separate room or section of the kitchen so that dust and earth from potatoes, carrots, turnips, and other root vegetables may be diverted from the main area of food preparation (Fig. 26). Figure 25 gives temperatures for the storage of various foods.

Fig. 26 Segregated vegetable preparation area

Other storage

In addition to refrigerated and cool storage there should be dry, light and airy cupboards or rooms for canned and other packaged goods stacked on shelves and marked for rotation. Powdered and granular foods such as flour, sugar, dried milk, tea, oatmeal, sago, rice, egg powder, and coconut should be stored in metal bins or metal or glass jars with close-fitting lids. Even these containers should be raised at least 450 mm (18 inches) above the floor to allow space for cleaning. Goods packed in cardboard or wooden crates or cases should be well clear of the floor and preferably on higher shelves. The rooms should be designed to discourage vermin, flies and dust and they should be easy to clean. Dried fruit, fish, or meat should be kept cool and dry. It is important to avoid conditions which could lead to condensation of moisture on the surface.

Cleaning materials require separate accommodation, which should be large enough to allow sufficient space for sinks for washing, boilers for the disinfection of cloths and mop heads, tubular steel racks for drying cloths, mops, brushes and other equipment and ample light to observe the state of cleanliness of materials. Utility rooms should be carefully designed and used.

Personal clothing and other belongings should not be left in the kitchen but stored in proper accommodation nearby.

Equipment for cooking, receptacles, utensils, crockery, and cutlery should be stacked and protected from dust.

The hygiene of food storage and preparation depends on a knowledge of the habits of bacteria, the foods they contaminate most frequently, and the temperatures they do and do not like for multiplication. When these facts are known, a common-sense view will enable the more susceptible foods to be protected against the potential danger of contamination with food poisoning and spoilage bacteria.

Preservation

Most of the methods devised for keeping food safe are concerned with controlling the growth of bacteria and moulds in the food. Details about preservatives including antibiotics are contained in the Preservatives in Food Regulations 1975 as amended 1976 (SI 1975, No. 1487; SI 1976, No. 509; SI 1976, No. 1887).

Preservatives

As well as heat and cold, chemicals such as salt, acid, and other preserving substances are used. Permitted preservatives include:

sulphur dioxide (50 to 2500 ppm) which may be added to sausages, hamburgers, dehydrated vegetables, dried fruits, various drinks, fruit juices and pulps, syrups, desiccated coconut, jam, and fruit yogurt, for example; benzoic acid (160 to 2000 ppm) which may be used for soft drinks, fruit juices and pulps, flavourings and liquid colouring matter, liquid coffee and tea extracts, and liquid rennet; propionic acid, which may be used in bread (3000 ppm calculated on the weight of the flour) and in Christmas pudding (1000 ppm); sorbic acid (1000 ppm), which is useful against mould growth in flour confectionery, cheese, marzipan, prunes, and solutions of food colouring, and it is sometimes included in wrapping papers although this use should be restricted to papers used for products in which this preservative is permitted. Sodium nitrite (200 ppm) may be used in cured meat and in small concentrations (10 ppm) in some types of cheese. For fresh fruit, thiabendazole (3 to 10 ppm) may be used on bananas and citrus fruit; biphenyl (70 ppm) may also be used on the latter.

Dehydration

Dehydration to powdered form reduces the moisture content to levels below which micro-organisms cannot grow. This process does not destroy all micro-organisms and the bacterial purity of the product depends on its state of contamination before dehydration. The addition of water will stimulate growth if temperature conditions are suitable and the substance is normally able to support growth of bacteria.

Antibiotics

The tetracyclines, chlortetracycline and oxytetracycline, were formally allowed to be used at a low concentration in ice (5 ppm) for the storage of fish, but present legislation bans this practice. Antibiotics are not permitted for the preservation of dressed poultry because experiments showed that when spoilage flora was repressed by chlortetracycline a strain of *S. typhimurium* resistant to the antibiotic grew more readily on dressed broiler chickens that were fed with the organism during life.

The proportion of antibiotic-resistant strains of *S. typhimurium* rose sharply when antibiotics were used freely in animal feeds and for prophylactic measures as well as for the treatment of animals. Recommendations to limit the use of certain antibiotics, except in treatment, to those not normally employed for treating man are given in the Report (Swann) of the Joint Committee on the use of

Antibiotics in Animal Husbandry and Veterinary Medicine, 1969; they will help to reduce the spread of antibiotic-resistant strains of salmonellae (see Chapter 4, p. 43).

Nisin, however, may still be used to repress the growth of spoilage organisms in cheese, clotted cream, and any canned food. The use of nystatin to prevent mould growth on bananas is no longer permitted, its place for this purpose having been taken by thiabendazole.

Gamma-rays

Irradiation with small doses of gamma-rays (0·5 to 0·75 Mrad) is recommended for the destruction of salmonellae in foods such as boneless meats, animal feeding meals (bone, fish, meat, cereals), and dried and frozen egg products, for example albumen, where destruction by heat may be difficult.

The use of gamma-irradiation for this purpose has so far been forbidden, but as no harmful effects have been demonstrated and changes in taste and smell are barely detected when small doses of 0·5 Mrad or less are given, it is hoped that the method may come into use and reduce considerably the distribution of salmonellae to animals and man in feeds and foodstuffs.

12

Preparation and cooking

General methods of cooking

Fresh food cooked and eaten immediately while hot should never be responsible for food poisoning due to micro-organisms. Nevertheless, heat-resistant bacterial spores frequently survive cooking and give rise to large numbers of bacterial cells when cooling is slow and the storage time of cooked foods in the kitchen is too long.

Short, high-temperature cooking is best for the safety of the foodstuff and thereafter there must be an understanding of times and temperatures of storage in relation to bacterial growth.

Steam under pressure, thorough roasting of small solid chunks of meat, grilling and frying are considered to be the safest methods of cooking. Infra-red rays and high-frequency waves have good penetration but may be patchy in action. The results of comparative experiments with small chickens inoculated with sporing and non-sporing organisms showed that some spores survived inside and on the outer surfaces of the carcasses after cooking in a microwave oven and also after conventional roasting. Both methods of cooking destroyed vegetative cells. The rapid reheating of chilled or thawed frozen meals in a microwave oven may have advantages in some circumstances and for certain foods, but the bacteriological condition of the cooked food before reheating is important. All the benefit of heat destruction of micro-organisms in raw food by cooking may be undone if manipulation and handling after heating allows recontamination of the cooked food.

Convection ovens

A fan in a forced air convection oven recirculates air in the oven, which improves heat transfer, and the cooking is faster, more even, and more effective (Fig. 27). The oven shelves can be filled with food without affecting efficiency, and similar articles of food will be cooked to the same degree. Cooking times generally can be reduced by one-third compared with those of the conventional oven. Forced air convection ovens are available in three types dependent on the speed of air movement and the input of heat. Care is needed to select the correct oven. As with conventional ovens vegetative cells of bacteria are killed but not all spores.

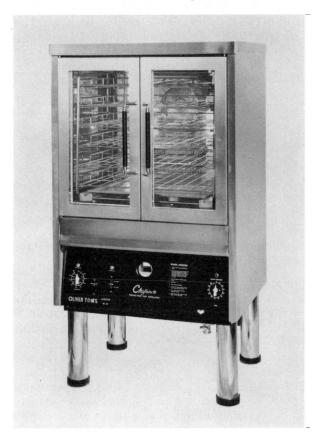

Fig. 27 Forced air convection oven

Microwave ovens

The microwave oven uses little electricity and it reheats cooked foods quickly; the oven can be used in conjunction with a deep freeze for fast food service. Microwaves boil food by the agitation of molecules, especially water molecules, but there is an inch limit to wave penetration into food. Metal containers will slow down microwave cooking by reflection and may even cause a breakdown in the system.

The drawbacks of microwave cooking are poor heat penetration and lack of browning; they are overcome by the Mealstream Micro-Aire oven, which is designed for a fast food menu. It cooks by continuous microwave energy or pulsed microwave at 7 second intervals, in combination with forced air convection making use of the adjacent infrared wave band as the source of heat. This appliance can be used to roast, bake, fry, grill, braise, and boil and it saves labour, food, power, space, and time compared with traditional cooking methods. There is less dirt and the hygiene is thereby improved; ventilation requirements are also reduced. A Code of Practice for hygiene in microwave cooking is available (see Appendix D) DHSS No. 9.

Pressure cooking

Pressure steamers enable food to be cooked to order within minutes and in conjunction with bratt pans, they can replace the boiling top and its battery of pans. Modern pressure steamers are of two types:

(1) dynamic or high pressure, where steam jets will rapidly defrost and cook frozen food at 12 to 15 pounds per sq. in.,
(2) low pressure, operating at about 6 pounds per sq. in. when there is greater flexibility and control of the cooking process.

Pressure cooking is similar in principle to the hospital autoclave, all bacteria and spores are destroyed by the combination of pressure and heat. As well as a steam generator, a water treatment plant is often an essential pre-requisite for trouble-free pressure cooking.

Slow cooking

Slow cooking dates back to ancient times when stone pots were first used for this purpose. With increasing costs of fuel and food there has been renewed interest in this method of cooking as a means of household economy; maximum tenderness can be obtained from less expensive cuts of meat when they are cooked slowly at low temperatures. Electric cooking casseroles have been popular in the USA for several years and they are now available in Britain.

A typical slow cooking vessel consists of a glazed earthenware bowl and lid set into an outer aluminium casing. The cooking heat comes from an element wound around the sides between the earthenware bowl and the outer casing. The heat used amounts to approximately 60 watts on low and 120 watts on the high setting, as little electricity as a light bulb.

Some concern was expressed about the possible bacteriological hazards of cooking food at low temperatures for long periods of time, particularly with respect to *Clostridium perfringens*. Experiments have shown that the hazards using an electric casserole are no greater than those for conventional cooking methods providing the manufacturer's instructions are followed. It is important that the food be eaten hot immediately, or removed from the casserole, cooled rapidly, and refrigerated, although these instructions should be followed when foods are cooked by any method.

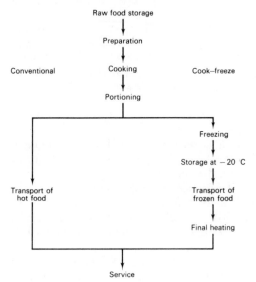

Fig. 28 Operation flow — conventional cooking versus cook-freeze

Cook–freeze

Cook–freeze can be defined as a system whereby high quality food is prepared and cooked in economic quantities, retained in a state of 'suspended freshness' by rapid freezing and freezer storage, and served when and where required from finishing kitchens with low capital investment and minimal staffing. Food is prepared, cooked, and frozen centrally with distribution of the frozen food to service areas for final heating and service (see Fig. 28).

The many advantages of the cook–freeze system include; centralization of stores, saving on staff, better portion control, and a better balance of the day's work thus avoiding the traditional peaks of production around mealtimes. From a microbiological point of view greater control can be exercised over preparation and storage as pressure to present meals at set times is eliminated. The dangers of cross-contamination from raw materials to other foods can be reduced by the preparation of single items at a time using equipment which will not be used for other foods on that occasion. If necessary, samples from large batches can be checked bacteriologically before they are eaten.

However, mistakes in batch preparation could lead to a far greater outbreak of food poisoning than small scale cooking on a day-to-day basis. In dealing with large quantities or bulks of food there is an increased hazard because it is difficult to ensure adequate heat penetration and rapid cooling after cooking.

The main emphasis in cook–freeze, as in any other catering system, must be placed on correct storage between cooking and service to prevent multiplication of organisms which may have survived the heat process, or which have reached the food after cooking.

Cooking frozen food

With the rapid expansion of the home freezer market there has been much discussion on the hazards of cooking food, particularly joints of meat and poultry, from the frozen state.

It has long been accepted practice to cook small items such as vegetables, fish fingers, beefburgers, and chops without preliminary thawing. These items are relatively small so there is no delay in heat penetration and adequate cooking is ensured in fairly short periods of time.

The main difficulty arises in the cooking of joints of meat and poultry. Although some frozen food companies and authors of books on home freezers and cookery advocate cooking most meat from the frozen state and give times and temperatures to use, it is safer to recommend proper thawing of frozen meats before cooking.

When a frozen joint is cooked, the outside may appear to be well done while the centre remains quite raw. Organisms present in the centre of a rolled joint or in the cavity of poultry, for example, may survive and if the cooked food is stored incorrectly, may multiply to numbers able to cause food poisoning when consumed.

Even if recommendations for cooking times and temperatures are laid down there will be times when rules are forgotten. The housewife tends to judge 'doneness' by the external appearance of meat and by probing with a sharp implement — how many use or would purchase a meat thermometer?

Joints for the average size family will be small and consumed quickly; the number of organisms surviving will most likely be small, probably too small to cause illness. Catering size joints are a much greater hazard as they are more likely to be cooked in advance of needs and may be improperly stored before use due to lack of cooling facilities. The cooking of large joints from the frozen state requires longer cooking times and hence more fuel; the practice should be discouraged.

Meat and poultry dishes

Heat penetrates slowly into joints, poultry carcasses, and made-up dishes such as pies, and adequate cooking times and temperatures should be allowed for the centre to reach boiling point. For instance, a 2·9 kg (6½ lb) meat pie requires a temperature of 177 to 204 °C (350 to 400 °F) for 2½ to 3 hours for the centre to reach boiling point at 100 °C (212 °F). An outbreak of food poisoning has already been described in which an organism of the salmonella group was isolated from several pies of two sizes: 453 and 113 g (1 lb and 4 oz). The minced meat, probably already contaminated with salmonellae, was hand-filled raw into the pastry cases and it was thought that the cooking, at 232 to 246 °C (450 to 475 °F) for 25 to 30 minutes, was either inadequate to destroy the contaminants or that there were temperature fluctuations. It was pointed out that pies made with raw meat should be cooked to the point of sterility even though the pastry may become a little over-brown in the process. It is worth while to note that for the red muscle colouring matter of meat to change to the familiar grey colour the temperature must be at least 73 °C (163·4 °F). Heat penetrates meat slowly and the English roast beef which remains red inside has not reached an internal temperature of more than 63 to 65 °C (145·4 to 149 °F). Slowly cooked rare beef used for sandwiches prepared for customers at their request has caused *C. perfringens* food poisoning.

Precooked meat is often used for making pies and pasties so that a final cooking time sufficient only to bake the pastry is given. The temperature reached in the centre of the mass of meat, sometimes mixed with vegetables, would not necessarily destroy sporing or even non-sporing organisms which would multiply actively while the meat was still warm.

Between 1973 and 1975, 141 of 632 (22 per cent) general outbreaks of food poisoning in England and Wales were due to *C. perfringens*; the foods most commonly mentioned were cold and reheated meat and poultry, and dishes such as mince, stews, and shepherd's pie which is often made with precooked meat. Thus a change in cooking methods and a greater awareness of the necessity for rapid cooling and cold storage would help to eliminate this type of food poisoning.

Part-cooking of meat in hot weather or at any other time is frowned on by the bacteriologist. Some organisms will be killed but others may be encouraged to multiply. The final cooking may be too light either to kill bacteria or to destroy toxins.

It is safer to keep meat in the raw state overnight, preferably in the cold, and to cook it thoroughly on the day when it is required. If, from motives of economy or for some other reason, it is essential to cook meat the day before it is eaten, it should be cooked thoroughly, cooled rapidly and refrigerated overnight. When there is insufficient refrigerator space, it should be a strict rule that all dishes of stewed or boiled meat, whether as stews, pies, or joints, must be cooked and eaten the same day, preferably with no delay between cooking and eating and certainly not more than 1 to 2 hours. The danger of eating meat and poultry cooked a day or two earlier seems to be far greater in the communal canteen dealing with large masses of meat than in the home, although in no instance should stewed or boiled meat be allowed to stand at a warm temperature for several hours. Well-roasted solid meats should be safe, but the rolled roast joint frequently gives rise to trouble because the contaminated outside is folded into the centre. The size and shape of joints of meat are important in relation to heat penetration and heat loss. Temperature recordings from thermocouples showed that during cooking the temperature at any point within the meat was dependent on the distance of that point from the outer surface of the meat. The centres of large bulky cuts of meat will, therefore, take longer to heat and cool than those of long slim portions of like weight. It was also shown experimentally that the centres of large portions of meat were slower to heat up in an hot-air oven than in a moist-air oven.

The degree of heat reached inside a grilled or fried sausage or a sausage roll will depend on the preference of the cook for a well-browned or lightly cooked article. Rissoles and fishcakes made with precooked meat or fish or potatoes, may be placed in the frying-pan or grilled for a few minutes only. Boiled rice may be quickly turned over in a little hot fat for frying. Raw foods such as fish, sliced or minced meat, and bacon are likely to be grilled or fried thoroughly on both sides in fat, which should ensure sterility.

The installation and use of pressure cookers for quick, high-temperature cooking might solve many of the difficulties associated with the preparation of foodstuffs on the day they are required to be eaten hot. Even heat-resistant spores would be killed by this method of cooking.

Canteen-prepared tongue has been a frequent vehicle of *C. perfringens* and staphylococcal food poisoning. *C. perfringens*, from the organisms already present in the raw tongue, and staphylococci from the hands of the cooks, will multiply in the cooked product. The following method is recommended for safety. The cured tongue should be washed and allowed to soak in water for 8 hours in a cold room overnight. It should be washed well and boiled quickly in a lidded saucepan or steamer. The skin should be removed while the tongue is hot, and the small bones removed from the thick end. The tongue is then ready to be pressed in a container which is scrupulously clean and either sterilized or disinfected in hot water; at this stage it is allowed to cool, but it is cooked again in the press, cooled rapidly, and refrigerated until required (see p. 88).

Outbreaks of poultry food poisoning frequently occur from cold or warmed poultry meat. Salmonellae and *C. perfringens* are commonly present in the frozen or chilled birds as they arrive. The spores of *C. perfringens* may not be destroyed by cooking and grow out later during long slow cooling and kitchen storage. Even a few salmonellae may survive in underthawed and undercooked carcasses, although they are most often picked up after cooking from traces of the raw product left on surfaces and utensils. Left unchilled, the organisms grow in the meat.

Outbreaks of salmonella food poisoning from spit-roasted chickens have been described in Chapter 6. Careful instructions are needed for thawing, cooking and, most important of all, for handling and storage of cooked poultry. Staphylococci are usually implanted by hands after cooking. Cooked carcasses may be cut and torn apart while still warm and the portions piled high on trays, so that even if refrigerated the cooling rate is far too slow. When removed from the refrigerator or cold room in good time next day the organisms continue to grow and produce toxin.

Milk foods

The hazards associated with the preparation of food a day or so ahead of requirements apply also to custards, trifles, blancmange, and other milk puddings; these dishes should be freshly cooked unless they can be stored in a refrigerator.

By heating (or cooking) milk gently, as in pasteurization, all the vegetative cells of organisms which are potentially dangerous are destroyed so that the milk is made safe unless recontaminated in the home. The term 'sterilized milk' means that a temperature is reached at which all or nearly all bacteria are destroyed, and the milk will remain close to sterility for an indefinite period, whilst it is kept in the sealed container. Ultra heat treated milk is subjected to a high temperature by injection of steam; not all spores are destroyed but the chilled shelf-life of the milk in unopened cartons may be as long as 3 months. There have been some noteworthy episodes of food poisoning from dehydrated milk. Two outbreaks are described (p. 73), one in the UK due to staphylococcal enterotoxin and the other in the USA due to *Salmonella new brunswick.*

The susceptibility of certain confectionery creams to bacterial contamination has already been emphasized, and their preparation and storage should be considered with care. All ingredients used in the vicinity should be free from pathogenic organisms and gross bacterial contamination. Equipment should be scrupulously clean and disinfected frequently, preferably by heat. Savoy bags for dispensing cream and other toppings and also mashed potato should be made of materials which can be washed and boiled after use, such as cotton, linen, or nylon. After boiling they should be dried thoroughly and stored in a special place protected from dust-borne or other contamination. Disposable paper bags may also be used for this purpose.

Although it may be considered necessary to ensure freedom from salmonellae of persons handling cream and milk, the presence of both these organisms in the cow herself may be of even greater importance. Little space has been devoted to *Brucella abortus* in cows and *Brucella melitensis* in goats but these organisms and others like the tubercle bacilli are scourges to cattle and to those who drink raw milk in countries without eradication schemes and without pasteurization. Nevertheless, most raw milk is boiled.

Infant bottle feeds

Careful precautions are necessary in the preparation and storage of bottle feeds for infants. Bacteria may be introduced into prepared feeds by constituents of the feed, bottles, teats, utensils, and also from hands used in the preparation. Investigations have shown that high counts may be due to bacterial growth during cooling and storage at atmospheric temperatures; unless care is taken at every stage of preparation, unsafe feeds contaminated with pathogenic bacteria and unclean feeds containing large numbers of bacteria, including *Bacillus cereus* and other aerobic sporing bacilli, may be given to infants.

There is a growing interest in the procedures of hospital milk kitchens and the preparation of safe infant feeds. Hospitals in the UK, in the USA and other countries are using terminal sterilization techniques. In one large hospital in India the incidence of *Esch. coli* enteritis in infants has been markedly reduced by this procedure. The cooked feed is poured into sterilized bottles; a sterilized or disinfected teat is placed on each bottle and covered with a paper cap; the complete bottled feeds with teats are placed in small crates, ready for feeding each child for a day, and given heat treatment in a pressure cooker or steamer. Special equipment is available for cleaning bottles and teats (p. 206). Milk remaining in infant feeding tubes used for premature babies may be a source of infection.

Much care, attention and legislation have been given to the hygienic production of milk, both liquid and dried, for the general public; similar care is needed to ensure a safe clean product for the infant consumer.

Other infant feeds

Bone or meat and vegetable broths and purées are common weaning foods for infants during the second 6 months of life. The care of these foods, which may be canned or prepared in large quantities in the home, is important because they are excellent media for the growth of bacteria. The sterile contents of small bottles or cans are intended to be eaten for one meal. There are closure methods for bottles designed to prevent opening by curious mothers anxious to know the smell of the product before purchase. The preparation in the home of small quantities for individual meals may be uneconomical and large quantities may be stored for a few days only in the refrigerator.

Contaminants can be introduced from hands or from utensils, and they will grow rapidly in warm weather without refrigeration.

Infants are more sensitive than adults to food infections and are more likely to succumb to the dehydration caused by diarrhoea and vomiting.

All foods and liquids intended for infants should be stored in covered containers in a refrigerator or, if canned, the portion left in the can should be refrigerated in the can and covered. Three days should be the maximum time of storage. Supplies prepared for 2 days should be separated into two portions to avoid further touching. Where there is no refrigeration the covered container should be stored in the coolest place and the food boiled immediately before the meal. When the indoor temperature is greater than 21 °C (70 °F) and there is no refrigeration, bone and meat meals ought not to be used unless the contents of a freshly opened can is consumed; anything left over should be abandoned.

All containers and utensils used for the preparation of infant feeds should be boiled after cleaning and allowed to drain dry.

Egg products

Small numbers of organisms of the salmonella group may be present in unpasteurized egg products prepared in bulk, including liquid and dried whole egg, white, and yolk. It is recommended that liquid egg mixes and rehydrated powders should be cooked within 2 hours of preparation unless refrigerated in small amounts. Such egg products should be used only in recipes requiring thorough heat treatment.

An outbreak of food poisoning which occurred in an army camp illustrates a number of these points. Reconstituted spray-dried whole egg was prepared early one morning; part of it was scrambled for breakfast and eaten by 70 men, only 1 of whom was affected. The portion which remained was allowed to stay in the cookhouse until tea-time when the original bacterial population, including salmonella organisms, would have increased enormously. The mixture was lightly scrambled with insufficient heat treatment to kill all the salmonellae, and of 20 men who ate it 16 were taken ill.

Infection from contaminated ducks' eggs can be avoided by boiling them hard — for at least 10 minutes — frying them well on both sides, or confining their use to baked products, such as cakes and puddings, which require cooking temperatures high enough to destroy the organisms. But care should be taken that all equipment used in the preparation of mixes containing ducks' eggs is thoroughly cleaned and disinfected. Outbreaks of food poisoning have been caused by the contamination of imitation cream mixed in a bowl previously used for the sponge or cake mixture containing ducks' eggs. Lightly cooked or uncooked dishes, such as scrambles, omelettes, meringues, mayonnaise, mousse, or similar foods, should not be made with ducks' eggs. Other outbreaks from eggs and egg products are described in Chapter 6.

Gelatin

Powdered gelatin is another substance which requires particular care in preparation and addition to foodstuffs, because it may contain a large and varied flora of bacteria. Melted gelatin in water for use in cooked meat pies and also for other purposes such as for glazing meat loaves should be nearly boiled, and used as rapidly as possible with the temperature maintained above 60 °C (140 °F). This procedure may involve the use of a higher concentration of gelatin than formerly needed at low temperatures to produce an effective gel. Microbiological standards for the various forms of gelatin used for cooking and also for feeding animals will reduce the hazards associated with this product. Gelatin has been responsible for outbreaks of food poisoning as glaze (p. 84) and as jelly for pies; poorly designed filling equipment may be at fault (pp. 98–102).

Coconut

Methods for the production of desiccated coconut are so much improved that contamination with salmonellae has been reduced to a minimum. When purchases of desiccated coconut are made from reputable firms, who know safe sources of supply, there is little danger from the use of this popular garnish. Coconut milk is sterile unless the outer husk of the nut or seed is damaged and bacteria pass through into the white flesh. Coconut milk is used as a refreshing drink in hot countries where the palm is common.

Rice

Dried polished rice has low counts of bacteria but *Bacillus cereus* is often present; this organism produces many spores which can survive cooking. The spores germinate into bacilli which multiply in cooked and moist cereal products left unrefrigerated, and a toxic substance is formed. Boiled rice intended for frying should not be stored in the kitchen, but should be prepared in small amounts and fried for customers as required. Outbreaks of food poisoning caused by the growth of *B. cereus* in boiled and fried rice are described on pp. 115–117.

Cake mixes

Packaged mixtures for cakes and sponges have given rise to many cases and outbreaks of salmonella food poisoning in the USA and Canada due to the inclusion of salmonella-contaminated egg products. It is recommended that such mixes should not be used unless there is assurance either that they do not include egg products, or that those included have been subjected to pasteurization prior to admixture with the other ingredients of the powder.

Salad vegetables and dessert fruit

In large-scale catering it is recommended that vegetables and fruits with thin skins used for salads and dessert should be washed in water containing a solution of sodium hypochlorite. There are opportunities for salmonella contamination from fertilizers and soil as well as from food handlers. To facilitate the correct use of hypochlorite a marked sink should indicate a known volume of water and a small measure used to add the required concentration of solution; 60 to 80 ppm hypochlorite is considered to be satisfactory for this purpose. The household use of hypochlorites for salad vegetables (including watercress) and fruits is also advocated. Exposure to solutions of hypochlorite should not be less than 30 seconds.

The poor sanitary conditions and polluted water in many countries, particularly in the Middle and Far East, emphasize the need for care of vegetables and fruits purchased in shops and local markets. As well as the direct transfer of bacilli and amoebae, causal agents of dysentery, from product to consumer, cross-contamination from raw to cooked vegetables may take place in the kitchen.

13

Retail sale and factories

Retail shops

The number of food-poisoning incidents traced to retail shops is small compared with those reported from hospitals, schools, works and institution canteens, and restaurants including cafés, hotels, and holiday camps. One of the reasons for this apparently low proportion is that home incidents are seldom reported and therefore their number is not accurately known. The opportunities for investigation are infrequent and, when they do arise, the responsible food is rarely found; the contaminated food was recognized in approximately 2 per cent of the 1278 family outbreaks of salmonellosis occurring in 1973–1975.

Much food will already be contaminated when it reaches the shop and the spread of the organisms will depend on the standard of environmental hygiene, personal cleanliness, and storage conditions.

Shops for raw and cooked meats

Each year most food-poisoning incidents are traced to contaminated meat and poultry dishes. Some of this illness is caused by the careless handling of cooked products in the home and canteen, and also by faulty cooking, cooling, and storage methods, but the spread of contamination within the retail shop plays an important role.

Many butchers' shops as well as provision stores sell cooked meats and there is a danger of contamination from raw to cooked meats and between different varieties of cooked meats. In the salmonella outbreak reported on p. 43 it was thought that one infected pig's carcass was responsible for spreading infection to other carcasses in the slaughterhouse where cloths were used to wipe them. More recent work suggests that several pigs were probably infected at the time of slaughter, and that the original infection acquired from contaminated feeding stuffs was distributed over a wide area. The degree of contamination, or the numbers of organisms on a carcass, will depend on various factors but obviously the greater the infection the greater the danger to the retail shop receiving raw meat. In the outbreak quoted several shops selling cooked as well as raw meat were involved. The spread of salmonellae from raw to cooked meat was facilitated by common knives, steels, surfaces,

Fig. 29   Meat products on sale in supermarket

benches, balances, and cloths used during the sale of both products. In 1947 few retail shops possessed chilled cabinets and meats of all types were displayed in the windows.

It is doubtful also whether cleaning methods included any form of disinfection and a quick wash-over with cloths would serve to encourage the spread of micro-organisms.

Raw meat should be free from salmonellae but until we have learned how to keep our food animals and poultry free from infection and how to improve the hygiene of slaughter it must be accepted that a variable proportion of the carcasses, boneless meats, and sausages sent to retail shops will be contaminated. They should therefore be treated as a potential source of danger to other goods and particularly to prepared meats sold loose from cans and open packs.

The greater the load of bacteria given to cooked meats by the retail shop the shorter their keeping time in the home and canteen and the greater the danger of the spread of food-poisoning organisms and the possibility of food poisoning. The sale of raw and cooked meats should be separated and individual staff, utensils, balances, counters, and chill cabinets used for each. In most large

Fig. 30   Wash-hand-basin in shop near meat display

shops or supermarkets meat and poultry products are prepacked and sold wrapped (Fig. 29). Care is needed in the sections behind the sales area where these operations are carried out. As in the smaller shops separate utensils and surfaces, used for raw and cooked products, should be cleaned and disinfected frequently in boiling water or chemical agent. Wooden blocks must be scraped and salted daily and where possible replaced by blocks made of impervious material. Five per cent of wood scrapings taken from chopping blocks used in shops for meat were found to contain salmonellae. Hands should be washed frequently and overalls and other apparel often changed.

Wash-hand-basins with running hot and cold water, soap, and paper towels should be installed within easy reach of all persons selling not only meat but all perishable foods (Fig. 30). Supplies of boiling water for the disinfection of equipment should be readily available; even a gas ring would suffice as a source of heat. The rules for general cleanliness and safety as recommended in the chapters on kitchen design and equipment and the disinfection of utensils also apply to retail shops.

Outbreaks of typhoid fever initiated by meat from cans contaminated by typhoid bacilli during production have emphasized the danger of the spread and persistence of disease-producing organisms in shops where sudden large foci of contamination appear accidentally, and with no visible evidence of their arrival. The management of every shop should question whether the routine cleaning procedures could withstand the spread of infection from a 2·7 kg (6 lb) block of corned beef contaminated with *S. typhi* or other food-poisoning organisms implanted without warning in the shop. Would the cases of illness which must follow the consumption of this meat be confined to those who purchase parts of the actual block itself? Or would the bacilli persist on equipment, spread from meat to meat and to other foods and thus give rise to a trail of cases for many days? How safe would the staff be under these circumstances and would those who succumb add to the spread of infection before diagnosis? Perhaps the bacteriologist alone can visualize the minute trail of bacilli left on the can opener passing rapidly from can to can, on to the hands and knives of those who make the first cut and then on to the slicing machine and other foods; crevices, ledges, and cogs are difficult to reach and they will harbour organisms indefinitely. Likewise, fragments of meat caught on the wide cutting blade will contaminate slices from other blocks of meat.

The customer served, the remains of the block may be placed on one side — or even in the window. The window pedestals, price tags, and trays will all play a part and so also will the sun encouraging a temperature suitable for multiplication. Overcrowded conditions will result not only in the jostling of those serving but of the meats they handle. The hands must be rinsed occasionally and without a wash-basin nearby a bucket of warm water may be used for hands, wiping cloths, and utensils so that the spread is ensured. Dilute meat and fat and warmth will encourage survival and growth; if there is no other way then the water in the bucket must be disinfected.

It is suggested that sliced meat should be prepared under carefully controlled conditions in a room equipped for the purpose at the rear of the shop, and that the remains of blocks of meat should be kept refrigerated and separated, as well as the weighed slices. When the remains of several blocks are gathered into a tray for refrigeration overnight, the chances of spread from portion to portion will be increased.

Toilet facilities for the staff should be kept clean and maintained in a good state of repair; bactericidal soaps and hand creams may be provided, and nail brushes frequently renewed.

Canned foods ought to be sterile and this is a justifiable assumption by the shop manager so that cool dry storage is adequate. There are a few notable exceptions. Large cans of ham and pork shoulder, chopped pork and, more exceptionally, tongue and veal may receive pasteurization temperatures only; these cans are marked 'keep cold' or 'keep under refrigeration' and it is important to obey this instruction. Organisms which have survived the processing may multiply at atmospheric temperature and spoil the meat, which may also become dangerous. Thus there should be cold storage for stocks.

Open packs, i.e. uncanned, cooked meats and pies, usually leave the factory with a small content of bacteria. If they are exposed in the shop window or on a shelf or bench the numbers of bacteria will increase, the rate depending on the atmospheric temperature and the strength of cure. Thus all such foods should be shown and stored in a chill cabinet maintained at approximately 4 °C (39 °F), until required for immediate sale. The chill cabinet serves many purposes; the food is cold, protected against dust and flies, and attractively displayed. Some cabinets have refrigerated shelves or drawers for storage below the display section, others may be combined with a deep freeze.

Various metal gadgets are available to replace the hand for steadying blocks of cooked meats; perforated Perspex covers and plastic plates and blocks are also useful and may easily be cleaned and disinfected.

The sale of vacuum-packed sliced goods increases yearly. Such foods are not sterile and both aerobic and anaerobic bacteria can grow when susceptible foods are stored at atmospheric temperatures; vacuum-packed goods should therefore be kept refrigerated. They should be coded with the date of manufacture and a careful rotation of packs maintained.

After being packed some sliced meats are scalded, and hams and large cuts of bacon may be plunged into boiling water to shrink the polythene bag into close contact with the surface. Heat-sensitive surface organisms are destroyed and the storage life is lengthened.

With highly salted goods, such as bacon, growth of many bacteria will be slow but low salt meats of normal pH will encourage microbial growth. When refrigeration arrangements failed for a large batch of film-packed hams delivered to various shops there was a widespread outbreak of staphylococcal food poisoning.

The domestic consumer may consider vacuum packs akin to canned goods and tend to store them in the larder for indefinite periods of time. Most manufacturers give code numbers with expiry dates and recommendations.

Fish shops

There are two recommendations for the fish shop — the closure of shop-fronts and the installation of refrigerated slabs and show cases (Fig. 31).

Fig. 31   Refrigerated slab and showcase of fish shop

All open-fronted shops, whether used for the sale of fish or of other foods, are subject to many sources of contamination from the air, passers-by, animals, and insects; furthermore, there seems no good reason why the smell of fish should so readily pervade the street. It is true that the closed shop must be well ventilated to prevent the same nuisance to employees. Most fish reach the shop already cleaned and deheaded; nevertheless a small amount of gutting and filleting is inevitable and a separate room or compartment at the back of the shop should be provided for this purpose. It has been shown that fillets of fish, because they have been much handled, are far more likely to contain food-poisoning bacteria of human origin than whole fish. There should be ample supplies of water and facilities for washing the hands, fish, and equipment.

It has already been noted (p. 68) that food poisoning from freshly cooked fish is uncommon, but when precooked or left-over fish is mixed with cooked potato, rice, or other material for pies, rissoles, and kedgeree, food-poisoning bacteria may be introduced and multiply.

Cooked shell-fish are subject to the same hazards of handling, and cockles may be contaminated at many points after their heat treatment in the cockle sheds and before they reach the consumer. Cockles for distribution to far distant places are heavily salted; those for local distribution are lightly salted only and more susceptible to contamination.

A greater use could be made of crushed ice in fish shops. On refrigerated counters or in refrigerated showcases the fish may rest or be embedded in the ice. Regulations for the manufacture of ice have recently been considered.

The organism *Vibrio parahaemolyticus* is associated in the Far East with food poisoning from seafoods eaten raw or cooked. A recent episode of food poisoning amongst passengers landing in London after a flight from Thailand was caused by *V. parahaemolyticus* in hors-d'oeuvre containing crab cooked in the eastern flight kitchen. The outbreak is described in detail on p. 117.

V. parahaemolyticus has also been isolated from samples of frozen cooked prawns imported from Malaysia, and in retrospect certain outbreaks of food poisoning may have been associated with prawn cocktails. There are reports that *V. parahaemolyticus* has been isolated from coastal waters and sea creatures in various parts of the world including England. Care should be taken in the sale of crab, shrimps, prawns, and fish. They should be stored and exhibited in the chilled state, and care in handling and separation from other foods are important factors.

Grocery and provision stores

Most articles for sale in small provision stores are canned, packaged, or otherwise wrapped and therefore protected from contamination. Fats such as lard, margarine, and butter may act as vehicles of infection for enteric illnesses and dysentery which may follow infection by small doses of organisms, but they do not usually allow multiplication of the common food-poisoning organisms. Nevertheless, an outbreak of staphylococcal food poisoning was reported from butter sauce. Matured hard cheese has too low a moisture content to allow multiplication, but bacteria can grow when the curd is forming during manufacture. Soft non-acid cheese should be covered and kept cold.

The large provision store or supermarket selling most foods as well as hardware goods is rapidly crowding out the small shop. Faults in technique will be magnified in their results because food is handled on a large scale and there are increased numbers of customers. Moreover there is a diversity of meats sold in large quantities. A single batch could spread contamination to other meats by a variety of means such as the slicing machine, knives and other equipment, surfaces, and hands, so that the number of persons infected could far exceed those who consumed the original contaminated article. Conversely the provision of good practices of cold storage and cleaning procedures will safeguard the health of large numbers of people. Meat slicers and other equipment should be easily and frequently dismantled, cleaned thoroughly and subjected to heat or chemical treatment to destroy as many organisms as possible. Convenient and adequate hand-washing facilities and disposable paper swabs should be provided.

Perishable foods ought not to be exhibited in the window unless chilled, and again it is important to separate raw and cooked meat products. Surfaces should be easily cleaned.

Bakers' shops

The preparation and service of confectionery containing fresh or imitation cream requires the greatest care and attention. Manufactured, pasteurized imitation cream may reach the bakery in a state of bacterial cleanliness but there are many opportunities for contamination in the bakery or shop. Such goods should be stored covered under chilled conditions and for a limited time. Commodities which are not wrapped should be handled with tongs and not with the fingers.

Bread is rarely a vehicle of food poisoning because it has a low moisture content and does not encourage bacterial growth. Nevertheless, the bacteria causing typhoid fever and dysentery in small doses may be transported from the hands of an excreter via bread to the victim; bread should therefore be wrapped. Moulds grow well on bread and particularly on sliced bread wrapped while still warm. Although they do not appear to give rise to gastroenteritis there is another serious hazard. Some fungi growing on or within foods are known to produce toxins; the most well known is aflatoxin, from *Aspergillus flavus*, which causes liver disease when fed in mouldy ground-nuts to poultry and fish. Evidence of harmful effects in man is slow to come but it is suggested that more attention should be given to acute or chronic illness in persons accidentally eating mouldy food and in peoples of nations habitually consuming fungi as food or in food.

Bakeries may play an important rôle in the spread of infection from contaminated egg products, meats, coconut, and creams. Equipment such as mixers, bowls, working surfaces, and Savoy bags should be frequently disinfected. Batches of cream, meats or rehydrated products left over from each day's supply should be discarded or refrigerated for one night only; they should not be mixed with freshly made-up batches. Care should be taken that egg mixes or other products used for glazing are known to be free from salmonellae. The premises should be kept free from dust to which they will be prone because of the flour and other powdered products used.

Dairy shops

The responsibility for the hygiene of milk is largely the concern of those engaged in pasteurization and bottling. Many dairy shops sell a variety of other foods including ice-cream.

There are no Regulations governing the hygienic quality of fresh cream; most supplies are made from pasteurized milk or they are heat-treated as cream, but many are still poor bacteriologically, and need stricter control with regard to both preparation and storage.

Buffets and stalls

Perishable foods displayed at buffets on stations, airports, fairs, street markets, and in mobile vans should be protected against dust, flies, airborne droplets, and animals. Sandwiches, pies, cakes, rolls, and similar foods should be wrapped in Cellophane or stand under glass covers or on shelves protected from the air on three sides. They should be freshly prepared and stored for a limited time only.

Fig. 32   Glass cabinets in railway buffet

In many modern glass cabinets the foods, packaged or prepared on plates, are accessible to the customer through glass flaps in the compartments (Fig. 32). Enclosed storage generates heat, thus food on display should be refrigerated and a minimum amount displayed at any one time. Small trolleys pushed around railway platforms are now covered in and the food protected with Cellophane (Fig. 33).

Fig. 33 Trolley at railway station

The automatic vending of food and drink

The automatic vending of food and beverages has become an important part of contemporary food distribution systems by making products accessible to the public on a 24-hour basis. Vending machines used for food services are subject to the Food Hygiene (Markets, Stalls and Delivery Vehicles) Regulations 1966 which require, amongst other things, that no food business shall be carried on at or from any stall which is insanitary or which is so situated or constructed, or is in such a condition, that the food is exposed to the risk of contamination. By definition, 'stall' includes 'vending machine', and 'food' includes 'drink' and 'chewing-gum'. The Food Hygiene Code of Practice No. 7 entitled 'Hygiene in the operation of coin operated food vending machines' is more important, though it does not have the power of legislation. It covers: (1) legal requirements, (2) construction, (3) cleaning, disinfection, and maintenance, (4) siting, (5) food handling, and (6) personnel. The factors which are important for food safety are:

(1) The food is stored in an enclosed system, thus a simple but efficient cleaning process is essential to avoid the accumulation of stale food, particularly in powdered form, or liquid, in parts of the machine invisible to the public eye.

(2) Many cold foods are perishable, for example meat sandwiches, pies, and sausage rolls, thus the temperature of storage is important as is the length of time the foods are held in the machine. The present Code of Practice gives general recommendations for temperatures of storage, but it does not give special recommendations for times of storage for perishable products.

(3) Machines must be sited away from the direct rays of the sun, or suitable protection provided.

(4) It should be compulsory to provide heat-treated milk only for vending machines.

Factory investigation and inspection

Unless a food factory possesses its own laboratory capable of microbiological examination of incoming foods, finished products, machinery, and other equipment, officers of local authorities in conjunction with public health laboratories should carry out periodic checks of the conditions in food processing establishments in their area. Collaboration with plant managers and hygiene officers is essential.

When outbreaks of food poisoning occur in association with factory produced goods, prompt notification and spread of information are essential. Investigations are required to find the source of the bacterial agents, the faults in production between raw and processed foods, and the storage conditions.

The investigations should not stop at the factory gate but extend back to the farm origin of animals and vegetables, as well as to the transport, market, and abattoir conditions. The combined efforts of medical, veterinary, and food technologists are usually required to find a solution and to establish preventive measures.

The origin of one factory outbreak of salmonellosis, spread by roast legs of pork, was traced to a high intake of pigs excreting the relevant serotype. Cross-contamination from raw to cooked products, and long, slow cooling periods for the cooked meat led to a major and widespread episode of food poisoning. Many human excreters were found in the factory, victims, no doubt, of the meat they were both handling in the factory and eating in the canteen.

Factories responsible for canned goods need careful inspection and checks on the time–temperature records for processes. The purity of water supplies used for cooling cans in the retorts is of primary importance, in view of the contamination of cans by pathogenic organisms in impure (unchlorinated) water and resultant outbreaks of disease. The handling of wet cans is another hazard, and automatic transport and means of drying cans after leaving retorts are also required. The concentrations of the ingredients of curing solutions is variable also; the regulation of some manufacturing processes, such as canning and curing, might be of value although difficult to enforce.

The hygienic condition of raw materials, methods, and equipment used in the preparation of food should be investigated periodically by laboratory examination of food and environmental samples. Instructions for cleaning machinery, the establishment in general, and the cleaning materials should be emphasized and clearly displayed.

14

Cleaning methods

Food may be contaminated from dirty utensils, surfaces, and equipment; pathogenic organisms may be left in food particles or moisture on imperfectly washed crockery and utensils. The word 'dirty' implies not only the presence of visible dirt but also the invisible presence of thousands and even millions of bacteria which might infect people and contaminate foodstuffs.

It is unsafe to use contaminated utensils and containers, particularly for cooked foods not intended for immediate consumption.

Dish-washing

Dish-washing is considered by some to be an unpleasant and tedious occupation, and the work is too often poorly paid. Yet the task is important both aesthetically in the presentation of appetizing food and the appearance of table equipment, and to safeguard health.

The methods in general use for cleaning cooking and eating utensils may be divided into two groups: hand-washing and machine-washing. Both these systems should start with the removal of left-over food, followed by a preliminary rinsing in hot water, to preserve the cleanliness of the wash water.

Hand dish-washing

The laboratory examination of crockery and cutlery, washed in one sink or bowl and immediately wiped without rinsing, has shown that large numbers of bacteria may be present. When a final rinse is given, either in a bowl of hot water distinct from the wash water or by means of running hot water, the results are much improved and the articles may be almost sterile. Running hot water supplied by a boiler system or a water heater is not always available, but a bowl of hot rinse water is practicable for everyone.

When there is a lack of facilities a detergent with bactericidal properties for the wash water or a disinfectant added to the rinse water is recommended.

Two-sink system

When two adjacent sinks are available the first should be used for washing in water with soap or other detergent as hot as the hands can bear, 46–50 °C (115–122 °F); the second sink should be used for rinsing with very hot water, and methods are available for maintaining high temperatures. The simplest and one of the most

Fig. 34   Twin-sink heat disinfection unit in a school kitchen

effective methods to cleanse and disinfect crockery and cutlery is the two-sink system which provides an efficient wash in a good detergent followed by rinse water thermostatically controlled at a temperature of 77–82 °C (170–180 °F). Galvanized iron or stainless steel sinks heated by steam, gas, or electricity may be used but the greatest uniformity of heat is provided by electricity. A thermometer should be placed in an obvious position on the sink so that the staff will be able to see it easily. Such units require little space, they are relatively inexpensive, and they are popular in school canteen kitchens, as well as in the kitchens of catering firms (Fig. 34).

The hot rinse not only rids plates, glasses, and utensils of wash water, cleaning agents, and bacteria, but it also allows them to drain and dry quickly without the use of drying cloths, which may serve to recontaminate the articles with bacteria. Wash and rinse waters should not be continually used when they have cooled, for lukewarm water will encourage the survival and multiplication of bacteria introduced from food particles. Drying cloths used to wipe a series of articles from such waters will become charged with bacteria —

sometimes of intestinal origin (Fig. 35). Laboratory experiments have shown that bacteria from contaminated drying cloths may spread from plate to plate.

There is danger, also, from plates stacked while wet with dirty wash or rinse water. The surface of clean, dry crockery will not encourage the survival of bacteria, whereas microbes left in pools or films of water not only survive but multiply. It is desirable, therefore, that crockery should be left clean, dry, and ready for the next meal; plates taken from hot water should be left to drain vertically in a rack. It has been proved that utensils artificially contaminated with

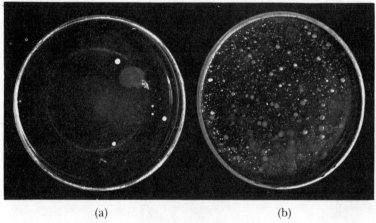

(a)   (b)

Fig. 35 Bacterial cultures from (a) a clean and (b) a dirty drying cloth

non-sporing bacteria can be disinfected by exposure to hot water at 77–82 °C (170–180 °F) for approximately 30 seconds and that china and utensils rinsed with water maintained at this temperature will dry rapidly in the air.

Disposable paper may be used for final drying and polishing (Fig. 36); but when it is considered necessary to use cloths they should be washed and boiled frequently, or washed and treated with hypochlorite or other bactericidal agent (Fig. 37).

There is another two-sink system made of stainless steel whereby hot water from a gas boiler flows continuously to the rinse sink, rinse water circulates into the wash sink containing a cleansing agent, and the wash water flows away. Thus it is impossible for food waste to accumulate either in the wash or in the rinse water.

Most materials used for containers and other articles of equipment, can withstand hot water and those which cannot should not be used for foods.

Fig. 36　Disposable absorbent paper used for final drying and polishing

Fig. 37　Disinfecting cloths by boiling

Chemical disinfection

Heat is recommended as the safest method to ensure the destruction of micro-organisms, but it may be impossible to maintain a continuous supply of nearly boiling water or steam. Treatment in rinse water containing chlorine, or in wash water containing a bactericidal detergent are the alternatives. The quantity of detergent used should be carefully controlled; too much may affect the flavour and odour of foods, too little will be ineffective; there may be no means of observing when the disinfecting action has been exhausted. The worker cannot assess the rate of decline in efficiency of chemical disinfection; therefore, the instructions given by the manufacturer must be followed carefully, and the correct quantities of substances added to a known volume of water.

Hypochlorite and quaternary ammonium compounds are used most commonly but other chemicals, such as iodophors, are available. Hypochlorites and iodophors have a wider range of antibacterial activity than is shown by the quaternary ammonium compounds. All three varieties of disinfectant are readily destroyed by food debris and some of the hypochlorites and iodophors are destructive to silverware, stainless steel, and aluminium, and may be harmful to cloth.

The names of bactericidal substances recommended by the dairy industry are given in a list of approved chemical agents issued by the Ministry of Agriculture, Fisheries, and Food.

Until another list is formulated for the food industry there seems no reason why guidance should not be sought from dairy usage.

To assist in hand-washing crockery and utensils, a mop with a plastic frame and Nylon bristles is recommended; it should be well cleaned and disinfected overnight in hot water or a suitable chemical solution.

Cloths for wet-mopping and cleaning should not be used in the kitchen; disposable paper is recommended to replace them.

In some countries the disinfection by heat of all eating, drinking, and cooking utensils is compulsory. Where there is no special apparatus to ensure adequate heat treatment, common receptacles such as bowls and saucepans are used. The containers may be placed on a perforated disk over boiling water heated on a gas ring or other convenient source of heat.

Machine dish-washing

Machines for dish-washing are used in many large-scale catering establishments. Most designs include detergent and rinse sprays, the temperatures of which can be controlled and maintained at 49–60 °C (120–140 °F) and 66–82 °C (150–180 °F) respectively (Fig. 38). A hand- or foot-operated spray may be installed for removing gross particles of food from plates and other articles before they are stacked. The plates are stacked in carrier racks, so that their maximum surface is exposed to the jets of water which play over them from above and below as the racks pass through the machine on a movable belt. The whole process is short and takes no longer than 40 to 45 seconds.

The wash water, containing a suitable detergent, is held in a tank and is continually re-used; the overflow runs away to waste. The concentration of detergent must be reinforced from time to time. Some machines include a gadget for automatically dispensing the detergent at regular intervals. The rinse water comes straight from the mains and is usually recirculated into the wash tank. On the more elaborate machines there may be a final row of sprays delivering mains cold water; this water is not recirculated but runs to waste. Usually the articles are delivered hot and steaming from the machine and they are rapidly air-dried.

Fig. 38   Large spray-type dish-washing machine

The efficiency of cleaning and disinfection by these machines depends largely on the maintenance of the wash and rinse waters at the correct temperatures and on the use of a good detergent at the recommended concentration. A machine used carelessly may give bacteriological results not better than those from the worst type of hand-washing.

In one establishment operatives were observed to be wiping the plates emerging after treatment in a newly installed machine. They explained that there were food particles on the plates; several faults were found. The plates were badly stacked on the racks, the detergent was unsuitable because it produced excessive amounts of froth and the temperature of the rinse water was too low. The results obtained from the examination of plate swabs gave very high bacterial counts, the highest noted for machine-washed articles. In another large washing machine the metal runway which should have drained the water from the exit end of the machine to the sink did not slope sufficiently to allow the water to run away. Pools collected, and the examination of this water showed that it contained many millions of bacteria. The plates were stacked in piles of 6 to 12 on the runway so that the bottom plate of each pile became heavily

Fig. 39   One-man-operated small domestic dish-washer

Fig. 40   Two-sink, turbulent dish-washer

contaminated with bacteria, which were passed on to a second plate when one pile was added to another.

There are smaller spray-type machines that can be worked by one operative, in which wash and rinse sprays are contained in one unit (Fig. 39). The articles are placed in racks which are lifted by hand

into the machine. A manually operated lever controls the flow of the
wash and rinse waters from the upper and lower sprays. The timing
is not automatically controlled, and therefore each operative must
judge the length of time articles should be exposed to the wash and
rinse waters.

Fig. 41   Machine washing of self-service trays

The less complicated types of dish-washing machines include two-
and three-tank systems employing brush or turbulent (Fig. 40)
mechanisms for the forceful removal of food particles. The brushes
have Nylon bristles, which are cleaned more easily than pig bristles;
these machines have heating elements to provide the correct
temperatures for wash and rinse waters. Small units with two or
three sinks may be seen in school canteens, as well as as in restaurant
kitchens. Wash and rinse waters are maintained at nearly boiling
point and the wash tank is supplied with a propeller which
continually churns the water. Racks containing the dishes and
cutlery are placed in the wash and rinse sections for a convenient

length of time. The method is probably too slow for establishments using a large number of plates at any one time, but the bacteriological results from articles washed in this way are good. The method shown in Fig. 41 eliminates the stacking of used tableware in the dining area. The self-service trays are flowed directly on the conveyor by the diner and dealt with by the machine operators who are engaged for the purpose. The machine used gives four separate washes, rinse, wash, heated rinse, and high-powered heated rinse.

In a survey of 20 restaurants and canteens the main divisions for classification were based on washing-up methods, and efficiency was judged by bacterial counts. The classification was carried out as follows:

(1) Premises with one sink only.
(2) Premises with twin sinks — wash–rinse arrangements.
(3) Premises having two sinks — the second being a disinfecting sink maintained at a constant temperature.
(4) Premises using a mechanical dish-washing machine.

In the first group, in which one sink only was used, 28 lots of articles were examined, such as plates, spoons, forks, and cups; 14 of these showed contamination with bacteria from the nose or throat, and 9 of them with intestinal bacteria.

In group two, the general bacteriological standard showed a slight improvement over that in the first group, but high counts, sometimes in the region of some thousands per utensil, were obtained. Thirty-one lots of articles were examined; 4 showed contamination with organisms from the nose and throat, and 6 with intestinal organisms.

In the third group, giving the best results, long-handled metal racks were used for the immersion of crockery and utensils for not less than 30 seconds in a disinfecting rinse sink maintained at a temperature of 77–82 °C (170–180 °F). Thirty-eight lots of articles were examined; 3 only showed contamination with nose and throat organisms and 3 showed contamination with organisms from the intestine. Plates were not wiped, but were stored in the hotplate containers; cutlery, however, was wiped to prevent rusting. At least 53 per cent of articles in this group attained the United States Public Health standard of 100 or less bacteria per utensil and absence of any respiratory and intestinal organisms.

The results for group four, using machine methods of dishwashing, varied widely according to the type of machine and the care with which it was run. The temperatures of the rinse waters from most of the machines were far below those recommended, and in many instances the utensils were hand-dried as they were taken out. In this fourth group the best results were obtained from a twin-sink machine, already described, fitted with a thermostatically controlled heating mechanism in both wash and rinse sinks. The wash water contained a cleaning agent and was agitated violently by means of a paddle, and water in the heated rinse tank was maintained at a temperature of about 82 °C (180 °F). In some models of this machine a third tank is included in which the crockery and

Fig. 42   Detergent dispenser

utensils are freed from cleaning agents before they are transferred to the disinfecting rinse. All tank waters were changed at intervals of 2 hours. Swabs taken from crockery and utensils were bacteriologically sterile.

The unsatisfactory results obtained from some machines were obviously due to lack of care in the supervision and running of machines. Thirty-five lots of articles were examined in this group; of these, 15 showed contamination with organisms of respiratory origin and 11 with organisms of intestinal origin.

A certain number of kitchens were visited daily for a week or more; the counts obtained from the samples taken each day varied considerably. Sometimes the variation was associated with a change of technique. For instance, damp cloths were used on some occasions to wipe the plates emerging from the machine, and counts from these plates were high. On other days, when plates were allowed to drain dry without further wiping, counts were much lower.

A few kitchens used a rinse solution containing hypochlorite; the results were regularly good for dishes rinsed in this way. A hypochlorite rinse, if carefully controlled, can produce clean articles almost free from bacteria. It is considered, however, that the routine use of hot-water disinfection is more efficient and practicable for a kitchen staff who may not take time or trouble to control the strength of hypochlorite.

A survey was carried out on six spray-type dish-washing machines used in the staff kitchens of various hospitals. Samples of wash water and swabs of washed articles gave satisfactory bacteriological results because high temperatures were maintained in wash and rinse waters. Experiments showed clearly the importance of high temperatures in both wash and rinse waters for maintaining low bacterial counts. When the temperatures were lowered experimentally the bacteriological results deteriorated and the counts rose in spite of the use of a bactericidal detergent dispensed automatically. A detergent dispenser would help to ensure that crockery and utensils are free from food and grease (Fig. 42). Where circumstances do not permit the use of a steady supply of hot water for washing dishes by hand a bactericidal detergent or another disinfectant agent should be used.

In this survey it was pointed out that a pre-rinse was desirable so that food debris would be removed and the wash water kept cleaner; this is applicable to both hand- and machine-washing of dishes. Racks and baskets specially designed for the size and type of crockery and to hold cutlery upright were recommended.

The small domestic dish-washer (Fig. 43) is useful for the large household or small canteen. The ease of stacking, the provision of a final hot rinse, and in addition steam, followed by time for articles to drain dry are essential considerations.

The visual criterion of efficiency is a clean plate or utensil, but a test in which fine powder, as used for finger prints, is puffed on to plates and sticks to areas which are not clean has proved to be of value.

Pot washing

It is equally important to have proper facilities to clean pots, pans, and other vessels and utensils used in the preparation of food. The large tanks so frequently designed for the purpose seem built for persons of giant proportions; their depth and width require reaching and bending guaranteed to cause backache and strained limbs. Furthermore, a considerable volume of water is required to fill them and, once filled, the same water may remain throughout the whole operation. Samples of water from these tanks give very high counts of intestinal bacteria. The installation of machines for pot-washing relieves congestion and gives rise to a higher standard of cleanliness. The King Edward Hospital Fund for London have

Fig. 43   Small domestic dish-washer

issued a report describing the efficiency of a mechanical pot-washer installed in the kitchen of a hospital supplying nearly 2000 meals daily.

A final rinse in very hot water is equally important for pots, pans, and utensils used for preparation and cooking, and they should be air-dried.

Detergents

A detergent is a cleaning agent made of soap or a soap substitute; it may be a mixture of alkaline materials and a substance which will soften the water, or it may be an organic surface-active agent. Its function in dish-washing is to facilitate the removal of food particles from the dishes and utensils and promote cleanliness so that all surfaces are readily accessible to the disinfectant action of heat or chemicals.

The selection of a detergent for a particular purpose will depend on certain factors, such as the nature of the substance to be removed, the material of the article or the surface to be cleaned, whether the hands must come in contact with the solution or whether it will be used in a machine, and the chemical nature of the water such as its degree of hardness. It may be an advantage to use a cleaning agent possessing some bactericidal power. Recommendations for the use of any type of detergent will depend on the particular set of circumstances.

The majority of detergents are cleansing agents possessing little or no bactericidal properties, but some organic substances, such as the quaternary ammonium compounds, are able to kill certain bacteria. Other detergents may combine good cleansing substances with a hypochlorite, so that the two functions of cleaning and disinfection may be accomplished by the one liquid or powder. Such mixtures may be used in small establishments with limited washing-up facilities, such as the small kitchen attached to an hospital ward, and the fair or sports ground, and for the bacterial cleanliness of ice-cream servers, cups, and other utensils used by mobile vans. They may be used also by the food vendors for washing their hands.

The general properties of a good detergent should include:

(1) Wetting — the ability to wet readily the utensils being cleaned.
(2) Emulsification — the ability to break up and disperse fat.
(3) Dissolving — the ability to dissolve food materials, principally protein.
(4) The ability to break up any solid food matter, no matter what it is.
(5) The prevention of scum and scale formation in hard water.
(6) Rinsing — the property of being easily rinsed away.
(7) Harmlessness to man.

No one substance possesses all the required properties, and most proprietary detergents contain a mixture of ingredients but the exact formulae are seldom divulged.

Soap is a simple detergent, but its use for washing-up is limited in hard water. It is well known that in hard water the washing of greasy dishes with soap results in scum formation. This scum is a mixture of dirt and hard magnesium and calcium salts from the water which have been precipitated out of solution by the soap. A water softener is an agent which keeps the salts of hard water in solution so that the cleaning agent itself may be more effective.

Most good detergents incorporate a water-softening agent. Some substances used for this purpose are common washing soda (sodium carbonate), trisodium phosphate, and sodium metasilicate and also the hexametaphosphate, tetraphosphate, and pyrophosphate salts of sodium.

Sodium hydroxide is a good dissolving agent but its caustic action is injurious to the skin. A good inorganic detergent powder may contain a mixture of sodium hydroxide or sodium carbonate, trisodium phosphate, sodium metasilicate, and sodium hexametaphosphate, thus combining cleansing and water-softening properties. The proportion of each ingredient must depend on the purpose for which the powder is intended and the hardness of the local water. These strongly alkaline powders are useful for many purposes, such as for crockery, cutlery, and milk, ice-cream, or other food containers. It must be remembered that they are hard on the hands and, therefore, best used in machine-washing where a cleaning agent which does not froth is of particular value.

The organic detergents include those which are manufactured as a by-product of the oil industry. Many are negatively charged (anionic) and can be used in combination with soap, which is also anionic. They possess most of the properties which make a good detergent; they wet readily, emulsify fats, break up dirt particles, and soften the water by keeping calcium and magnesium salts in solution. They are not usually alkaline and are preferable to the caustic inorganic powders for hand-washing. On the other hand, they often froth too much to be of value in dish-washing machines. The anionic detergents are sometimes mixed with a hypochlorite to combine cleaning and disinfecting properties. The quaternary ammonium compounds are cationic detergents, that is, they are positively charged and cannot be mixed with soap. Some foam readily while others do not. They exert a bactericidal action on some germs and may be mixed with inorganic materials to form satisfactory cleaning and bactericidal agents.

There is another group of organic detergents, or surface-active agents as they are called, which are non-ionic — that is, they have neither a negative nor a positive charge. They have good wetting properties in cold water and are useful detergents with good stability towards hard water, acids, and alkalis.

All articles should be rinsed free from cleaning agents as it is not always known whether harmful effects could arise from the accumulation within the body of small doses of some of the wide range of substances used.

The washing of glassware in licensed premises

The washing of glasses requires special care to ensure that fingerprints and lipstick are removed, and disinfection by heat or by chemicals is necessary. The conditions which are available for washing glasses in licensed premises are different from those for dish-washing in other catering establishments. All cleaning is done at the bar counter, and at rush hours there is a considerable turn-over of glasses in a short time. A system for quick washing and for disinfection is required. Each bar should be provided with a double sink or a suitable glass-washing machine, and an adequate supply of glasses should be available to allow time for the glasses to cool before they are required for use. As for all washing up in double sinks, the first sink should contain the recommended detergent

Fig. 44   Detergent dispenser for public house

solution and the second water at 77–82 °C (170–180 °F) for immersion for at least 2 minutes. The rinse water in the second sink may contain 40 ppm of available chlorine. In places where it would be difficult to install two tanks, a combined chemical agent and detergent should be used in the single sink, but its use must be carefully controlled with sufficient changes of water. Glasses should drain dry and receive a final polish with clean paper if necessary. A bactericidal detergent added to the wash water will reduce the number of residual bacteria on the glass. Quaternary ammonium compounds can be used for cleaning and disinfection, but their effectiveness may be limited by the possible loss of beer-head retention. This factor should be considered when choosing a sanitizing agent for beer glasses. It is recommended that an automatic dispenser (Fig. 44) be used to deliver a constant dose of

Fig. 45   Glass-washing machine

Fig. 46   Another type of glass-washing machine in a special aluminium module. The drainers on the left and right of the machine deflect all surplus water into the discharge trough of the machine

the cleaning and disinfecting agent into a sink or tank of known capacity. A quick rinse in a bowl of tepid water should not be tolerated.

Special small washing machines for glasses are available, which can be fixed to the bar itself. They have a detergent wash and a hot rinse spray with automatic temperature and flow control; some models have brushes and a final cold spray may be used (Figs. 45 and 46). Dregs should be drained from the glasses before washing.

A water softener is necessary for machine-washed glasses in hard water areas. The cheaper alkaline detergents can cause hard white deposits which may be mistaken for hardness salts in dish-washing and glass-washing machines. A clean glass should be provided each time a drink is served. The use of over-sized glasses and metered pumps is recommended to prevent spillage of beer; overspill must be discarded.

The large food container

Amongst the more important articles to be kept clean and free from bacteria are the large food containers used to transport meals from central school kitchens to the children in surrounding schools and also those used for carrying food from the kitchen to the wards of hospitals. There should be provision for the disinfection of these containers and for their subsequent drainage. Food residues, if allowed to remain, may retain bacteria able to contaminate the next batch of food.

When freed from all residual food particles, each container should be thoroughly washed in a warm detergent solution, rinsed free from the wash water, steam heated and drained; the inside should not be touched again before it receives the freshly prepared food. It has been shown that high bacterial counts are common from containers washed in the ordinary way and cloth dried. Cooked food may remain in these containers for a considerable time, and it is necessary to ensure that bacteria which remain on the inner walls, in spite of thorough cleaning, are destroyed by steam and that more bacteria are not introduced by contaminated cloths. The lids of the containers should also be steamed.

The time of exposure to steam, from a jet or in a cabinet or in a machine, should be adequate. Immersion in tanks of boiling water can also be used.

As an alternative measure, where there are no facilities for treatment with steam, a final rinse in hypochlorite solution should be given.

It is not intended here to give detailed information on the cleaning of plant equipment used in food manufacture; it is necessary only to stress its importance. This is particularly true for ice-cream equipment, the cleanliness and disinfection of which is essential for the purity of the ice-cream mix and for the maintenance of Grade I samples. It is probable that the same applies to many other foodstuffs manufactured with the help of machines.

The basic principles of any cleansing technique include a hot detergent wash, followed by some method of disinfection by water, which should be nearly boiling, steam or chemical agent. Hand cloths to dry equipment should be used only when hot water is unobtainable and there is chemical disinfection. Drying cloths should be washed and boiled frequently or replaced by paper. Preferably, articles should be air-dried rapidly, or wiped with absorbent paper.

Infant feeding bottles and other food containers

Infants and young children are very susceptible to intestinal infections and the proper care of feeding bottles, both glass and plastic, and teats is an important factor in preventing the spread of enteritis amongst infants.

The Medical Research Council Memorandum No. 11 (Revised Edition 1951) recommended that, when feeds are finished, the bottles should be thoroughly rinsed in cold running water, cleansed with a detergent to remove milk film and rinsed again in running water. Brushes used for cleansing bottles should be disinfected after each period of use. Teats and valves should be turned inside out after each use, gently scrubbed to remove all traces of feed, and boiled for not less than 2 minutes before being used again. Between each feed, bottles should be disinfected by boiling for not less than 2 minutes in special equipment. Chemical disinfection with a hypochlorite solution may be used also. The results compared with those from the boiling method showed that a safe level of disinfection could be obtained by the use of either hypochlorite or heat provided the correct technique was used; care is needed to submerge teats. Although the recommendations were prepared for glass feeding bottles they may also be applied to the plastic (polycarbonate) type of bottle. Most mothers nowadays use the chemical disinfection method.

When milk feeds for infants are prepared in bulk, terminal sterilization of the assembled feed in the glass bottle is the safest method. The prepared feed is boiled and added to clean sterilized or disinfected bottles. The clean and disinfected teats are placed in position and capped. The whole unit is sterilized by steam under pressure in an autoclave or pressure cooker.

All containers and utensils used for broths and purees fed to infants should be disinfected in boiling water and drained dry without wiping.

Cleaning premises and equipment

Cleaning methods employed in most kitchens are based on the domestic system with manual labour and hand tools for the arduous cleaning of surfaces. The result in catering kitchens is often a low standard of hygiene and a schedule that takes at least one-quarter of staff time and may require up to half of the total working time in order to achieve satisfactory results. To reduce costs and improve cleanliness new kitchens should be designed to accommodate mechanical cleaning methods — two systems are recommended.

Cleaning by machinery

Cleaning of floors is a major task in kitchens and elsewhere, therefore mechanical floor scrubbers, drying, and buffing machines are available that will quickly and safely clean and shine vinyl/asbestos tiles without the need for polish. Care should be taken to cleanse the water and detergent tanks daily and the machines must be cleaned and dried after use. Figure 47 shows a floor

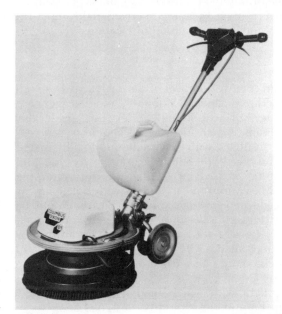

Fig. 47 Floor scrubber; detergent tank can be autoclaved

scrubber with detergent tank which can be autoclaved. The kitchen design should permit the full use of machinery, for example, the floor must be accessible beneath fittings and equipment, or fitments should be mobile. Dish-washing machines are often installed in catering premises not only for crockery and utensils but also for pots and pans.

High pressure cleaning lances

A method of cleaning by high pressure jets may be installed as a built-in system or operated from a mobile plant. It is used by specialist firms to 'deep clean' kitchens and the system is a routine operation in some food factories. High pressure hot water with detergent has several advantages over steam, but it can only be used by skilled staff when the kitchen is closed. Large savings in cost result from daily pressure cleaning, although buildings and equipment need higher specifications than would otherwise be necessary. For example, electrical switch gear, wiring, and connections must be specially water resistant in kitchens intended to be pressure cleaned. Surfaces and equipment must withstand the pressure jet and be designed to avoid the collection of water; special precautions are also needed to prevent flooding of gas equipment. High pressure lances generate a low volume of water (11·4 litres, 2·5 gallons per minute) and may be used with advantage by trained personnel throughout a kitchen built to accommodate this method of cleaning.

To summarize

Daily cleaning should remove all traces of the day's activities, with no remnants of food scraps or smears. Hot water and detergent are the basic requirements. Surfaces should be left dry, preferably mopped up with disposable paper. Meat blocks should be scraped, rubbed over with salt, scrubbed with detergent, and finally treated with hypochlorite solution. With hand cleaning, sweeping and dusting should be done with damp cloths and dust-damping powder. All surfaces must withstand treatment with hot, soapy or detergent water. Fixed carpets, mats, and furniture should be vacuum-cleaned daily (Fig. 48). A vacuum cleaner may also be used for overhead fittings, otherwise the exposed framework of roof or ceiling, light bulbs and shades, as well as service pipes, and floor-drainage channels, should be washed or dusted with a damp cloth.

Articles and equipment with which food comes into contact should be kept clean. Equipment should be designed so as to be readily taken apart and should be so placed that all parts can be easily reached. Disinfection should be applied to equipment used for perishable raw ingredients such as egg products for glazing and for cake, sponge, and other flour confectionery mixes, for meats, gelatin, milk, and coconut, and to all equipment used in the preparation, storage, and dispensing of fillings, decorations, and toppings.

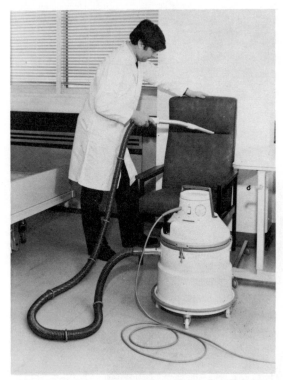

Fig. 48   High powered suction cleaning

The general principle of cleaning for all equipment including can openers, meat-slicing machines, and mincers should be to pass all disassembled parts through the following stages: hot detergent water, a rinse at 76·7 °C (170 °F) by means of a washing machine or a two-sink system in which the second sink is thermostatically controlled at a temperature of 76·7 °C (170 °F) or higher. When possible there should be a final exposure to steam or immersion in boiling water for about 1 minute. Immovable equipment, covered metal containers, and mixers should be exposed to steam from a hose for 10 to 15 minutes, unless high pressure jets are available. As an alternative to steam or boiling water a chemical disinfectant should be used; probably the most effective are the hypochlorite, iodine, or bromine preparations. All surfaces must be thoroughly wetted with the disinfectant, diluted according to the maker's

Fig. 49 Double sink with small section for hot disinfection

instructions. After a suitable contact period of at least 5 minuts the treated equipment may be rinsed with clean mains water and dried with absorbent paper.

Small articles such as ladles, palette knives, and piping bags should be cleaned and boiled or replaced by treated articles after meal breaks. The double sink unit shown in Fig. 49 is useful for this purpose.

15

Sterilization and disinfection
(Isobel M. Maurer)

The word 'sterilize' is often used incorrectly. Sterilization means the destruction of all micro-organisms of all kinds, including bacterial spores such as those produced by clostridia. Sterilization is not normally necessary in food hygiene. Prevention of the growth of spores is sufficient for the prevention of food poisoning; the spores need not be killed. Unfortunately, the word 'sterilize' is commonly used in the literature of food hygiene and in some official publications where the word 'disinfect' would be correct. Cleaning products are often described as 'detergent/sterilizer' when 'detergent/disinfectant' would be an accurate description. The title 'sterilizing sink' is used although water in a sink cannot be heated above boiling point (100 °C; 212 °F) and the lowest temperature recommended for sterilization is 121 °C (229·8 °F). Most young mothers imagine that they 'sterilize' a baby's bottle when they disinfect it by boiling or chemical treatment. Sterilization of feeding bottles is not necessary although disinfection is required.

The British Standard's Institution has now published a Glossary of terms relating to disinfectants (BS 5283, 1976). This is in two sections; the first definitive terms, and the second terms in common use. Some of these are reproduced here as the definitions were worked out very carefully.

Section one

Sterile — free from all living organisms;
Sterilization — a process intended to destroy or remove all living organisms;
Sterilizing agent — a chemical agent leading to sterilization.

Section two

Disinfection — the destruction of micro-organisms, but not usually bacterial spores; it does not necessarily kill all micro-organisms, but reduces them to a level which is harmful neither·to health nor to the quality of perishable goods. The term is applicable to the treatment of inanimate objects and materials and may also be applied to the treatment of the skin and other body membranes and cavities;

Disinfectant — a chemical agent used for disinfection;

Sanitization — a term used mainly in the food and catering industry. A process of both cleaning and disinfecting utensils and equipment;

Sanitizer — a chemical agent used for sanitization;

Detergent/sterilizer and chemical sterilizing agent — misnomers for sanitizer and disinfectant.

It must be emphasized once again that the word 'sterilize' should be used only for a process which can be depended upon to destroy bacterial spores. Disinfection cannot be depended upon to destroy such spores. They are tough organisms and are difficult to kill. No chemical disinfectant should be described as a sterilizer, or a sterilant.

Disinfection is essential in food hygiene. It may be brought about by:

(1) Cleaning.
(2) Heat.
(3) Chemical disinfectants.

Disinfection by cleaning

Disinfection by cleaning is probably the most useful of the three methods. It may be used alone or in combination with either of the other two. A high proportion of microbial contamination may be removed from premises, equipment, and also the hands by thorough cleaning. The standard of cleaning premises and equipment and the level of decontamination achieved depends on several points.

(1) The design, materials and condition of the surfaces and equipment to be cleaned. The design should make it possible to reach all parts with ease and to dismantle equipment, exposing all the soiled areas. Soft and porous surfaces such as plain wood or untreated cork are more difficult to clean than those that are harder and non-porous. Worn, scarred, scratched, or chipped surfaces are always difficult to clean.

(2) Individual care and effort affect the level of cleaning more than does the use of a particular cleaning agent. Much depends on the training and supervision of the staff. Failure to change

cleaning water when it is dirty will mean failure in decontamination.

(3) Choice of cleaning agents, the wide variety on the market is confusing for the user. No one of them is ideal and more depends on the method by which they are applied than on the choice of a near-perfect agent. In general the costly, fancy cleaning agent of unusual perfume or colour should be avoided as unnecessary. Inexpensive, old-fashioned washing soda is a fine cleaner for greasy equipment, grids over drainpipes and the pipes themselves. Pouring a washing soda solution into sink waste pipes will do much to keep the sinks unblocked. Scouring powders should not be so harsh that they damage surfaces or eventually cleaning will be impossible. Perfumes are suspect because they hide the bad smells which come from failures in cleaning. References to claims for results obtained from non-standard tests should be regarded with caution. On some occasions it may be thought advisable to treat kitchen surfaces or equipment with a chemical disinfectant as an extra weapon in the battle against bacterial contamination. Where this is done the maximum benefit is obtained by cleaning first of all and applying the disinfectant afterwards. Combined detergent/disinfectants are of questionable value since they are inevitably applied to a dirty, usually food-soiled, surface. Dirt of many kinds, including scraps of food, inactivates chemical disinfectants. For this reason the use of the chemical disinfectant is always recommended as the second step of a two-step process. Clean first and disinfect afterwards.

(4) Care of the cleaning apparatus, which must itself be kept in a clean hygienic condition, affects cleaning standards. Time is saved by eliminating apparatus where possible. Hot dish-washing means spontaneous drying of crockery and avoids the use of tea towels. Disposable paper towels are hygienic when thrown away after using once. Although this seems to be extravagant there is a saving in labour required to launder linen towels. Disposable cloths for wet work also save labour but, with all disposables, attempts to re-use them must be resisted. Where mops, brushes and cloths are to be used more than once, it will be safer to avoid disposable models and choose varieties which are tough enough to withstand decontamination after use. Cleaning apparatus used for wet work is likely to become heavily contaminated with bacteria unless it is disinfected by heat, or chemicals, as well as being kept clean. In this situation washing mops, cloths, and brushes will remove large numbers of bacteria but the few which remain may multiply in a few hours while the apparatus is wet. Next time the apparatus is used it will no longer

remove bacteria from soiled surfaces but will increase the
bacterial load on the surfaces.

The most effective treatment for wet-cleaning apparatus is heat
disinfection combined with the laundering which is described below.

Disinfection by heat

Disinfection by heat is the most reliable of the three methods.
Immersion in water at 65 °C (149 °F) for 10 minutes, or at higher
temperatures for shorter times, can be depended upon to destroy
most micro-organisms harmful to health, with the exception of
bacterial spores. For many years it was believed that boiling water
could be used to sterilize but now it is known that bacterial spores
may survive boiling. However, boiling water is an effective and
cheap disinfectant.

Heat disinfection may conveniently be included in a cleaning
process. In machine dish-washing, the temperature of the washing
or rinsing water may be adjusted and the time arranged to include
heat disinfection in the cycle. In manual dish-washing also, this can
be arranged in a so-called 'sterilizing' rinsing sink. It would be more
accurately described as a disinfecting sink. Here the water is hot
enough to disinfect the crockery, and a rinsing temperature of 65 °C
(149 °F) or more, will enable it to dry spontaneously and avoid
recontamination by unhygienic tea towels.

Similarly, a disinfecting temperature may be included in a
laundry cycle, in either the washing or the rinsing process. Heat
treatment in laundering will ensure the disinfection of all the tea
towels (if they must be used), all dish mops and sponges, floor cloths,
damp dusters, and floor mops; also the scrubbing brushes used for
floors, hands, pans, or vegetables. As previously described, all
cleaning appartus used for wet work should be disinfected daily in
order to prevent bacterial growth. Heat is not only the most reliable
disinfectant, but also the cheapest. A combination of heat disinfection with daily cleansing of the apparatus is hygienic, time saving,
and economical.

In making up a list of cleaning apparatus needing heat treatment,
bowls, buckets, and scrubbing machines should not be forgotten,
and in all cases materials should be chosen which will withstand the
disinfection temperatures. Manufacturers of cleaning equipment
are now, in most cases, aware of the need to use materials which will
withstand heat. Some new designs for floor scrubbing machines are
planned which can be dismantled and heat treated daily to disinfect
all parts which become wet.

The practice of applying steam from a hose, in food premises, is a useful method of heat disinfection, although its efficacy is difficult to assess accurately because the conditions are variable. Steam treatment of equipment in a cabinet may also be recommended, but the results are also variable. Times normally quoted for steam disinfection are 5 to 10 minutes' application from a steam hose and 10 to 15 minutes in a steam cabinet.

It must be remembered that bacteria may multiply rapidly in stagnant water. Neglected puddles or wet dregs in food premises, may present a hazard to health. Equipment should always be stored dry and protected from dust during storage.

In some situations individual cleaners may have to be responsible for the hygienic care of their tools; means for washing and disinfecting the tools should be provided.

Disinfection by chemicals

Disinfection by chemicals is widely advertised but is more costly and less reliable than heat disinfection. The effectiveness of chemical disinfection depends on a number of variables which are not always understood.

Some chemical disinfectants are active against a wide range of bacteria but others have a narrow range of antibacterial activity. Staphylococci are among the bacteria which are killed fairly easily by chemical disinfectants. Salmonellae are more difficult to kill by chemicals and the spores of clostridia will usually survive chemical treatment. Some chemical disinfectants are bactericidal, they kill vegetative bacteria but not spores. Others are no more than bacteriostatic, they prevent the growth of vegetative bacteria.

Effectiveness of chemical disinfection depends, to some extent, on the time of contact, the temperature, and the concentration of the solution. At least 2 minutes' contact is desirable for the most rapid disinfectant and as long as 30 minutes may be necessary for the effective action of some others. Higher temperatures of disinfectant solutions increase their effectiveness and accurate measurement of the recommended concentration is all-important.

The numbers of bacteria present and their accessibility to a chemical disinfectant must be considered. A few bacteria are more easily killed than many. Those which are hidden by pieces of equipment or under layers of grease may be protected from the chemical action. Dismantling equipment and washing it before exposure to a chemical disinfectant will increase effectiveness.

Many chemical disinfectants will kill some micro-organisms and the best of them will kill a great many, but only if the conditons are favourable. It is unfortunate that many materials which are likely to be present in food premises inactivate chemical disinfectants and by their presence create unfavourable conditions.

A common inactivating material is the hard water which is found in many districts. All chemical disinfectants perform less well when diluted with hard water than when in distilled water. It is not suggested that distilled water be used for diluting disinfectants but it is worth remembering that some reported results of disinfectant tests refer to dilution in distilled water. A favourable report of the disinfectant's performance in a test may therefore be quite true but unrealistic and a poor guide to the performance which may be expected of the disinfectant in practice.

Chemical disinfectants are inactivated by all kinds of organic material, including food, and the greater the quantity of such material present the greater will be the extent of the inactivation. The advice that equipment be washed first, to remove organic material, and that the disinfectant solution be applied to a clean surface has already been given but it is worth repeating. Large quantities of chemical disinfectants are regularly wasted because they are applied to dirty surfaces. Scraps of food may not only prevent access of the chemical disinfectant to the organisms but may also inactivate the disinfectant. If a chemical disinfectant is to be used at all it is worth while providing it with conditions which will enable it to work well.

Anionic disinfectants such as hypochlorites and phenolics are compatible with anionic or non-ionic detergents but they are inactivated by cationic detergents. Similarly, cationic disinfectants such as quaternary ammonium compounds are compatible with cationic or non-ionic detergents but are inactivated by anionic detergents. Manufacturers of detergents and disinfectants may be consulted on this point. Where a chemical disinfectant rinse is planned to follow a detergent wash it is wise to choose compatible products, otherwise the disinfectant may be inactivated by the detergent which has previously been used to clean the surface. Many other materials have been found to inactivate some chemical disinfectants. These include wood, cork, rubber, cotton, Nylon, cellulose sponge mops, and many plastics. It is not unusual to find a disinfectant solution in a bucket of plastic material which inactivates it and which also contains an incompatible detergent which completes the inactivation of the disinfectant and is inactivated in its turn. The solution therefore neither cleans nor disinfects, money is wasted on both detergent and disinfectant, the standard of hygiene is low, and food poisoning may result. Elsewhere a chemical disinfectant solution may be used alone, but it may be applied with a mop, cloth, sponge, or scrubbing brush made of material which, in its turn, inactivates the disinfectant and renders it ineffective.

Another cause for anxiety is the fact that dilute chemical disinfectant solutions may deteriorate with time. A recommended dilution of a well-chosen chemical disinfectant which is measured accurately into a clean bucket, on a Monday, may be effective in disinfecting surfaces or cleaning cloths soaked in it. However, the same solution allowed to remain in the bucket until the following Friday, may not only be too feeble to disinfect, owing to deterioration, but it may have become a source of infection because bacteria are growing in it.

The best chemical disinfectant, working under the best conditons, will rarely, if ever, kill 100 per cent of the bacteria present. There are likely to be a few survivors, over and above any bacterial spores present. The few survivors are most unlikely to present a hazard unless they have the opportunity to linger in the disinfectant solution for several days as it deteriorates. Under these conditions they may multiply rapidly and become a source of infection. It is therefore of great importance that staff be supervised and, where chemical disinfectants are used, fresh preparation daily be insisted upon, in clean containers. The containers should preferably be not only clean but heat treated as described earlier, to destroy bacteria which may remain in them. It is most unsafe to empty yesterday's disinfectant solution from a bucket, and make up today's new solution in the same wet bucket. The dregs of the old solution will contain a few bacteria at best, and many bacteria at worst. They will have acquired some slight resistance to the particular chemical disinfectant and thus will survive with more than usual ease in the new solution. Where refilling of wet containers continues day after day there may be a carry-over, into the fresh solutions, of bacteria with increasing resistance to the chemical disinfectant, which enables them to multiply rapidly in the solution.

The practice of 'topping up' disinfectant solutions is one which must be sternly condemned.

The correct use of a chemical disinfectant is likely to have more effect on the standard of hygiene achieved in food premises than is its chemical nature, but a brief summary of the properties of the different types available for use in food premises is given here. A few commercial brand names are given for each type. They are examples only and are arranged in alphabetical order, not in order of preference. The list is not exhaustive.

Properties of some different varieties of chemical disinfectants

HYPOCHLORITES are probably the most useful for food premises and they are inexpensive. This group has a wide range of antibacterial activity including some activity against bacterial spores which is not shown by other varieties. Hypochlorites have little taste or smell. They are anionic and are incompatible with cationic detergents. The addition of a little (anionic) detergent may be necessary to ensure the wetting of shiny surfaces. Where there is no wetting with the solution there is no disinfection. Hypochlorites are inactivated more easily by organic material than are most other disinfectants; this is their chief disadvantage, but apart from incompatible detergents they show very little inactivation by other materials. Owing to the risk of corrosion, metallic equipment should not be left to soak in a hypochlorite solution.

Examples: Brobat, Chloros, Domestos.

IODOPHORS resemble hypochlorites in antibacterial activity, but they are less sporicidal. They are more expensive but are equally acceptable as having little taste or smell. Iodophor disinfectants all incorporate a detergent which may be anionic, non-ionic, or cationic. They are considerably inactivated by organic material but show little inactivation by other materials.

Examples: Betadine, Vanodine, Wescodyne.

QUATERNARY AMMONIUM COMPOUND (QAC) disinfectants are popular in some food premises but they have a more limited range of antibacterical activity than hypochlorites and iodophors. They are cationic and are incompatible with anionic detergents but are, in themselves, good detergents. They are considerably inactivated by organic material, by soap, hard water, wood, cotton, Nylon, cellulose sponge mops, and a few plastics. Some bacteria grow with ease in QAC solutions and for this reason it is advised that where they are used great care is devoted to the preparation of fresh solutions daily in clean, heat-treated containers.

Examples: Hytox, Nonidet, Shield.

QAC DIGUANIDE mixtures are widely advertised as skin disinfectants. They have the disadvantages of the QACs, they are expensive and are not the best choice for food premises.

Examples: Resiguard, Savlon.

PHENOLIC DISINFECTANTS are of several types. The white fluid phenolics and the clear soluble fluids of the lysol type have a wide range of antibacterial activity which is similar to that of hypochlorites and iodophors while being much less easily inactivated by organic material. Their disadvantages lie in inactivation by some plastics and by rubber and, in some brands, a powerful smell. The chloroxylenol phenolic disinfectants show a more narrow range of antibacterial activity and greater inactivation by organic material.

Phenolic disinfectants are anionic and they are incompatible with cationic detergents. Some brands incorporate a detergent. Most phenolic disinfectants have a taint and consequently are not suitable for use in food premises.

Examples: White fluid phenolics: Izal, White Cyllin.

Clear soluble fluid phenolics: Clearsol, Hycolin, Stericol.

Chloroxylenol phenolics: Dettol.

AMPHOLYTE DISINFECTANTS have a narrow range of antibacterial activity and are readily inactivated by many materials and in particular by hard water, organic matter, wood, rubber, cotton, Nylon, cellulose sponge, and plastics. They are good detergents but are costly and they are not recommended as disinfectants.

Example: Tego.

PINE FLUIDS show little disinfectant activity and are not recommended. Many brands are available. All of them have the word 'pine' either incorporated in the brand name or mentioned in the advertising literature.

Those responsible for maintaining a high standard of hygiene in food premises should:

(1) Choose heat for disinfection wherever possible.
(2) Use a chemical disinfectant when, and only when, the application of heat is impossible.
(3) Arrange for equipment and surfaces to be cleaned before disinfection by heat or a chemical solution.
(4) Select a chemical disinfectant, where one must be used, from a variety showing a wide range of antibacterial activity. A good choice will be a hypochlorite solution used at a concentration giving 100 to 200 ppm of avilable chlorine for scrupulously clean surfaces. Slightly lower concentrations are permissible for salads. Where absolute cleanliness cannot be assured, a concentration giving 1000 or more ppm of available chlorine will be required.
(5) Ensure the fresh preparation, daily, of chemical disinfectant solutions, in clean, dry and preferably heat-treated containers.
(6) Remember that the effectiveness of a chemical disinfectant depends, very much, on the user.

16

Kitchen design and equipment[1]

In the construction of buildings for catering purposes a wide range of structural methods and materials are employed, but the basic requirements of any place to be used for the preparation and service of food must comply with the ordinary standards of stability, durability, and protection against the weather which are applicable to all buildings.

It is not appropriate here to describe the many details of construction involved in the erection of building; these may be studied. It is sufficient to say that the traditional forms of construction using proven materials, brick, concrete slates, and tiles cannot be improved upon for impermeability. Developments in materials have lead to lighter forms of construction supported by steel or concrete frames. Provided these materials are used within their performance specification, and the insulation and fire protection meet the required standards laid down in the current Building Regulations, these constructional methods are quite acceptable for catering purposes.

There are many types of catering business, and this large diverse industry served between 20 000 000 and 30 000 000 catering meals each day during 1976; school meals alone totalled 6 000 000 daily. Whilst catering, in many instances, is a small part only of another operation, it is the third largest industry in Britain employing about 1 000 000 people.

The interior

When it is clear that the building fulfils its primary function as a shell or impervious box the internal arrangements which would be specially suitable for food premises can be considered. For obvious

[1] Mr J. B. Simpson, Senior Environmental Health Officer, City of Canterbury and Mr David Ward, Principal Architect, North Yorkshire County Council, provided expert advise and revision of Chapter 16 and the authors are grateful.

reasons, a kitchen should be on the same storey as, and adjoin, the dining room. Though the delivery of stores and refuse removal is easier from ground floors, the natural lighting, ventilation, and outlook are usually better on upper storeys.

It is generally agreed by those interested in food hygiene that there is less likelihood of food becoming contaminated when the kitchen staff work in congenial surroundings. Certainly it may be assumed that staff made conscious of their responsibilities to the public, and employed in premises where work can be done in an orderly and unhurried manner, can and will pay attention to the demands of hygiene. Fatigue and strain brought about by cramped conditions, inadequate equipment, a dim light, overwork, and noise will predispose to carelessness; while good ventilation and lighting, readily accessible and easily cleaned surfaces make efforts to attain hygienic conditions less arduous.

The design, construction, and equipment of a commercial kitchen should satisfy two basic criteria — first, the proposed menu and scale of operation, and second, the intended method of cleaning the premises and equipment.

Lay-out

The minimum size of kitchens serving the public, and of certain staff canteens, is, in common with several kinds of other workplace, subject to requirements laid down by the Offices, Shops and Railway Premises Act, 1963. No such room may be so overcrowded as to cause risk of injury to the health of the people working therein, nor may there be less than about 3·7 square metres (40 square feet) of over-all floor area, and about 11·3 cubic metres (400 cubic feet) of over-all air space per person. These statutory figures refer to basic room capacity rather than to the space available after allowing for equipment; since kitchen equipment usually occupies a considerable amount of space compared with the number of persons using it, it seems unlikely that there will be many kitchens 2·4 to 3 metres (8 to 10 feet) high where the standards are not met.

The working space needed in kitchens will vary greatly depending on the menu, the extent that pre-prepared or convenience foods are used, and the type of equipment installed; every plan must be subject to the basic legal requirements. This chapter is based on ideal kitchen construction but it is possible to use the recommendations to improve existing premises.

There are heavy duty large scale installations which provide three full meals each day, and also the lighter catering kitchens. So far as working space is concerned, school kitchens designed and erected to the standards of the Department of the Environment and the

Department of Education and Science may be taken as reasonable: 1·2 to 1·8 metres (4 to 6 feet) of working and passage distance is allowed between island cookers and wall sinks or benches. As a rough guide to floor area of kitchens and other essential accommodation, Table 19, based on post-war school-meals service premises, may be of interest, bearing in mind that midday meals only are prepared.

The British Standard Code of Practice, CP3 (1950) Functional Requirements for Buildings, Chapter VII, Engineering and Utility Services, however, suggests a much more generous scale of kitchen area.

For	100 persons	69·7 sq. metres	750 sq. feet[1]
,,	250 persons	120·8 ,, ,,	1300 ,, ,,
,,	500 persons	232·3 ,, ,,	2500 ,, ,,
,,	750 persons	278·7 ,, ,,	3000 ,, ,,
,,	1000 persons	348·4 ,, ,,	3750 ,, ,,
,,	1500 persons	464·5 ,, ,,	5000 ,, ,,
,,	2000 persons	557·4 ,, ,,	6000 ,, ,,

plus space for cloakrooms accommodation, lavatories, rest rooms, and the manager's office.

The present trend in kitchens is to install preparation equipment at the sides (where waste can be conveniently drained away), and to erect island cooking apparatus in the centre of the room where there can be localized ventilation; but even in the smallest kitchen there is need for division into further compartments for the preparation of different kinds of food prior to cooking, and for washing-up.

Work and production should flow progressively from delivery of goods to storage, preparation, and service without return or 'cross-traffic'. There are good reasons for siting vegetable storage and preparation nearest the point of delivery in an area separated from the other parts of the kitchen, to prevent soil from root crops contaminating other foods. The sections for raw meat and raw fish should be well separated from those dealing with cooked and prepared products, including the pastry work, in order to prevent contamination passing from raw to cooked foods. Stores for each department should be adequate.

Most of the dirt generated in a kitchen comes from food material and this organic matter attracts vermin. Thus the preparation of food should involve the minimum number of processes that will cause spoiling, consistent with the menu. Deep fat frying is expensive and generates greasy dirt, therefore it should be reduced to a minimum. For bulk cooking it may be better to use frozen vegetables instead of fresh vegetables so that the production of waste is reduced. In general the size, design, and lay-out of a kitchen will

Table 19 Approximate floor areas (in square metres/square feet) of school kitchens

No. of meals	Kitchen	Vegetable store	Dry store	Larder	China store	Boiler house	Staff rooms	Refrigerator capacity (cubic metres/cubic feet)
750 in two sittings	176·5/1900 including two serveries and wash-up	9·3/100	7·4/80	8·8/96	—*	—†	17·1/184	4·6/50
600 in two sittings	131·9/1420 including servery and wash-up	9·3/100	7·4/80	6·7/72	—*	—†	13·9/150	2·3/25
500 in two sittings	111·5/1200 including servery and wash-up	9·3/100	6·7/72	7·4/80	—*	9·3/100	14·9/160	2·3/25
350	69·7/750	8·4/90	8·4/90	6·2/67	4·4/48	6·7/72	6·2/67	1·7/18
250	55·7/600	6·5/70	6·5/70	3·3/36	2·8/30	4·6/50	3·3/36	1·7/18
150	39·0/420	3·3/35	←——— 6·5/70 ———→		2·2/24 →	3·3/36	3·3/35	1·7/18
100	27·9/300	3·3/36	←——— 3·8/42 ———→		↗	3·3/36	2·8/30	—‡
75	19·5/210	1·5/16	2·6/28		↗	—	—	—‡
40	15·8/170	1·4/15	2·2/24		↗	—	—	—‡

* Provision made elsewhere than in the kitchen.
† Hot water supply from main building.
‡ Domestic refrigerators included.

depend on the menu, type of service, method of cleaning (by hand, machine, or high pressure lances; p. 207), and the energy used for cooking. Although the provision of services such as gas, electricity, water supply, drainage, and ventilation are primary considerations in planning a kitchen, the surface finishes of floors, walls, and ceilings are considered first.

Floors

Floor surfaces should be smooth and impervious and they should be durable enough to resist damage from the metal wheels of trolleys. As well as being impervious to moisture they should not be adversely affected by grease, salt, vegetables, or fruit acids or other materials used in the preparation of food. The surface finish of the floor should not have joints and crevices in which dirt, bacteria, and

Table 20   Comparison of floor surfaces

Material	Advantages	Disadvantages
Asphalt	Dust-free and waterproof jointless surface which can easily be coved to form skirting. Dull colours only	Will not tolerate excessive heat and concentrated weights. Not resistant to some acids and fats
Quarry tiles	Very hard wearing in all conditions. Non-slip if faced with an abrasive material	Numerous joints which can retain dirt and moisture unless well laid
Welded sheet vinyl	Smooth sheet material, impervious provided the joints are welded. Vinyl cove skirting can be incorporated. Wide range of patterns	Subfloor must be smooth and level. Will wear in dense traffic areas. Can be slippery when wet
Granolitic concrete	Low initial cost. Non-slip surface	Can be subject to dust and cracks. Difficult to colour
Epoxy resin composition	Virtually indestructable. Joint free. Non-slip finish to degree required. Joint-free and can incorporate cove skirting. Wide range of colours	High initial cost

insects can lodge. Angles at floor level should be avoided and the junction between floor and walls should be coved.

Tessilated quarry tiles coved at the junction with walls are still recommended for the floors of heavy duty kitchens. With light catering and in dining rooms, properly laid vinyl–asbestos tiles of at least 3·2 mm thickness provide a good floor surface. Sheet vinyls impregnated with graphite particles are available but may be difficult to clean. Patent non-slip floors should be inspected under operating conditions before purchase. Non-slip footwear may be a better investment than supposedly non-slip floors that retain dirt and become slippery from deposits of grease and water.

Table 20 on p. 224 outlines the advantages and disadvantages of the most commonly used floor finishes. Timber floors, either soft or hardwood, are not satisfactory because they are absorbent, wear quickly, and the joints harbour moisture and dirt. Rubber and cork tiles are not satisfactory as rubber is slippery when wet and cork is not durable where traffic is heavy. The main objectives for floors are that they should be impervious, easily cleaned, and durable.

Walls

Smooth, impervious, and durable wall surfaces from floor to ceiling are required to allow cleaning without deterioration. The basic material for wall structure should be either brick or concrete blocks. Faced stud partition walls of plaster board should not be used as they are liable to harbour vermin which can reach the cavity by gnawing through the plaster board, skirting, or duct work; also, fittings or equipment cannot be attached because of the light weight. A plastered finish will provide a smooth and reasonable non-porous surface, especially if the final skin coat is 'hard' plaster. The vitreous-faced sheet materials are acceptable, although only the standard glazed tiles are suitable as larger sheets must be screwed to the walls and cover strips to the joints, so that the smooth surface is destroyed. The joints on small glazed tiles are narrow and can be made smooth and flush. The better wall surfaces have no hollow places, such as solid-bedded ceramic tiles; any spaces should be filled with lightweight concrete.

Localized protection against damage by impact may be necessary. Glazed tiles will protect walls behind working surfaces, they should extend at least 450 mm above the surface. External corners subject to contact with trolleys or other movable equipment should be protected with suitable polyvinyl chloride (PVC) extrusion which can be simply fixed to the wall with adhesive. Areas such as trolley parks should be protected by either a PVC or timber rail at handle or any other height where there are projections liable to damage the wall surface. An almost indestructable impervious surface is provided by stainless steel as tiles or sheets. Resin-bonded fibre-glass provides an excellent finish that withstands severe impact blows without damage and remains impervious; it also withstands heat providing fire-retardent resins are used.

Ceilings

A ceiling is necessary in a kitchen to prevent dust falling down from the roof or floor structure. Two types of ceiling are described, both of which have advantages and disadvantages in particular situations. In the design of school kitchens a smooth impervious surface is favoured, plaster-board finished with a skim coat of plaster to eliminate the joints. It may be combined with a hot-air blower suspended from a corner of the ceiling to help remove condensation. Such a surface is easily cleaned and where midday meals only are prepared each day condensation is unlikely to be troublesome. In kitchens with continual service it is considered that with impervious walls, floor, and equipment one surface should absorb some sound and condensation. Patent suspended ceilings in absorbent 600 mm square acoustic tiles (fibre-board) are recommended. The tiles, laid loose on aluminium bearers, are cheap and easy to replace. Polystyrene tiles present a fire hazard under certain conditions. The objections to absorbent tiles include difficulty in cleaning, a tendency to deteriorate when saturated, and that the tiles are subject to attack by vermin. The alloy suspension grids are also said to corrode in humid atmospheres. Services to equipment are usually accommodated in floor zones for easy access to equipment. Services to lighting run in the ceiling void and are usually free from trouble. Any insulation to the roof should be placed between the plaster-board or tiles and the structural roof.

Decorative finishes for walls and ceilings

The purpose of decorative finishes for the walls and ceiling is two-fold — firstly, to protect the wall finish from damage caused by cleaning, and secondly to provide a visually acceptable and pleasing environment. Oil-bound eggshell paints are generally the most widely used, with gloss finish on the fittings; other paints may help to reduce condensation, but they tend to provide less of a sealed surface than that covered with an oil-based paint, and, therefore, are more difficult to clean.

No rules can be laid down regarding colour schemes for kitchen areas as orientation and the amount of natural lighting are important factors. White ceilings are generally best as they reflect the light from artificial sources. All-white walls give the area a stark clinical look. Pastel colours with perhaps bolder tones on some of the fittings are better. Colour for the floor finish should not be too dark as this renders cleaning difficult to assess.

Lighting

Good lighting in kitchens improves concentration and safety. The Offices, Shops and Railway Premises Act, 1963, requires that effective provision shall be made for sufficient and suitable lighting in every part of the premises. The Department of Employment Code of Practice No. 39 on Lighting, sets out minimum requirements, whilst the Illuminating Engineering Society's Code gives recommended values. Five hundred lux is the generally accepted over-all level of lighting on working surfaces and 100 lux elsewhere, with a limiting glare of 22 lux. Artificial illumination is necessary even though the suggested standard could be met during normal working hours by natural lighting in a kitchen with a high window-to-wall ratio. Good natural lighting is desirable in kitchens but without glare from direct sunlight, which may cause reflection from polished surfaces. North light is preferable, otherwise overhanging eaves, tinted glass, or some form of blind should be fitted to the windows to obtain indirect light; venetian blinds are difficult to clean.

Of the two forms of electric light, tungsten filament and fluorescent, the running costs of fluorescent lighting are lower than those of tungsten and the light distribution is more even, if the tubes are covered by diffusers. Twin tube 'natural', Kolor-rite, or 'warm white delux' fluorescent tubes are recommended to improve colour rendering or perception of food. The tubes lose 20 per cent efficiency within a year or earlier and should be replaced when flicker and black ends are observed. The IES Code for interior lighting gives guidelines on designs to improve texture, contrast, and direction. Light fittings should be vapour proof and the actual layout of the lighting should consider the sites of equipment and preparation areas including sinks, stoves, and tables. Lighting is important where food is dispensed, since it can enhance the appearance of the food. Spot lights can be placed directly over the servery counter to compliment the over-all lighting. Additional lamps may be required to aid cleaning of less accessible dark areas. In kitchens proofed 'luminaires' (whole light fittings) are necessary to withstand both the heat and the possibility of explosions if tubes are defective.

Windows

Window boards and ledges situated behind kitchen equipment are not easily accessible for cleaning. Sills should be higher than equipment and constructed with an angled ledge to prevent their use as shelves. Louvre windows provide good control of ventilation and may be easily fitted with nylon mesh fly screens. The windows in a kitchen should not face due south without taking precautions to eliminate glare and the effect of solar heat.

Ventilation

It cannot be overemphasized that an efficient ventilation and extraction system is essential for kitchens. The operations of preparation, cooking, serving, and washing-up generate large amounts of water vapour, steam, which unless it is extracted will strike the colder surfaces in the kitchen and condense to create moisture dripping from the ceilings or running down walls. In addition, with high humidity there may also be volatile fat. The most satisfactory method of controlling the humidity and cooking odours is to use localized systems of extraction analogous to the methods employed to remove dust from sanding and polishing machines. The commercial fish fryer used in fish and chip shops provides an example of an integrated design that includes ventilation matched to the equipment, but this system can still contravene the law by releasing objectionable smells. A ventilation system cannot operate without a supply of sufficient air for the extract fans. When there are gas appliances, balanced ventilation is essential so that the open flames burn steadily. When there is insufficient oxygen to gas jets, there is danger of unburnt gas reaching ducts — drawn in by suction.

The grouping of cooking appliances in islands is a convenient method of concentrating this equipment in order to extract the steam and odours before they are diffused throughout the kitchen area. The equipment shown in Fig. 50 is modular in plan and is assembled like unit furniture with all the services located in a central spine; the arrangement is popular in school kitchens. This type of equipment saves space and lends itself to a localized extraction system. The items cannot be moved for cleaning and it may be difficult to reach the services. Figure 51 shows another well designed kitchen used to prepare a wide variety of lunches and snacks only.

Although the traditional canopy and extraction fans are still highly efficient methods of extraction, they do visually interrupt the kitchen space and are difficult to clean. Where electric fans are used, their speed should be adjustable to a maximum rate of extract of air,

Fig. 50 Efficient and hygienic grouping of equipment

Fig. 51 Kitchen used to prepare luncheons and snacks

through grease filters, up to 20 cubic metres per minute per square metre of hood area. Simple baffle boards placed below extraction fans are now used in school kitchens. The boards, usually made from block-boards covered with plastic laminate, are about 1 metre square and are suspended below the ceiling on adjustable straps. The distance between the baffle board and the ceiling can be readily adjusted until the desired extract velocity is achieved. The whole

Fig. 52   Baffle board centred over extract duct

baffle board can easily be removed, cleaned, and replaced within minutes (Fig. 52). Ducts are reduced to a minimum, especially if the extraction fan is roof mounted; they should be air-tight with properly sealed joints.

Other items of equipment which produce large quantities of steam, for example, large automatic dishwashers, should have their own extraction system ducted to the atmosphere, likewise tea and coffee urns. Where grease filters are incorporated into an extraction system over cooking ranges, the filters should be so placed that they can readily be removed for cleaning or replacement, and a spare set should be available. In small kitchens where localized extraction is not possible, small wall extraction fans can be placed in walls or windows to supplement the natural ventilation (Fig. 53). Their position should be considered carefully in order to prevent the short

circuit of air from the window to the fan. In action, windows should
be closed.

If the vegetable store is not situated on an outside wall, ducted
mechanical ventilation must be introduced. The dry store will also
need ventilation although to a lesser degree. Where mechanical

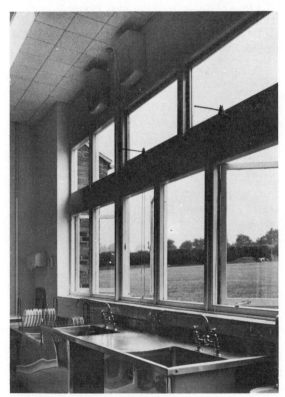

Fig. 53   Vent-Axia extraction fans

extraction units are incorporated in food storage areas to form
'Rapid Cooling Larders', it is important to ensure that air inlets draw
in fresh air and not air from the general kitchen area.

Heating

The legal minimum air temperature of 16 °C (60·8 °F) is required in
work rooms. This temperature must be reached within the first hour
of starting work. Usually, heating appliances are only necessary in
the staff rooms and offices of kitchens.

Services

Services into a kitchen include water, drainage, electricity, gas, and ventilation. Numerous additional points are required around a kitchen so that services may readily be tapped. Ducts can provide routes whereby vermin enter, leave, and infest entire buildings. Holes for services must be completely sealed and proofed against vermin. Floor ducts that may be flooded by wash water or provide harbourage for vermin, should be filled with lightweight concrete or a similar inert material.

Gas

This fuel is popular with chefs, but pressure in each installation must be carefully balanced using a water gauge. Automatic ignition to burners is essential to reduce wastage of energy, and devices to stop flame failure will help to prevent an accidental build-up of gas. The possibility of explosions can be eliminated by installing alarms for gas detection.

Flexible supply pipes with bayonet fitting connectors for each appliance, together with in-built mobility, permit effective cleaning and maintenance. Gas appliances should have governors fitted, to prevent variations in gas pressure affecting the efficiency of the burners.

Electricity

Electricity may be expensive, but it is the most suitable source of energy for many catering processes. As a fire precaution, one master switchboard, clearly identified, is necessary indicating each piece of equipment; it should be situated close to the kitchen.

Single phase electricity may be satisfactory in a few light catering kitchens, but usually a 415 volts supply consisting of three phases and a neutral wire, is essential. Electric wiring should be either mineral insulated copper-covered cable (Pyro), or water-resistant heavy gauge conduit, with points at about 1·5 metres off the floor. All electrical devices in the buildings, and equipment in heavy duty catering kitchens should be waterproof.

Water supply

To ensure constant and adequate supplies of hot and cold water, pipes should be installed as a ring main whereby water circulates continuously; stop taps should isolate every fitting. A supply direct from the mains is required in kitchens except at wash-hand-basins, shower baths, and dish-washing machines. Water softening is necessary for effective dish-washing in hard water areas and it halves the amount of detergent used. A cold water tap for culinary use can be conveniently situated adjacent to cooking appliances. An ample supply of hot water at 82 °C is essential in a kitchen, but the actual quantity of hot and cold water needed depends on the type of menu and the scale of equipment. Boiling water for tea and coffee rapidly produces hardness scale so that the boilers should be connected to a soft water supply.

The temperature of the water in the sink used for the disinfecting rinse may be raised by means of a thermostatically controlled gas burner or electrical unit, or by steam. This reduces loss of heat from the rinse water while work is in progress. Alternatively, an independent boiler may provide hot water directly to the disinfection sink from which there may be a constant overflow to the washing sink as the water cools. Where a piped supply for hand-washing is not practicable from the main hot water system, small gas geysers or electric appliances are useful; they cannot supply water at high temperatures for washing-up.

Sanitary and washing facilities

In all premises where persons are employed, including buildings used for the preparation of food, toilet and washing facilities must be incorporated to satisfy the Sanitary Convenience Regulations, 1964 and Offices, Shops and Railway Premises Act, 1963. Local Authorities are now empowered to require that sufficient specified sanitary appliances (water closets, urinals, and wash basins) be provided and maintained in a clean condition at any relevant place. A relevant place is where there is public entertainment or the sale of food and drink to members of the public for consumption at that place. The suitability and adequacy of sanitary accommodation is considered before a licence is granted by the Brewster Sessions. In general terms the provision of one lavatory for every multiple of 15 males or females will meet the regulations, but special conditions may require more.

Standard sanitary ware is acceptable for installation in kitchen premises. Low level WC cisterns are recommended as they are more readily adapted to a pedal-operated flush system (Fig. 54).

The siting of toilet accommodation in relation to food preparation areas and other rooms in danger from pollution is subject to statutory control. All toilets must be entered through some intervening and separately ventilated lobby or corridor. Artificial ventilation should provide 6 air changes per hour, and also static inlet ventilation in the lobby to supply air for the fans. Two fans should operate continuously and an emergency fan should be supplied. For small places, individual double fan units can be operated by the light switch and continue to function 20 minutes after the light is switched off. Mechanical ventilation serving sanitary facilities must not communicate with other ventilation systems within a building.

Wash-hand-basins must be placed in or adjacent to toilet cubicles, as well as in food preparation areas where workers' hands will

(a) Household adaptation   (b) Permanent installation

Fig. 54   Foot-operated flush

become dirty and contaminated from raw foods and other materials during the course of the work — foot-operated control is recommended (Fig. 55).

When food handlers are engaged in work on more than one floor of a multistoried building, conveniences and adjacent wash-hand-basins are desirable on each storey; they should, at least, be situated so that each serves not more than two floors. Toilet areas should be adequately lighted and ventilated either by natural or artificial means.

Facilities for hand washing may comprise fixed wash-hand-basins, troughs, or washing fountains (circular bowls at least 0·9 metres in diameter). With troughs, a length of 0·6 metres is regarded as equivalent to a wash-basin; with fountains, 0·6 metres of circumference is allowed. Foot-operated water control (Fig. 56) is recommended for food factories.

The Washing Facilities Regulations, 1964, require basins or their equivalent in troughs or fountains to be provided on the same scale as toilet accommodation.

Fig. 55 Foot-operated wash-hand-basin

For hand washing there must be supplies of running hot and cold water, or water blended to a suitable temperature. Where a piped supply of hot water is not available there are several excellent alternatives such as thermal storage units and instantaneous water heaters using electricity or gas as a source of heat.

Spray taps which discharge water at a temperature of 48·9 °C are economical in the volume of water delivered and consequently in the amount of fuel required for heating. Lever-arm taps, as installed in hospitals, which can be operated by the elbow or forearm, greatly reduce chances of cross-contamination; alternatively, pedal-operated taps or sprinklers should be used (Fig. 56).

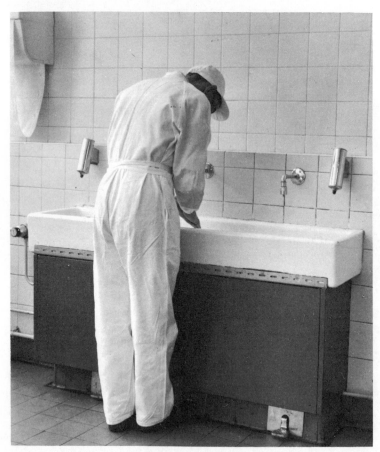

Fig. 56   Foot-operated water control and sprinkler

Washing facilities include the provision of soap, nail brushes, and some means to dry the hands. Liquid or dry soap dispensed from fitted containers is preferable to tablets of soap left in wet dishes. Liquid soap containers must not be topped up, but must be washed and disinfected in hot water before being refilled. Nail brushes, too, need care. They should be made of plastic with Nylon bristles to permit disinfection, preferably by heat although some plastics do not withstand heat. They should be stored dry, up-ended, and not in disinfectant solutions. Satisfactory means for drying hands include paper towels, the patent continuous roller towel providing a clean portion for each person, and efficient electric air blowers. Sanitary and washing facilities must be separate for each sex, unless the number of persons employed on the premises does not regularly exceed five at any one time.

The facilities provided for customers may be used for employees but the number must be increased by one extra closet and wash-basin when more than 10 persons are employed. A notice drawing attention to the necessity for washing the hands must be displayed in all sanitary facilities for staff, and should be brought to the attention of customers also.

Sinks and washing-up units

Various dish-washing machines and sink units are available for crockery, cutlery, glassware, pots, pans, and utensils. A separate sink for vegetables and salad preparation is essential. Guards (upstands) of 150 to 300 mm integrated with the back of sink units protect adjacent walls. Sinks should be installed under wall-mounted taps with stopcocks fitted at low level on the water pipes. When the taps and plumbing are not fixed directly on to a sink it is a simple operation to unscrew the waste trap, when the unit becomes easily movable to permit the previously concealed wall area to be cleaned.

Articles can be disinfected in a dish-washing machine or by means of a stainless steel double sink unit with the water temperature in the rinse sink maintained at 77–82 °C (170–180 °F). An ample supply of deep wire baskets is required. A double sink with a small section for hot disinfection of knives, choppers, and other articles is useful (Fig. 49).

Drainage

The design and construction of drainage systems for all classes of buildings have to meet the requirements of the Building Regulations, 1972. All relevant design drawings must be inspected and approved by the local authority before construction takes place. It is essential when designing a drainage system for a kitchen to prevent blockages either by solids or grease. Much of the grease discharged into the drains from a kitchen comes from the washing up area where it enters the pipes in a molten state but solidifies in the system unless intercepted. Grease traps consist of a tank in the ground, which holds a volume of cold water sufficient in quantity to cool the inflow of washing up water to a temperature below the melting point of the grease. The inlet and outlet are submerged so that the solidified grease forms a layer at the top of the tank. This layer is skimmed off at regular intervals. Nevertheless, grease traps are not entirely satisfactory and if correct procedures are adopted the accumulation of grease should be avoided. It is important that all drains be rodded from the fitting to the entry into a manhole so that blockage can be rectified easily. Large cast-iron and copper waste pipes should be used. PVC will soften in contact with the near boiling water which runs to waste in kitchens. Large waste pipes (50–75 mm in diameter) will prevent siphonage and also permit clearance. One large pipe can be used in common to drain several fittings and should discharge as a back inlet over a gully. Drainage channels are required in the floor around cooking equipment — they should be covered with galvanized metal gratings which can be easily removed. Sinks and basins should be discharged either into or over trapped gullies. Items of equipment such as potato peelers, dish-washing machines, or waste disposal units which are connected directly into the drainage system should be trapped to prevent the waste pipes acting as vents to the system.

Waste disposal

Unlike the scrap from many industrial and commercial processes, kitchen waste can putrefy and demands particular care and

Fig. 57   Waste disposal unit

Fig. 58 A refuse compactor

attention while awaiting final disposal. Undoubtedly, the principle of immediate disposal by disintegration and flushing to the drainage system, is most attractive. Waste disposal units which discharge into the drainage system may be fixed under metal sinks or stand in a frame with their own receiving hoppers. An electrically driven macerating unit breaks down waste food to a fine mash which is washed away through a trapped waste pipe. In one type the machine is automatically switched on only when water is flowing through the grinding chamber (Fig. 57). Units designed for the domestic market have motors of 1/3 hp, but generally a heavier duty motor should be used in commercial premises. Refuse compaction is economic in large food businesses where skips are provided — machines are available that reduce bulky refuse to a convenient size (Fig. 58). In large catering premises, refuse disposal by incineration can also be considered but this must not be accompanied by smoke.

The system of storage in paper or plastic sacks is popular (Fig. 59). The filled sacks are light and clean to handle and they can be sealed easily with a bag twist tool which rapidly fixes 254 mm (10 inch) wire twists; the tool and twists are available from agricultural merchants.

Fig. 59   Paper sack and holder

Fig. 60   Dustbins on stands

Dustbins should be made of stout and impervious material, and 22 gauge galvanized iron is recommended. Lids should be close fitting with an overhanging lip; lids of hard rubber reduce noise. There is a British Standard Specification for the construction of dustbins.

All members of staff should be aware of the necessity for daily removal of refuse from the kitchen, and of the care needed in storage. A properly constructed storage area for refuse is essential, with concrete floor and a hose tap for use in flushing the yard; the drainage gully should be fitted with a straining basket. The wall surfaces should be smooth, impervious, and withstand water from high pressure hoses. Refuse bins need to be washed each time they are emptied and stored inverted to drain dry on metal racks above the yard surface (Fig. 60). A daily collection of refuse is necessary for large quantities of putrid waste; if such frequent collection is impossible, a secure refrigerated refuse store, away from food, should be provided.

Equipment

Equipment must be so designed and sited that all surfaces are accessible for cleaning. Every item should be readily removable or accessible. Large equipment should be free standing and clear of the floor and walls. Mobile equipment with wheels which can be locked facilitates cleaning as well as helping staff to reduce the movement of foods (Fig. 61). It is recommended that there should be at least 300 mm (12 inches) under appliances or they should be mounted or sealed to a solid base such as a concrete plinth approximately 150 mm (6 inches) high, topped with quarry tiles, and with a coved tile skirting. Dirt is liable to accumulate in the framework and outer casing which should be as smooth as practicable, and spaces in the

Fig. 61 Food mixer mounted on mobile table

supporting structure should be totally enclosed and sealed or open for cleaning purposes. For example, legs to standing equipment are best formed of sealed tubes rather than of angle or channel section. The basic material for food equipment must be non-absorbent and not subject to injury by cleaning or by disinfectants.

Surfaces

Tables and worktops should be constructed for ease of cleaning, strength, and durability. Stainless steel tables with tubular legs and braked castors are recommended. Wood is not satisfactory for direct contact with food because it is porous and cannot be effectively cleaned and disinfected. Large numbers of intestinal bacteria may be cultivated from teak sinks even after thorough washing and scrubbing with soda solution. As with sinks, a stainless steel upstanding back, 150 to 300 mm at the rear of worktops, will help to prevent the adjacent wall surfaces from becoming soiled and damaged. Worktops should be movable to facilitate cleaning, otherwise at least 300 mm (a broom width) should be left behind fixed equipment.

Open shelves of stainless steel or cantilevered plastic laminate are recommended for the storage of small equipment and foodstuffs in preference to cupboards or drawers. Fixed shelves sited over cooking equipment should be made of stainless steel. A hollow plinth should not be incorporated under shelves because the space harbours dirt and it is a favourite nesting place for mice. Wooden shelves should be avoided. Free standing wire shelves allow air circulation and dust will fall through to be washed easily from the floor, but such shelves are not suitable for open food. Detachable shelves are convenient for cleaning and redecoration.

Cooking equipment

The traditional method of cooking, using pots and pans on an open ring, is wasteful of energy. As much as half the heat produced is not used to cook the food but is removed by ventilation and is thus useless. Excessive heat in the kitchen causes unpleasant and debilitating working conditions. Furthermore, warmth and humidity encourage bacterial growth.

The accessibility and adaptability of cooking equipment is improved by separating the boiling top from the oven. Ovens should be situated at waist height on movable stainless steel tubular frames.

Aluminium or soft alloys should not be used for burners and handles; such metals are difficult to clean and are easily damaged by caustic cleaning agents.

Polished stainless steel (type 302 and thickness 14/16 gauge) is the best construction material for catering equipment with rounded corners and deburred edges. The design of appliances should enable the removal of heavily soiled parts for cleaning; each piece should easily fit into a sink, or better still, into the dish-washing machine, directly before emptying the water tanks. Several washes may be necessary to soften heavily soiled trivets, trays, and shelves but if the process is carried out on a daily basis, a high standard of finish can be maintained.

Equipment is now available to cook food in batches with only small flavour and nutrient losses, and such plant may be easily cleaned, for example, pressure steamers, bratt-pans (that can be tipped to empty) and forced air convection ovens. All these items can be raised above the floor surface and the underneath cleaned.

Faults in bulk cooking often arise when practices that suited the domestic kitchen are used for the catering industry. Cooking a large amount of food in one container above several open burners requires much water and constant stirring which is dangerous for staff who, furthermore, may have to carry these heavy containers full of hot food. Cooking large amounts of food too far ahead of requirements without adequate cooling and refrigeration facilities will inevitably lead to food poisoning.

Convection ovens, microwave ovens, and pressure cookers are described in Chapter 12.

Cooking vessels

Cooking vessels and other utensils may be made of a wide range of materials, including various metals and vitreous substances. There have been no reports of illness following the consumption of food prepared in contact with the more common metals such as aluminium and its alloys, iron, and tin, except from corroded cans, or stainless steel. Zinc poisoning has been reported from fruit and fruit juice prepared in galvanized iron containers, and lemonade prepared in chipped enamel containers has caused antimony poisoning. Copper from tea urns and from tin-coated steamers from which the tin layer has been worn has been reported in chemical food poisoning. The use of cooking pots and pans which are heavily carboned wastes energy.

Fryers

Deep frying causes fat deposits and dirt in the kitchen, in ventilation systems, and outside the building. Deep fat fryers hold large quantities of cooking oil which undergoes a physical change at prolonged high temperatures and reduce the quality of fried food. A system of frying must ensure that oil is not used for an excessive length of time. The breakdown of cooking oils is caused by many factors:

(1) High temperature frying and oxidation.
(2) Food can introduce excessive moisture, common salt, potato whitener, and charring by food particles; the charring can be reduced by providing a deep cool zone in frying equipment.
(3) The catalytic action of copper and brass in old cheap fryers or filter valves rapidly darkens fat or oil.

To overcome some of the difficulties associated with deep fat frying, staff should be trained to use equipment correctly; several small capacity fryers give a greater flexibility and better results. All frying equipment should be fitted with thermostatic controls and heat should be applied slowly to avoid thermal shock to cooking oils. Whilst enclosed filter systems are useful for clarifying oil, open filters may lead to oxidation of the oil. Oil manufacturers recommend a minimum oil level during frying and frequent topping up with new oil. For fish and doughnuts a complete change of cooking oil is required regularly; doughnut plant needs careful operation and supervision like other deep fat equipment. Thermostats should be calibrated and checked against a thermometer at least once each week.

Hot cabinets

The hot cupboard is satisfactory for heating plates but not for keeping food hot since food dries out quickly, losing flavour and nutritional quality. Furthermore the temperatures in some cabinets may be suitable for the growth of bacteria. The appliances are not designed to cook food and the system of holding food in this manner can provide conditions necessary for multiplication of food-poisoning organisms. Food should be served directly from cooking appliances, dry bain-maries, and cold cabinets.

Cutting 'boards'

Synthetic cutting pads are easily cleaned and disinfected although they may sustain cuts. Hard synthetic rubber pads are good although they may be deformed by heat; this can be corrected if they are softened in hot water and allowed to harden on a flat surface. Polypropylene pads can be put in a dish-washer. Hardwood boards should be constructed without joints.

Separate cutting blocks and 'boards' should be used for different foods, particularly for raw and cooked foods, to reduce the risk of cross-contamination. Hard synthetic rubber chopping blocks or table tops are useful in many food trades. The surface is suitable for boning meat, cutting pastry, and filleting fish without causing damage to knives. Rubber is impervious, unlike the cellular structure of wood that permits the absorption of food particles and juices. Sandpaper may be used to resurface a rubber pad after prolonged periods of heavy use. Rubber table tops of 1 or 2 inch thickness, should be supported on stands of tubular aluminium, stainless steel, or galvanized steel with adjustable feet.

Slicing, mixing, and mincing machines

These machines can facilitate the cross-contamination of food. Food machinery should be designed to be easily dismantled for cleaning and disinfection, and easily reassembled; safety is another important factor in the selection of machines. Hygiene and safety considerations should come first in the choice of equipment and should outweigh the initial cost. In dual purpose machines with interchangeable parts, the hazard of cross-contamination will be increased.

Milk packs

Refrigerated milk packs are useful in restaurants, canteens, and hospitals and other large-scale eating places. The machines will accommodate three or five gallon packs of milk, singly or in pairs, and they can be used in conjunction with automatic vending of milk. The use of milk packs overcomes the risk of contamination of milk after arrival on catering premises and resolves the nuisance of empty milk bottles.

Food storage

Refrigeration

The multiplication of bacteria will be reduced by rapid cooling and the refrigerated storage of food. The temperatures at which certain foods must be kept, laid down in Regulation 27 of the Food Hygiene (General) Regulations, 1970, are above 62·7 °C (145 °F) or below 10 °C (50 °F), the lower temperature could be reduced advantageously to 7·2 °C (45 °F) or even 4 °C (39 °F). Refrigerators should provide separate storage at the temperature recommended for each particular type of food, or separate refrigerators are required. Cold storage facilities should be provided for vegetables and fruit, a temperature of 10 °C (50 °F) is adequate. Cooked and uncooked food should be refrigerated and stored separately and not on the cold room floor or beneath other foods that may spill or drip and

Fig. 62   Mobile chill cabinet

cause contamination. Cold store evaporators should be defrosted regularly, otherwise temperature control cannot be maintained and there will be a rise of temperature inside the refrigerator. Automatic defrosting is recommended. Refrigeration is a heat exchange process and heat removed by the refrigerant must be dissipated elsewhere; a well designed cold room should have ample ventilation to the compressor and no obstruction of the plant. Wherever possible, large refrigerator motors should be sited outside the building and always outside the kitchen. They are a source of heat and dust, and the motors can become nesting places for mice. A warning device for refrigerator or deep freeze failure is essential. Two separate motors are valuable in case the compressor fails. Mobile refrigerated cabinets are recommended for use in large-scale catering (Fig. 62).

Deep freeze

Frozen foods should be maintained at a constant temperature in a cabinet operating at a temperature of $-18\,°C\,(0\,°F)$; the temperature should be checked frequently. The cabinet should be placed in such a position that it is not affected by draught or heat from the sun or radiators. The air compressor motors or coils should not be obstructed.

Rapid cooling larder

The provision of rapid cooling facilities is strongly recommended, particularly for foods refrigerated after cooking. They are especially necessary for meat and poultry dishes intended to be served cold or refrigerated for use the following day as cold food. A room should be allotted on the north side of the kitchen with an extract fan and means to maintain the temperature at $8–10\,°C\,(46–50\,°F)$. Such facilities are also useful for the storage of dairy products. Mobile cabinets provided with fans and air filters are desirable for large-scale catering.

Larder for dry goods

The vermin-proof room or cupboard, depending on the size of the kitchen, for dehydrated and canned goods should have impervious surfaces to floors, walls, and shelves, and also fly screens. Good ventilation can be supplied by 9-inch air bricks in an external wall, together with an extractor fan to aid air movement. The inlet and extract vents should be on opposite walls, the inlet at low level and the extract at higher level to ensure good air circulation.

Cleaner's equipment room

Nominally clean articles used for cleaning are often heavily contaminated with bacteria and should not be stored in food rooms.

Cloths, mops, and brushes can contaminate otherwise clean surfaces, so provision must be made to disinfect all cleaning equipment; there should be racks to drain buckets and facilities to dry cloths. There is a risk that spillage of chemicals may contaminate food and therefore separate storage facilities are essential for cleaning materials. Figure 63 gives a plan for a cleaner's equipment room. Sinks and wash-basins in kitchens should not be used for the disposal of wash water used in cleaning processes. A separate slop sink or

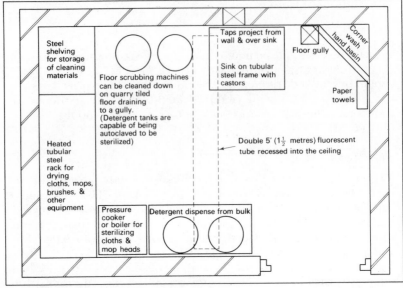

Fig. 63   Plan for cleaner's equipment room

gully should be provided in the cleaners' room, together with supplies of hot and cold water, wash-hand-basin and extract fan. If cloths are used for equipment, cutlery, surfaces, and glasses they should be disinfected in boiling water or bleach solution at least daily; after the bleach solution, cloths must be thoroughly rinsed. Paper swabs and disposable cloths are recommended. Twin bucket trolleys are available for washing floors manually using a mop. One bucket contains detergent water and the dirty water is wrung out into another bucket (Fig. 64).

Staff room

Facilities away from food rooms must be provided to store and dry the outdoor clothing of employees. If clothes lockers are used they

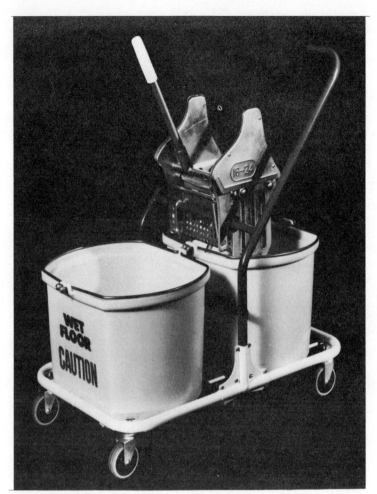

Fig. 64   Twin bucket trolley

should be constructed of open wire, heated, and situated close to the staff sanitary and washing facilities. It may be preferable to hang clothes freely on rods and supply a source of heat for drying purposes. It is desirable to provide showers for the staff and also a receptacle for discarded protective clothing.

First aid

The provision of first aid materials is a legal requirement laid down in the Food Hygiene (General) Regulations, 1970 and in greater detail in the Offices, Shops and Railway Premises First Aid Order, 1964, Number 970. Blue waterproof dressings will be noticed more easily than skin coloured dressings and are less likely to become extraneous matter in food.

Licensed trade

In the public house or hotel bar there may be a mixture of business and domestic arrangements. The preparation of food intended for customers should be separated from domestic occupations. In particular, laundry activities should be carried out in a different room; this should be borne in mind for all domestic households. It is obvious that soiled clothes and bed linen should not be washed where food is prepared; the bathroom is more appropriate, but special accommodation should be provided.

Food displayed on bars, or anywhere else, should be kept cold and a rapid turnover ensured. A Code of Practice would be helpful not only for public houses but for hotels and restaurants where cold meats, salads, and sweet dishes are often exposed on tables and trolleys during service for lunch and dinner.

17

Control of infestation

It is probable that estimates of the material damage caused by rats and mice are often overstated, and the implication of these rodents in the spread of infection in Britain is probably not considerable, although not insignificant, at the present time. Nevertheless, the presence of such animals in and around food stores is repugnant, apart from being a source of material loss, and a potential danger to health.

Local authorities invariably maintain a staff of pest operators trained in methods of rodent destruction, and the occupier of infested premises can call for practical assistance. It should be pointed out that the onus for keeping premises free from infestation rests upon the occupier or owner. Councils are entitled to charge for such services, but rarely do so in domestic premises. Where there is serious damage to food caused by any infestation the occupier is under an obligation to report it to the authorities (Prevention of Damage by Pests Act, 1949, section 13).

Block control of rats and mice

The Black death in the fourteenth century was bubonic plague caused by *Yersinia pestis* which was spread from rat to rat and from rat to man by fleas carrying the organisms; 25 million people died. Certain countries still suffer this disease. The rat is clever, breeds prolifically, gnaws voraciously, and may carry agents of other diseases such as leptospirosis, and viral and food-borne infections.

An infestation is not always confined to one part of a building which may be occupied by different families or firms, nor to a single building; the rat or mouse colony may spread through several adjoining premises. Thus a tenant might kill off the rodents on his own premises, only to find them replaced in a very short time by an overflow from his neighbour's property. Concerted action over the whole infested territory or block is necessary before all the rats and mice can be destroyed. Usually this is carried out most conveniently by the local authority and it is known as block control (Fig. 65). A contract with a commercial pest control organization will minimize the risk of reinfestation.

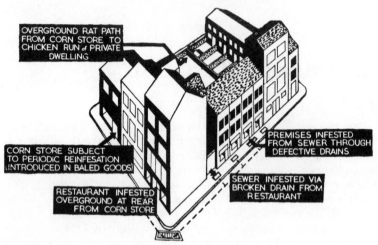

Fig. 65 Block control: an example of related infestation in separate buildings which require simultaneous treatment

Vertical block control

An infestation may extend below ground to drains and sewers, so that vertical block control schemes must include treatment for the destruction of rats in underground pipes as well as in the buildings above. Black rats may be present in the roof and brown rats at ground level.

Rodent-proofing

Some comments have already been made (p. 225) on structural materials and their properties of resistance to penetration by rodents. Naturally, stony and metallic materials have basic advantages over those of a fibrous nature. Impenetrable materials, however, are of little value if the building is constructed so that apertures or cavities are left for rodents to use as a means of entry or passage, or as a place to nest in. Furthermore, thoughtless methods of food storage, careless stacking, and general untidiness may allow a considerable infestation to become established in an otherwise sealed building; a rat or mouse family may be introduced through the store entrance, for example, in straw packing materials.

The major requirements for survival and family life in the rodent world are food, warmth, and housing, and to deny any or all of these is a means of discouraging infestation. Therefore, material which is likely to be suitable for rat food, e.g. cereals, starchy vegetables, and fatty compounds, including even tallow and soap, should be kept in rodent-proof metal bins or containers, and refuse of the same type in properly covered metal dustbins, whilst awaiting removal. As far

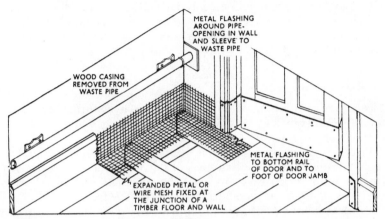

Fig. 66   Rat-proofing: methods of protecting some vulnerable points

as possible access to water should be denied by attending to dripping taps and keeping grids on gully traps, for example. Articles temporarily unused should not be allowed to accumulate in odd corners nor remain undisturbed for more than a week or two, thus providing refuge for rats; anything which may afford cover to rats should be eliminated from the building and attached yards. Mice obtain sufficient water from their food and their small size enables them to enter buildings and move about easily.

Cartons, boxed goods, or sacks should be neatly stacked close together on wooden pallets at least 0·6 metres (2 feet) from a wall. Although rats hesitate to cross open spaces, the space behind should be inspected. Incoming goods must be inspected and segregated from packaging and existing stock.

Drains often provide an entrance to a building and should be maintained in good repair with all inlets, manholes, and rodding eyes properly sealed or covered. There are other vulnerable points such as broken air-gratings in walls, openings for pipe-work sometimes below ground, ill-fitting doors, worn thresholds, the gnawed bottoms and jambs of doors, and corrugation in the wall or roof. Structural harbours may occur below hollow floors, in hollow walls and partitions, in pipe ducts and casings, and less commonly in roof spaces above false ceilings.

Figure 66 illustrates remedies for some of the common defects mentioned above. It shows some of the means by which the passage of rodents from one part of a building to another (for example, from a subfloor space and the room above) may be prevented. It will be seen that to proof a building against rats, openings must be sealed by cement mortar, sheet metal, or mesh. Similar materials should reinforce vulnerable points such as door edges and junction points of walls and floors. Coarse wire wool should be embedded in the cement used to block holes in walls. Metal plates can be used in the base of ill-fitting doors.

Rat destruction

Rats are creatures of habit and are suspicious by nature; they avoid new objects. They may be trapped, but poisoning, when practised methodically is generally more effective.

A good measure of success has been achieved for some years by the use in suitable bait (e.g. oatmeal) of a material known as warfarin which after several doses, prevents the coagulation of blood and produces spontaneous haemorrhage. During the feeding period of 3 to 8 days before death, the rat appears to experience no pain or significant loss of appetite and no 'bait-shyness' develops. As the poisoned bait is acceptable immediately, no pre-baiting is carried out, but it must be replenished or renewed for a period up to 10 days or until feeding ceases. The proportion of warfarin used in the bait is small, normally giving a final concentration of 0·05 per cent, so that there is a large margin of safety in case of accidental ingestion by man or domestic animals. Also, as the poison is effective only after repeated doses, the danger to creatures other than rodents is remote. It is considered advisable, however, to lay the baits in containers or under cover in positions where the poison will be readily accessible to rodents only; thus the bait, approximately 85 g (3 oz) should be laid in established and currently used rat runs or where smears or droppings indicate rat activity. Liquid warfarin is also available. Before baits are laid it is necessary to carry out careful surveys of the area to determine the extent of the infestation, rat runs, and harbourages, and to estimate the number of baiting points required. Each point should be baited with 227–454 g (8–16 oz) of material; frequent inspections are necessary.

Populations of rats in various parts of the UK have become resistant to warfarin; resistance is reported in Denmark and in other parts of the world. The selective destruction of non-resistant strains by the continued use of an anticoagulant reduces the natural competition amongst the rats in a neighbourhood, and can lead to a less restricted reproduction and overflow of resistant rat colonies into wider areas.

When rats become resistant to warfarin it should be assumed that other anticoagulants such as chlorophacinone and coumatetralyl will also prove to be ineffective. In such areas, difenacoum or calciferol should be used. Acute poisons such as zinc phosphide are not recommended unless it is essential to obtain a quick kill — for example, on agricultural land where swine vesicular disease has occurred. Zinc phosphide tends to induce shyness to bait and it is subject to the Poisons Rules for purchase and use. It should be handled by a trained operator only and care must be taken to ensure that food and water for human consumption are not contaminated. It should not be placed in dwelling houses or in any establishment where food is prepared. Furthermore, zinc phosphide cannot be considered humane under the Animals (Cruel Poisons) Act, 1962, and its use will be discontinued. Difenacoum and calciferol are proving to be useful alternatives. The vasoconstrictor norbormide has not lived up to its early promise. It is a selective rat toxicant and expensive; it is not toxic to mice. Poisonous contact dusts containing lindane may be used; the rat picks up the dust on its feet and fur and the poison is ingested by the action of grooming, since the rat is clean in its personal habits.

Fluoroacetamide is a liquid rodenticide used in sewers only; it is subject to the Poisons Rules and may be used only by fully trained operators. It should not be used in agriculture, horticulture, the home, or any place where food is handled. Similarly sodium monofluoroacetate (1080) may be used in ships only.

Mice

The mouse appears to be less a creature of habit than the rat, less suspicious of unfamiliar objects, and less consistent in travel routes and established feeding points. Thus the individual trap may be quite useful, whilst wholesale extermination by poisoning may be more difficult with chronic poisons than for rats. Mice appear to be on the increase, due to the development of resistance to warfarin, which has given rise to the so-called 'super mouse'.

Of all traps, the spring break-back type is most used although it suffers from the disadvantage that once sprung it is of no further use until reset. A substantial number of traps set in a mouse-infested area over a period of several nights usually has a good effect. A treadle or plate is better for holding bait than a prong, because cereal bait such as oatmeal, dried fruit, nuts, or chocolate may be used and, contrary to belief, they are more attractive to mice than the traditional cheese. It is desirable to place the trap at right angles against the wall so that it will be sprung from either direction, and the treadle should be nearest the wall or vertical surface.

Baits containing 0·25 per cent of warfarin and in quantities of 28 g (1 oz) are also used with reasonable success against some mice, although resistance is developing. The hypothermic poison, alpha-chloralose, is now in use; it kills quickly and humanely. The metabolic rate is reduced and the mice die from heat loss. Alpha-chloralose is used indoors only where floor temperatures are less than about 18 °C (65 °F); at higher temperatures mice may recover from the stupefying condition. A contact dust based on lindane is also used for mice and a new rodenticide in bait form which contains 1 per cent calciferol is proving to be effective.

Food animals, especially pigs, and domestic pets have been known to eat dead rats and mice and themselves be killed by the poison used to destroy the rodents. Therefore, it is essential that the minimum effective dose of poison be used, so that it gives the minimum effective toxicity.

The Animals (Cruel Poisons) Act, 1962

Red squill, phosphorus, and strychnine have been prohibited in the UK by a regulation under the above-mentioned Act, and certain other poisons may eventually be prohibited in the same way. Thallium compounds are dangerous to human life besides being very inhumane. Permits for their use for rodent control must be obtained from the Ministry of Agriculture, Fisheries and Food; their use as insecticides was prohibited in 1967. Rodenticides may not induce apparent symptoms of pain or suffering.

Flies

House-flies, bluebottles, and greenbottles are still prevalent and potentially dangerous, although nowadays less significant as a result of two major changes in our way of life over the past half century. These changes are: firstly, the disappearance of horse-drawn traffic and the consequent diminution in the amount of horse manure, which is the fly's first choice of breeding ground; secondly, the water-carriage system of drainage in use throughout urban areas, which greatly reduces the risk of access by flies to infectious material.

In spite of these improvements there are often far too many flies about in their season, and any uncovered and undisturbed vegetable refuse, fish and meat offal can serve as breeding grounds. The chance that a fly may spread communicable diseases by infecting food is a possibility and there are circumstances where flies may gain access to infected material. For example, this may occur in earth closets or pail closets where they are still used; in creches and day nurseries where very young children are still at the 'pot' stage; at slaughter-houses and knackers' yards; and in places where there are stools of rats, mice, cats, dogs, and other animals which may excrete food-poisoning organisms. Food should be protected from contamination by flies.

Whilst the danger of fly-borne contamination of food must not be overemphasized, and certainly not to the extent of diverting the public mind from the really vital safeguards of personal cleanliness, temperature control, animal husbandry, and refrigeration, it would not be safe to ignore completely the possibility of contamination and all steps should be taken to deny flies access to food intended for human consumption.

Four methods of approach may be suggested, but since none of these is likely to be effective independently, a combination of all four should be practised. Control may be exercised (1) by the elimination of breeding places; (2) by measures to destroy the fly at some period of its life cycle; (3) by protecting foodstuffs, or better still by making food premises fly-proof as far as practicable; and (4) by obtaining practical advice from the environmental health officer or contractor responsible for pest control.

The elimination of breeding places is the responsibility of the food trader, but others have a duty in the matter too. Refuse is universal and the public should be aware of the sources of material used by flies for breeding, so that they too may play a part in its control. Likewise the local authorities should be vigilant in detecting and dealing with accumulations of offensive material. With modern methods of on-site disposal, refuse collection, and the availability of suitable refuse containers, there is no reason why waste which is attractive to flies should be left putrefying and uncovered anywhere.

Measures against flies, as with all pests, depend primarily on a knowledge of the life cycle and habits of the insects. Flies pass through four stages, the time spent in each depending upon the species and weather conditions, especially temperature. The stages are: (1) the egg, which is laid by the female in some material which provides food for (2) the larva or maggot which hatches from the egg after 8 hours to 3 days. The larva burrows into its food supply, eating vigorously until fully grown, which takes from 42 hours to as much as 6 to 8 weeks, when it seeks a dry and cool spot in which to pupate. The pupa (3) or chrysalis remains motionless in its cocoon for a period of 3 days to 4 weeks, when (4) the adult fly emerges.

The most vulnerable stage is the adult. Although there are many forms of fly trap and many insecticides, the most effective way to destroy adult flies is by sprays containing natural or synthetic pyrethrins, iodofenphos or fenitrothion, bromophos, or dichlorvos. Liberated as a fine mist, a spray of pyrethroids immediately knocks down flies on the wing. The other compounds sprayed on walls, ceilings, and hanging fixtures have a residual action, killing flies which come in contact with the surfaces over a period of weeks. Deposits of insecticides on food or on equipment in direct contact with food must be avoided because of possible toxic effects. Aerosol

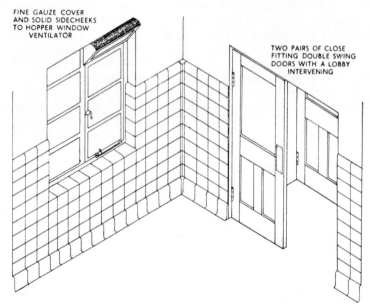

FINE GAUZE COVER
AND SOLID SIDECHEEKS
TO HOPPER WINDOW
VENTILATOR

TWO PAIRS OF CLOSE
FITTING DOUBLE SWING
DOORS WITH A LOBBY
INTERVENING

Fig. 67   Fly-proofing: protecting common places of entry

devices which release pyrethrins at regular intervals and resin strips or blocks impregnated with dichlorvos can be used to control flying insects. The manufacturers' instructions with regard to excess ventilation should be observed.

There is a danger that flying insects affected by insecticides may drop into food mixes and escape detection. An electrical device avoids this risk by using ultraviolet fluorescent tubes as a lure to attract flying insects on to an electrified grid; the insects are immediately killed and fall into a collecting tray.

Migrating maggots may be destroyed by boiling water or contact insecticides, and where manure bins are used there should be a larva trap either beneath or around them.

Thorough cleanliness and an absence of uncovered food scraps both inside and outside the kitchen will make the premises less attractive to flies. Whilst it is not always easy to fly-proof premises, at least all external doors should be self-closing, and windows and ventilators covered with fine gauze (Fig. 67). Flexible fly screens (stixcreens) using the velvo fastening system are suitable and effective for all types of window. It is said that a net, which moves in the wind, may be hung loosely over doorways to exclude flies for even though the mesh be quite large flies fear entanglement; hanging plastic strips are used widely on the Continent for the same purpose. In buildings which are not fully proofed against flies — and many are not — larders should be safeguarded and displayed foods covered; crockery and cutlery should be protected after they have been cleaned.

Cockroaches

Cockroaches most commonly found in Britain are the Oriental cockroach or 'black beetle', and the German cockroach or 'steam-fly' which is dark yellow-brown in colour. The two species are sometimes present in one building at the same time. They are both nocturnal in habit, occupy crevices in walls and floors, especially in warm places, and they are catholic in their choice of foodstuffs, with a notable taste for beer. Hitherto they have rarely been implicated as the proven vector in outbreaks of disease; nevertheless, salmonella organisms were isolated from cockroaches infesting a children's ward in an hospital where there had been an extensive outbreak of gastro-enteritis. The creatures are known to carry other pathogenic organisms, including dysentery and tubercle bacilli, the cholera vibrio, streptococci, and staphylococci.

Before commencing an insecticidal treatment it is important to determine the extent of the infestation by means of a thorough inspection carried out after dark when the premises are quiet. Cockroaches are readily repelled by some insecticides and for this reason treatment should start beyond the infested area so that insects attempting to disperse cannot avoid contact with the insecticide.

Cockroaches are susceptible to most classes of insecticide, including organochlorines (dieldrin, chlordane, and chlordecone), organophosphates (fenitrothion, diazinon, iodofenphos), carbamates (propoxur, bendiocarb, dioxacarb), and pyrethroids (pyrethrins, resmethrin). In choosing an insecticide it is important to remember that some strains of the German cockroach (*Blatella germanica*) possess a high level of resistance to organochlorine insecticides and treatments with these compounds against such strains are doomed to failure. Insecticides are formulated and can be applied in various ways to make optimal use of their properties.

For example, dieldrin formulations are extremely persistent, particularly the lacquers, and retain their effectiveness for many months. Chlordecone is formulated as a bait, whilst the organophosphorus and carbamate insecticides are usually applied as sprays. However, cockroaches will often avoid sprayed or lacquered surfaces and pest control officers sometimes use baits containing chlordecone gelor, a paste based on carbaryl. In hot, dry ducts and voids a light dusting of boric acid dust will remain active for long periods, whereas other insecticides may break down and become ineffective in a very short time. The selection of the appropriate insecticide and formulation, and its application so that maximum effect is achieved, requires skill and experience, and is often best entrusted to professional pest control personnel. This is particularly so if the more toxic insecticides are to be used, when great care must be taken to prevent the accidental contamination of food and food preparation surfaces during application.

Ants

Two kinds of ants occur in buildings — garden ants which nest outside but enter in search of food, and Pharoah's ants, which nest in warm buildings. Garden ants are not known to be of public health importance, but they may be a nuisance in kitchens and other food premises. Pharoah's ants have been shown to carry organisms of significance in human disease and they constitute a health hazard in hospitals by roaming from open wounds and soiled dressings to sterile equipment and dressings or to food.

Much can be done to avoid attracting ants, by careful observance of cleanliness, removal of waste food, even the smallest crumbs, and the repair of structural cracks and crevices in walls and floors which afford nesting sites to the ants. Garden ants can be destroyed by treating the nest with boiling water, paraffin, malathion, or lindane. Established infestations of Pharoah's ants indoors will involve many nests, each with several queens, over a large area. Control must be carried out systematically. The infested area should be determined by placing small pieces of fresh liver to attract the ants. Treatment should start beyond the infested area and consists of applying bands of insecticide at the wall/floor junction of rooms and corridors, around pipe exits, sinks, air vents, cracks, sills and on the under side of cupboard shelves in infested buildings.

Lacquers containing dieldrin or sprays of chlordane, dieldrin, propoxur, or fenitrothion are suitable. An alternative method of control is by poison bait using chlordecone mixed with an attractive base such as liver.

Wasps

Wasps can be a nuisance in food premises although there appears to be no evidence that they have been implicated in the spread of food infections. From mid-summer onwards the foraging workers are attracted by and feed on fruit juice, sugar, syrup, and other sweet substances, but in early summer they will also take insects, fresh and decaying meat or fish to feed the grubs in the nest. Wasps seem to find their way into premises which would normally be regarded as fly-proof although they cannot penetrate mesh as fine as 3 mm ($\frac{1}{8}$ inch).

The workers may range a mile or more from their nest and when an infestation occurs a search should be made for nests in the vicinity and steps taken to destroy them. This work is best carried out in the evening when most of the wasps are in the nest and drowsy, and it is a wise precaution for the operator to wear gauntlets and a bee-keeper's hood. When the nest is in a suitable position it can be soaked with a rapid 'knock-down' liquid insecticide and burnt or broken up. Equally quick results can be obtained for nests outside by pouring or syringing 1·4–2·8 decilitres ($\frac{1}{4}$ to $\frac{1}{2}$ pint) of carbon tetrachloride into the entrance hole of the nest and then plugging the hole, but this must be done with care and not in a confined space.

A rather slower process is to place BHC, lindane, or derris powder dust into the entrance hole so that the insecticide is carried into the nest by the insects. It is not necessary to remove the disused nest as reinfestation does not occur. Baits containing carbaryl in an attractive material may be placed around the perimeter of vulnerable premises.

Where it is impossible to find or to deal with the nests, attractive baits set outside the premises will often intercept and divert wasps from the building. The bait may be jam, syrup, molasses, fermenting fruit, or beer, mixed with enough water in a wide-mouthed jar to drown the insects. The addition of detergent (about a teaspoonful per 4·5 litres or 1 gallon) causes the trapped wasps to sink more quickly. The use of chlordane, applied by brush to alighting points, is also effective. The ultraviolet light traps, used for flies, are also effective against wasps inside buildings.

Other pests

Large numbers of insects and mites are of significance in the spoilage of stored food; they are often imported in the raw materials. Although they are severely destructive and may impart an odour to the infested food, they are not a hazard to health. Bread baked from mite-infested flour has an unpleasant musty smell. The grubs of many moth species produce large amounts of webbing which causes granular products to adhere and form sticky masses which may block elevators, augers, and screening equipment. Most of these spoilage insects can fly so that they can reach neglected areas where there are deposits of waste food, and thus they reach other areas of food plants.

Methods of control include careful surveillance of raw materials and even fumigation of incoming goods. The general hygiene and warehousing should be inspected frequently.

Birds

Birds are hazards in food establishments because their droppings may contaminate food with organisms of the salmonella group and other pathogens. Also they may be vectors of pests which spoil stored products. Screens on windows and doors would help to exclude birds, but this may be impracticable. The treatment of window sills with certain materials would help to deter the birds from alighting on strategic points.

Safety precautions

A wide range of formulations are available to obtain effective control of all insect pests found in Britain. They can be purchased under the various proprietary names as sprays, dusts, lacquers, or aerosols. The mixtures as purchased contain the correct percentage of insecticide and should be safe to use provided the manufacturers' instructions are followed. The use of any rodenticide or insecticide in food premises can present risks to those who apply the materials, to those who work or dwell in the buildings, and to those who consume the food that is present when the premises are treated.

Pesticides must always be applied strictly in accordance with the instructions given by the manufacturer. Before use the label should be read and the advice followed carefully.

Reputable manufacturers and contractors will clear their materials through the Safety Precautions Scheme. Free advice is available from most pest control authorities; a directory of members is available from the British Pest Control Association.

18

Legislation[1]

In England and Wales measures designed to prevent the spread of food-borne infections and to control outbreaks of food poisoning are contained in several Acts and their subordinate legislation.

With the reorganization of local government and of the National Health Service on 1 April, 1974 came changes in the way in which this legislation is administered and enforced. Former counties, boroughs, and urban and rural districts disappeared, although in some instances the names have been retained for reasons of sentiment. The operational unit of local government for matters concerned with the hygiene, safety, and fitness of food is now the 'district' except for Greater London which is divided into the City of London, the Temples, and the London boroughs. Where the term 'local authority' is used in this chapter it means the council of the district or similar unit. A council may appoint a 'proper officer' for a particular purpose in local government and persons holding these posts can be contacted through local health departments.

Some of the statutory functions formerly carried out by the medical officer of health are now the responsibility of a medically qualified 'proper officer', frequently referred to as the medical officer for environmental health, who is generally a community physician seconded to the local government district from the relevant health district of the National Health Service. Other statutory functions are dealt with by an environmental health officer acting in his own right as a 'proper officer' of local government. Efficient administration of the legislation covering public health and food safety requires good communication and co-operation between all persons concerned.

The Public Health (Infectious Diseases) Regulations, 1968 as amended 1969 and 1974 (SI 1968 No. 1366; SI 1969 No. 844; SI 1974 No. 274) apply specific sections of the Public Health Acts of

[1] Expert advice on legislation was provided by Dr H. E. Schefferle, Food and Dairy Officer, Scottish Office; the authors are grateful.

1936 and 1961 and the Health Services and Public Health Act, 1968 to various infectious diseases including diphtheria, scarlet fever, tuberculosis, typhoid and paratyphoid fevers, dysentery, viral hepatitis, and poliomyelitis. The Acts apply directly to cholera. The obligation to notify cases of these diseases now rests on medical practitioners who must notify the medical officer for environmental health (proper officer) of the local authority for the district in which the patient resides. Under the 1936 Act it is an offence for any person knowing he is suffering from such a disease to engage in any occupation where there is risk of spreading the disease. In a like manner cases of food poisoning or suspected food poisoning are required by the 1968 Act to be notified, this provision being previously contained in the Food and Drugs Act, 1955.

The medical officer for environmental health sends a weekly return of the number of cases of each of these diseases, and cases and suspected cases of food poisoning to the Registrar General and Area Health Authority. A three-monthly return is also required which allows time for corrections of diagnosis. In addition the Chief Medical Officer to the Department of Health and Social Security or Welsh Office and the Area Health Authority must immediately be informed of any case of cholera or serious outbreak of any of the other diseases including food poisoning.

When it is considered, from the available information, that measures are required to prevent the spread of infectious diseases and food poisoning, the public health legislation gives a local authority power to request any person concerned to discontinue his work. With typhoid, paratyphoid, and other salmonella infections, dysentery, and staphylococcal infections likely to cause food poisoning both cases and carriers may be requested to discontinue and refrain from engaging in any occupation while there is a risk of causing infection. The local authority has power to ask for the medical examination of any person engaged in a food trade or business who is suspected of being such a carrier. Persons suffering from other forms of food poisoning which may have been caused by an infection may likewise be excluded from working with food or drink. There is provision for the payment of compensation. Similar provisions relating specifically to milk are contained in the Milk and Dairies (General) Regulations, 1959.

Certain Regulations made under the Food and Drugs Act, 1955 also contain measures aimed at preventing the spread of food-borne infectious diseases and food poisoning by taking account of the place where a person is employed. Any person engaged in the handling of food or meat in food premises or in a slaughterhouse who becomes aware that he is suffering from, or is a carrier of, typhoid, paratyphoid, or any other salmonella infection, or dysentery, or any staphylococcal infection likely to cause food poisoning, must notify his employer who must notify the local authority for that district. Similar notification is required when a person with access to milk or equipment used for milk becomes aware that he or any member of his household is suffering from any notifiable disease (Food Hygiene (General) Regulations, 1970; Slaughterhouse (Hygiene) Regulations, 1977; Milk and Dairies (General) Regulations, 1959).

Other legislative controls are applied to the production, preparation, manufacture, and sale of food in order to combat existing or potential microbiological hazards from the aspect of both safety and freshness or keeping quality. These measures are contained in the Food and Drugs Act, 1955 and in Regulations made under this Act an outline of which follows. The safety of all persons working in food businesses is covered by the Health and Safety at Work etc. Act, 1974.

The Food and Drugs Act, 1955

This Act seeks to provide consumers with a pure and wholesome food supply and provides for the punishment of persons found guilty of offences under the Act.

It is prohibited to sell food for human consumption which:

(1) has been made injurious by addition or subtraction of substances or by any treatment;
(2) is not of the nature, substance, or quality (e.g. of a different kind, adulterated, or inferior food);
(3) has false or misleading labelling or advertisement;
(4) is unfit (e.g. decomposed or contaminated food).

The Act enables an authorized officer of a local authority to examine any food, including materials in transit under certain conditions, intended for human consumption and to take samples for analysis or for bacteriological or other examination. When it is suspected that food is likely to cause food poisoning its further use for human consumption may be prohibited while a sample is being examined.

Food considered to be unfit may be seized and brought to the attention of a Justice of the Peace who, if satisfied that the food is unfit, will condemn it and order its destruction or disposal so that it cannot be used for human consumption. Food likely to cause food poisoning comes within the category of unfit food.

Further restrictions

It is prohibited to sell for human consumption any meat from knackers' yards, or the milk from cows suffering from certain diseases, including tuberculosis, and any infection of the udder or the teats which is likely to convey disease.

There is restriction on the use of premises for certain purposes. Dairies, and premises used for the manufacture of ice-cream, sausages or for the preservation of food may only be used for these purposes if they are acceptable as regards hygiene and are registered by the local authority. In a similar way the Slaughterhouses Act, 1974 provides for the licensing of private slaughterhouses.

Powers under the act

The Act gives powers to Ministers (the Minister of Agriculture, Fisheries and Food, and the Secretary of State for Social Services) to make regulations for securing sanitary and clean conditions in connection with the importation, preparation, transport, storage, packaging, and sale of food, other than milk, for human consumption. Regulations made include those dealing with hygiene in food premises, slaughterhouses, and poultry slaughterhouses, and those covering meat inspection, meat 'sterilization', shell-fish, and imported food. A local authority may make by-laws relating to the hygiene of the handling, wrapping, and delivery of food and the sale of food in the open air; if by-laws conflict with regulations made by Ministers, the regulations prevail.

Ministers may make regulations, when it is in the interests of public health or for the protection of the public, for requiring or regulating a process or treatment used in the preparation of food intended for human consumption. The Regulations dealing with the heat treatment of ice-cream and liquid egg, foods particularly liable to contamination at source, come in this category as do also the Regulations controlling the irradiation of food.

Regulations may also be made to control the labelling and description of food, other than milk for which there are special provisions, and this can be of interest to consumers, e.g. cream which has not been heat treated must be labelled 'Untreated'.

Ministers may make regulations with regard to milk similar to those pertaining to food. There are General Regulations relating to milk and dairies, particularly hygiene, and legislation has also been made to cover the colour coding of milk bottle caps and the treatment of skimmed and semi-skimmed milk. In addition, regulations may be made for prescribing 'special designations' to milk and to grant licences permitting their use. Regulations have been made to cover the use of the special designations 'Untreated', 'Pasteurized', 'Sterilized', and 'Ultra Heat Treated'. The use of these special designations for retail sales was at first only obligatory, with certain exceptions, in specified areas detailed in orders made by Ministers. By 1962, the specification of the whole of England and Wales had been virtually completed.

The Food and Drugs (Control of Food Premises) Act, 1976

The Act amends the Food and Drugs Act, 1955 by prohibiting the preparation, storage, and sale of food in certain circumstances. Where a person has been convicted of an offence under Regulations made under section 13 of the Food and Drugs Act, 1955 and the offence relates to a food business where food is exposed to the risk of contamination, a 'closure order' may be applied to the premises concerned if it is considered that the unsatisfactory conditions are likely to continue and be a danger to health. In addition an 'emergency order' may be made in circumstances where there is imminent risk of danger to health and this would prohibit the use of the premises pending the outcome of legal proceedings under the Regulations as a result of which a closure order might operate.

Premises covered by the Act include stalls and there is power to make regulations to cover corresponding situations on ships.

Model by-laws

Model by-laws on various hygienic measures applicable to food indicate the form of clause which would be approved by the Secretary of State for Social Services for adoption by local authorities; originally they were made by many councils under the earlier Food and Drugs Act, 1938. Such by-laws continue in force and authorities may still make them. However the Food Hygiene Regulations have to a large extent taken their place administratively, if for no other reason than that the penalties for contravention are greater under the Regulations. It is not proposed, therefore, to consider the details of the requirements contained in by-laws.

The Food Hygiene (General) Regulations 1970 (SI 1970 No. 1172)

These Regulations aim to secure a standard of construction and equipment in food premises and in home-going and moored ships where food is handled, and of conduct of food handlers, to protect foodstuffs against contamination. The requirements may be outlined as follows:

(1) *Premises*

No food business may be carried on at insanitary premises where the condition, situation, and construction is such that food may be contaminated. The premises must be well lit and ventilated, clean, in good repair, and free from accumulation of refuse. There must be facilities for the storage of waste material. Food rooms may not be used as sleeping places and food rooms which communicate directly with a sleeping place or a room containing a sanitary convenience may not be used for the handling of open food. Sanitary conveniences must not be located in a food room. Fresh air inlets of ventilation pipes connected with the soil drainage system may not be situated in a food room and inlets into such a system in such rooms must be trapped. Accommodation must be provided for the outdoor clothing of food handlers.

(2) *Washing and sanitary facilities*

A clean and wholesome water supply must be available and there must be facilities for washing food and equipment. With certain exceptions such as the washing of fish, fruit, or vegetables, or the special washing of drinking vessels where only cold water is required, sinks must be provided with both hot and cold (or blended) water. There must be a similar supply of water to wash-hand-basins which must be provided in readily accessible positions. The basins must not be used for any purpose other than for the use of food handlers for hand washing, and they must be provided with a supply of soap or other suitable detergent, nail brushes, and clean towels or other suitable drying facilities.

Sanitary conveniences must be kept clean and in good working order; rooms containing them must be well lit and ventilated and have notices displayed requesting users to wash their hands.

(3) *Equipment*

Articles or equipment which may come into contact with food must be kept clean and in good repair. Their construction must allow them to be thoroughly cleaned. They must be, as far as possible, non-absorbent and not liable to cause contamination of food.

(4) *Food handlers*

Food handlers must protect food from the risk of contamination. Some specific aspects included are contamination from surroundings, particularly when food is displayed for sale, and contamination from contact with unfit food or unsuitable wrapping materials. When carried in a container food must be protected from contamination from other articles, live animals, or live poultry. In the open, food must not be placed within 450 mm (18 inches) of the ground unless adequately protected.

Persons handling food must keep themselves and clothing clean, keep open cuts and sores covered with a waterproof dressing, and refrain from spitting or smoking. Persons handling open food must wear clean and washable overclothing except in specified cases.

A supply of first-aid materials, including waterproof dressings, must be kept in an accessible place on food premises.

(5) Catering practice

Where food premises are used for catering purposes, i.e. for the supply of food for immediate consumption, certain foods must be kept at temperatures either below 10 °C (50 °F) or at not less than 62·8 °C (145 °F). These foods include meat, fish, gravy, and imitation cream, foodstuffs prepared from or containing any of these substances or egg products, including dried or frozen whole egg, yolk, or albumen, or milk including separated or skimmed, dried, or condensed milk, and cream.

This requirement does not, however, apply to food actually exposed for sale, or to: (a) bread, biscuits, cake, or pastry in which egg or milk is used only prior to baking, (b) chocolate or sugar confectionery, (c) ice-cream to which Regulations requiring heat treatment apply, (d) food which is canned, bottled, or otherwise preserved in an effectively closed container which remains unopened, (e) butter, margarine, lard, shortening, cooking fats, or beef suet, (f) cheese, uncooked bacon, uncooked ham, dry pasta, dry pudding mixes, dry soup mixes, or dry mixes for the preparation of beverages, or (g) unskinned rabbits or hares or unplucked game or poultry.

Most of the foods which are exempt from temperature control are those which will not support the growth of micro-organisms because of factors such as low moisture content, high concentration of sugar, fat or salt, or because they are to be subsequently prepared and cooked.

A notable omission from the Regulations concerns the storage of perishable foods exposed for sale. Ideally, cooked meatstuffs and fresh sausages, for example, should not be kept in food premises unless there are facilities to maintain them at a temperature of about 4 °C (39 °F), i.e. cold storage should be provided for display of food in windows and elsewhere in shops, and for food in catering establishments including open buffets.

It is a common practice in certain retail shops whose main business is not concerned with catering to sell warmed pies from a heated display cabinet. Pies, pasties, and spit-roasted chickens also may be kept warm under conditions which would not satisfy requirements of the Regulations as regards safe temperatures for storage of meat products.

In connection with personal hygiene and cross-contamination there should be included in the Regulations a requirement to indicate to food handlers the risk to themselves of handling raw meat, offal, and poultry and that their hands should be washed after contact with these products both for their own protection and to prevent spread of contamination to cooked foods. Although legal terms such as 'risk of contamination', 'suitable and efficient', 'adequate and effective' appear to be vague, they are intended to allow action in differing circumstances.

(6) *Agricultural activities*

The business of packing or storing eggs, fruit, and vegetables on farm premises is made subject to certain requirements.

The Food Hygiene (Docks, Carriers, etc.) Regulations, 1960 (SI 1960 No. 1602)

These Regulations prescribe requirements to secure the hygienic handling of food at docks, warehouses, cold stores, certain food stores and also premises used by goods carriers.

The Food Hygiene (Markets, Stalls and Delivery Vehicles) Regulations, 1966 as amended 1966 (SI 1966 No. 791; SI 1966 No. 1487)

These prescribe food hygiene requirements for markets, stalls including vehicles used as stalls and coin-operated automatic vending machines, and delivery vehicles; they are similar to those required for fixed premises and ships contained in the Food Hygiene (General) Regulations, 1970. Certificates of exemption from certain of the requirements may be granted by a local authority.

Delivery vehicles as well as stalls must bear the owner's name and address, and both must identify any other place where they are normally kept or garaged. There are specific requirements relating to the transport of meat.

The Slaughterhouses (Hygiene) Regulations, 1977 (SI 1977 No. 1805)

These new Regulations, which came into operation in May, 1978 replacing the 1958 legislation, are designed to improve further the hygienic production and handling of meat from cattle, swine, sheep, horses, and goats.

Operators of slaughterhouses and other persons must comply with requirements for construction, layout, ventilation, lighting, drainage, water supply, equipment, hygienic operation, and personal hygiene.

Suitable lairage must be provided and because infection rate increases when animals are kept in lairs for 1 or 2 weeks, the waiting period is limited to 72 hours except with the consent of an authorized officer. Lairs must be kept clean, a requirement also of the Slaughter of Animals (Prevention of Cruelty) Regulations, 1958 (SI 1958 No. 2166), and it is hoped that this will ensure the disinfection of lairs prior to the reception of each new group of animals. Animals known or suspected to be diseased must be kept isolated and slaughtered apart from other animals.

Accommodation must be provided for emptying stomachs and intestines and there must be separate accommodation for the retention, locked, of meat rejected as unfit for human consumption. Hands must not be used for stirring blood intended for human consumption; carcasses may not be inflated in any manner and the use of wiping cloths in the dressing of carcasses, including offal, is prohibited. Knives and other implements which come into contact with meat must be cleaned and disinfected in water at a temperature of not less than 82 °C (179·6 °F) frequently during each working day and after contact with meat known or suspected to be diseased; handles of implements and cutting or chopping surfaces may not be made of wood.

Certain provisions apply only to new slaughterhouses but in 1980, existing premises also must meet more stringent requirements. These include: taps for washing hands must not be hand operable; bleeding and dressing processes must not be carried out on the floor; clean operations must be separated from those liable to cause contamination; separate accommodation must be provided for the preparation of casings and tripe and also for the storage of hides and skins; and refrigerated storage will be required for meat held for longer than 48 hours. In new premises only there must be facilities for cleaning and disinfecting livestock vehicles.

The Poultry Meat (Hygiene) Regulations, 1976 (SI 1976 No. 1209)

These Regulations implement in national legislation the provisions of the European Economic Community's Council Directives No. 71/118/EEC and No. 75/431/EEC which deal with health problems affecting trade in fresh poultry meat.

The Regulations apply to poultry meat derived from domestic

fowls, turkeys, guinea fowls, ducks, and geese. They prescribe conditions which must be satisfied for the production, cutting-up, packaging, storage, and transport of poultry meat intended for sale for human consumption down to, but excluding, retail sale in a shop. There must be ante- and post-mortem inspection of birds with certain exceptions.

Premises used for the slaughter and cutting-up of poultry must be licensed by the local authority and comply with requirements for structure, ventilation, lighting, drainage, water supply, equipment, and hygienic operation. There must be separate areas for ante-mortem inspection, stunning, scalding, plucking, and evisceration. Accommodation at slaughterhouses must be provided for diseased poultry; poultry meat rejected as unfit for human consumption must be kept separate.

No person may handle poultry meat if suffering or suspected to be suffering from typhoid, paratyphoid or any other salmonella infection, dysentery, infectious hepatitis, scarlet fever, infectious tuberculosis or an infectious skin disease; symptomless excretors are included.

In England and Wales certain temporary exemptions have been granted to occupiers of some slaughterhouses and cutting premises from the requirements of the Regulations although all the terms of the EEC Directives apply to production for export from the United Kingdom to other Member States. Some of the specific requirements of the Regulations are: taps for washing hands must not be hand operable; water at 82 °C (179·6 °F) must be supplied to disinfect implements; implements and equipment which come into contact with poultry meat must be made of an impervious material other than wood; and poultry meat in store or during transport must be maintained at a temperature of not more than 4 °C (39·2 °F). Eventually all poultry meat will bear a health marking indicating the country of origin and the approval number of the slaughterhouse or cutting premises.

Originally it was intended that the use of immersion chilling ('spin chilling') of poultry be prohibited, but all chilling methods for poultry are being reconsidered. The sale of uneviscerated plucked birds, i.e. 'New York dressed', will be permitted at least until 1981.

Certain sales of poultry meat by those who keep live poultry are excluded from many of the requirements applicable to slaughterhouses and cutting premises.

The Meat Inspection Regulations, 1963 as amended 1966 (SI 1963 No. 1229; SI 1966 No. 915)

These require that, except where the Regulations permit, carcasses of animals slaughtered for sale for human consumption must not be removed from the place of slaughter until they have been inspected and, if passed as fit, until they have been 'marked' in the manner prescribed.

The Meat (Sterilization) Regulations, 1969 (SI 1969 No. 871)

These Regulations require all knacker meat and meat (other than the meat of a rabbit or hare) which is imported for purposes other than human consumption, as well as all butchers' meat or imported meat which in either case is unfit for human consumption, to be 'sterilized' before entering the chain of distribution. Transport of such meat in the untreated state must in most cases be under locked conditions.

Certain establishments such as zoos may obtain such meat untreated but it must be transported in locked containers or vehicles; other exemptions are listed in the Regulations.

'Sterilized' means treated by boiling or by steam under pressure until every piece of meat is cooked throughout; or dry-rendered, digested, or solvent-processed into technical tallow, greases, glues, feeding meals, or fertilizers.

The Public Health (Shell-Fish) Regulations, 1934 as amended 1948 (SR&O 1934 No. 1342; SI 1948 No. 1120)

These empower a local authority to prohibit the sale for human consumption of shell-fish, including mussels and cockles as well as oysters, from a laying within a district known to have produced shell-fish which have caused illness or are likely to be dangerous to public health, unless subjected to an approved process of cleansing or disinfection by steam.

The Imported Food Regulations, 1968 as amended 1973 (SI 1968 No. 97; SI 1973 No. 1351)

These contain measures for the protection of public health in relation to imported food. They also implement requirements contained in certain Directives of the European Economic Community. Any food commonly used for human consumption if imported for sale is presumed, unless proved otherwise, to have been imported for sale for human consumption; the same applies to ingredients used in the preparation of food.

The enforcement of these Regulations comes within the responsibility of the port health or local authority at the point of entry but examination may be deferred until the food reaches its final destination in which case the port health or local authority must inform the receiving authority which then assumes responsibility. This particularly applies to the examination of food carried in bulk in sealed containers.

It is an offence to import food which has been rendered injurious to health, is unfit for human consumption, or is unsound or unwholesome. Samples of food may be taken for analysis and where special examination is necessary the food may be held for periods up to 6 days pending results of the examination.

With certain exceptions meat and meat products cannot be imported without an official certificate from the country of origin which is recognized by the Minister of Agriculture, Fisheries and Food and guarantees that the meat or meat product has been prepared in accordance with satisfactory standards of hygiene.

The amended Regulations require specified kinds of meat from any country of the EEC, the Channel Islands, and the Isle of Man to be accompanied also by a health certificate, and poultry meat from all sources by both an official certificate and a health certificate.

Quite apart from control by means of regulations made under the Food and Drugs Act, 1955, and as a safeguard against the introduction of animal diseases, the importation of meat and meat products, and poultry meat, with certain exceptions, is also subject to licensing; this is required by the Importation of Carcases and Animals Products Order, 1972 as amended 1976 (SI 1972 No. 287; SI 1976 No. 708) and the Poultry Carcases (Landing) Order, 1971 (SI 1971 No. 1593) — both made under the Diseases of Animals Act, 1950.

The Ice-Cream (Heat Treatment, etc) Regulations, 1959 as amended 1963 (SI 1959 No. 734; SI 1963 No. 1083)

These Regulations require mixtures intended for the manufacture of ice-cream, other than those of a pH of 4·5 or less used in the manufacture of water ices or similar frozen confection, to be subjected to one of the following heat treatments of pasteurization or 'sterilization':

(1) pasteurization at a temperature of 65·6 °C (150 °F) for 30 minutes, or 71·1 °C (160 °F) for 10 minutes, or 79·4 °C (175 °F) for 15 seconds;

(2) 'sterilization' at a temperature of 148·8 °C (300 °F) for 2 seconds.

Mixtures must not be kept for more than 1 hour at a temperature higher than 7·2 °C (45 °F) before heat treatment.

After pasteurization or 'sterilization' the temperature must be reduced to not more than 7·2 °C (45 °F) within 1½ hours and so kept until frozen. The cooling requirement need not apply to a mix held at 148·8 °C for 2 seconds which is transferred aseptically into sterile airtight containers which remain unopened until required for freezing; once opened the temperature must be reduced to 7·2 °C (45 °F) and so kept until frozen.

Complete cold mixes which during manufacture have been subjected to comparable heat treatment, evaporated, dried, and put into airtight containers, need not be given a further heat treatment when mixed with water before manufacture into ice-cream; they must, however, be frozen within 1 hour of reconstitution.

After being frozen, all ice-cream must be stored at a temperature not exceeding −2·2 °C (28 °F); if the temperature rises above this level during storage the mix must again be heat treated, cooled, and frozen.

Apparatus used for the manufacture of ice-cream must have means of recording that heat treatment and cooling requirements have been met. For short time methods (2 and 15 seconds) there must be an automatic mechanism to divert the flow if the required temperature is not reached or, as an alternative in the case of 'sterilization', a device to stop the apparatus.

The amended Regulations add sugar to the list of materials which may be added to pasteurized and 'sterilized' complete cold mixes without further heat treatment being necessary.

The Liquid Egg (Pasteurization) Regulations, 1963 (SI 1963 No. 1503)

These prohibit the use as an ingredient in the preparation of food of liquid egg, meaning a mixture of yolk and albumen, which has not been pasteurized. The requirement does not apply to shell eggs broken on the premises where the food is prepared and either used at once or kept at a temperature not exceeding 10 °C (50 °F) and used within 24 hours.

The pasteurization treatment requires the liquid egg to be held at a temperature not lower than 64·4 °C (148 °F) for at least $2\frac{1}{2}$ minutes followed by immediate cooling to below 3·3 °C (38 °F). Automatic flow diversion and means of recording heat treatment and cooling must be supplied.

The Regulations prescribe the method of sampling and examination by the alpha-amylase test which the treated egg must satisfy.

The Food (Control of Irradiation) Regulations, 1967 as amended 1972 (SI 1967 No. 385; SI 1972 No. 205)

These prohibit the application of ionizing radiation to food, an exception being made in the case of low levels of radiation associated with the use of certain nucleonic measuring instruments. The amended Regulations permit the use of ionizing radiation, under certain conditions, of food intended for consumption by medical patients who require a sterile diet as part of their treatment.

The Milk and Dairies (General) Regulations, 1959 (SI 1959 No. 277)

These provide for the registration of milk producers, distributors, and their premises.

There is provision for the veterinary inspection of cattle and the procedure to be used where milk is infected or liable to be infected with disease organisms communicable to man. When there is evidence that milk has been responsible for disease or food poisoning a notice can be given requiring its treatment before consumption so that it is safe.

Buildings used during the handling and processing and for storage of milk must be constructed and maintained in such condition that there is no risk of contamination; premises must be provided with a satisfactory water supply. Care must be taken throughout milking and subsequent handling, processing, and storage to prevent contamination of the milk.

At the dairy farm the hands of the milker and the flanks, tail, udder, and teats of all cows must be cleaned before milking and the foremilk inspected and discarded. The milk must be cooled to a temperature of 10 °C (50 °F) or not more than 2·8 °C (5 °F) above the temperature of the water supply if the temperature of that supply is 7·2 °C (45 °F) or above. Where a system of refrigerated bulk storage of milk is being used this temperature requirement will automatically be met.

All vessels and equipment which come into contact with milk must be kept clean and before use must either be scalded with boiling water or steam, or be treated with an approved chemical agent; this requirement, however, does not apply to glass bottles effectively cleansed in a bottle-washing machine. Cartons and other non-returnable containers must be protected from contamination.

A list of approved chemical agents is published by the Ministry of Agriculture, Fisheries and Food (HMSO).

The Milk (Special Designation) Regulations, 1977 (SI 1977 No. 1033)

These specify conditions for the granting of licences to milk producers and dealers allowing the use of the special designations

'Untreated', 'Pasteurized', 'Sterilized' and 'Ultra Heat Treated' (UHT).

'Untreated' milk must come from a herd accredited as free from brucellosis; it has undergone no heat treatment. For 'Pasteurized' milk the raw milk must either be heated to a temperature of between 62·8 °C (145 °F) and 65·6 °C (150 °F) and held at this temperature for a period of at least 30 minutes, or heated to a temperature of not less than 71·7 °C (161 °F) for at least 15 seconds. After heat treatment the milk must be immediately cooled to a temperature of not more than 10 °C (50 °F) and put into bottles or other appropriate containers. Both designations must comply with the prescribed methylene blue test and in addition 'Pasteurized' milk must satisfy the phosphatase test.

'Sterilized' milk must be filtered or clarified, homogenized, and heated to a temperature of not less than 100 °C (212 °F) either in bottles or by a continuous-flow method followed by aseptic filling into bottles. The heating time must be sufficient for the product to comply with the prescribed turbidity test and the bottles must be sealed so that they are airtight. 'Ultra Heat Treated' milk must be heated to a temperature of not less than 132·2 °C (270 °F) for not less than 1 second. Sterile containers must be filled aseptically and sealed so that they are airtight. This designation of milk, and also 'Sterilized' milk where heating is followed by aseptic filling into bottles, must satisfy a bacterial colony count of less than 1000 per millilitre after preliminary incubation of a sample.

The production of 'UHT' milk by the direct application of steam is permitted provided the steam is free of impurities and the process is controlled so that the contents of fat and solids not fat are the same after treatment as before it. The process is not considered as one of adulteration of milk by the addition of water and is authorized by the Food and Drugs (Milk) Act, 1970.

The heat treatment and cooling of milk must be recorded. An automatic device to divert the flow of milk which has not been raised to the required temperature must be provided except where pasteurization is by the low temperature method, or 'sterilization' is in bottles.

The Milk and Dairies (Semi-skimmed and Skimmed Milk) (Heat Treatment and Labelling) Regulations, 1973 (SI 1973 No. 1064)

These require that semi-skimmed and skimmed milk, as defined, must be heat treated by pasteurization, 'sterilization', or by the ultra high temperature method. The conditions of heat treatment and tests with which the various types must comply are the same as those applied to whole milk subjected to the same processes. There is, however, no provision at present for ultra heat treatment by the direct application of steam.

The Milk and Dairies (Milk Bottle Caps) (Colour) Regulations, 1976 (SI 1976 No. 2186)

These Regulations prescribe the colours of caps and lettering which must be used in labelling milk of specified descriptions sold in bottles sealed with an aluminium foil cap. 'Untreated' milk has a green cap which in certain circumstances has a single gold stripe. 'Pasteurized' milk has a silver cap but, if in addition it is homogenized, the cap is red and if from Channel Islands or similar breeds of cows the cap is gold. Provision is also made for pasteurized Kosher and Kedassia milk.

Newer forms of packaging have made it possible to market long life milks in bottles with aluminium foil caps and these may be distinguished by a blue cap for 'Sterilized' and a pink cap for 'Ultra Heat Treated' milk.

Cream

Cream is included in the definition of milk in the Milk and Dairies (General) Regulations, 1959 and its provisions relating to registration and hygiene therefore apply to cream. A recent amendment to these Regulations (SI 1977 No. 171) exempts cream imported in bottles or cartons from the requirement that it be put into these containers on registered premises. The Milk (Special Designation) Regulations, 1977 which deal with licensing and the statutory tests applicable to milk of various designations do not, however, apply to cream.

A Government Code of Hygienic Practice for Cream, revised 1972, deals with heat treatment methods, requirements for plant and equipment, personal hygiene and laboratory control. As a result of a survey and suggestions by a working party of the Public Health Laboratory Service during which the effectiveness of the Code of Practice was considered, the Ministry of Agriculture, Fisheries and Food recommended (Circular FSH 2/71, HMSO, 1971) that a methylene blue test be used as a screening or advisory test for cream by local authorities. The test is not a statutory one but, as an advisory test, should help to indicate unsatisfactory production methods to which more attention could be given.

For the information of consumers, it is a requirement of the Cream Regulations, 1970 (SI 1970 No. 752), which deal with the composition of cream, that, except for clotted cream, one of the following terms must appear on the label, namely, 'Untreated', 'Pasteurized', 'Sterilized', or 'Ultra heat treated'.

The Diseases of Animals (Waste Food) Order, 1973 (SI 1973 No. 1936)

Measures designed to prevent the spread of disease to animals may also have a secondary effect in reducing disease in man. This Order, made under the Diseases of Animals Act, 1950, is aimed at ensuring that precautions are taken to prevent the spread of disease to livestock and poultry from the use of waste food, and swill as a feeding stuff.

Waste food is defined as meat, bones, blood, offal, or other part of the carcass of livestock or poultry, or products derived from these, and also hatchery waste, eggs, or eggshells. It also includes kitchen waste which contains or has been in contact with any of these materials. Meal manufactured from protein originating from livestock or poultry is, however, excluded.

Waste food must not be fed to livestock or poultry unless it has been processed at premises, licensed for the purpose by the Minister of Agriculture, Fisheries and Food, by holding it for at least 60 minutes at a temperature of not less than 100 °C (212 °F) or given an equivalent authorized treatment. Care must be taken to ensure that processed waste and other feeding stuffs do not become contaminated from untreated waste; if this does occur the material must be reprocessed.

If waste food is brought to premises for use there as a feeding stuff it must already have been processed or, if not, the person concerned must hold a licence authorizing the processing at the premises. There is an exception for the need to hold a licence where the waste food originates solely from the household on the premises but it must still undergo processing. Another type of licence is required for premises where unprocessed waste food is held prior to removal to processing premises.

Road vehicles used for conveying unprocessed waste food must be covered and constructed so that spillage, including drips, can be prevented; after use for this purpose they must be thoroughly cleaned and disinfected. Processed and unprocessed waste food must not be conveyed in the same vehicle, and neither type may be carried in a vehicle being used for the transport of livestock, poultry, or other feeding stuffs.

No waste food, whether processed or not, originating from the stores of a ship, aircraft, hovercraft, road, or other vehicle and brought into Great Britain, may be used for feeding to any animal or bird.

The Zoonoses Order, 1975 (SI 1975 No. 1030)

This is the first Order of its kind to be made under the Agriculture (Miscellaneous Provisions) Act, 1972 and makes a number of provisions dealing with zoonoses, i.e. diseases which man can contract from animals or birds. Its purpose is to give greater power to act where there is a risk to human health as a result of infection in animals or birds. It was one of the recommendations of the Joint Committee on the Use of Antibiotics in Animal Husbandry and Veterinary Medicine (Swann Report, Cmnd 4190, HMSO, 1969) that a veterinary officer should be given powers to deal with infections in animals that threaten human health.

The Order designates organisms of the genera *Salmonella* and *Brucella* and applies certain provisions of the Diseases of Animals Act, 1950 to the presence of these organisms in an animal or bird. It is anticipated that in practice the Order will be of more significance for salmonella than brucella infections because of the systematic eradication scheme for brucellosis which is already in operation.

Restrictions on movement and isolation, if necessary, of infected animals and birds may be made and there is power to require the disinfection of infected places, vehicles, and associated things. Persons who know or suspect the presence, as a result of isolation, of designated organisms in live or dead animals or birds of certain species, whether or not there are clinical symptoms, or from materials associated with them, are required to notify the Ministry of Agriculture, Fisheries and Food. It is not intended that the reporting procedure should extend to foods where it is no longer possible to identify that food with any particular individual or group of animals or birds and their source; neither is it intended that the Order be used for dealing with infected food or milk for which there is already provision to act in the Food and Drugs Act, 1955 and in the Milk and Dairies (General) Regulations, 1959.

Recent developments and additional needs

Legislation cannot be introduced in advance of the results of informed opinion in technical investigation and, although there are instances of control being rapidly applied to new and undesirable practices, e.g. the Meat (Treatment) Regulations, 1964 (SI 1964 No. 19) — which prohibit the use of certain additives to meat — measures for the prevention of bacteriological food poisoning have been slow to come. Dried egg was implicated as a vehicle of infection in 1940 and liquid whole egg in 1955, yet the pasteurization of this product was not made compulsory until 1963. The delay was due partly to industrial and commercial objections and partly to difficulties in perfecting the alpha-amylase test as a control means to check the efficiency of pasteurization at the required temperature and time.

The widest implications of the failure to maintain a disease-free animal population are perhaps insufficiently appreciated. Although there has been success in the eradication of tuberculosis from dairy cattle, and measures can be readily instituted to contain outbreaks of animal diseases which are notifiable, there is still a substantial reservoir, for example, of salmonellae in farm animals including cattle, pigs, and poultry. The Zoonoses Order, 1975 now gives veterinary officers of the Ministry of Agriculture, Fisheries and Food more power to act where salmonella infection or the presence of salmonellae in those animals commonly consumed by man, has been reported. This will mean that investigation of cases in animals and poultry can be carried out and emergency measures, to safeguard human health, taken if necessary. Co-operation between the veterinary service, medical officers for environmental health, chief environmental health officers, and the Public Health Laboratory Service, by the setting up of liaison groups, should help to improve knowledge of the incidence and distribution of serotypes of salmonellae in animals, birds, and in man. This information may lead to a better understanding of how and under what conditions infection is acquired and spread in animals and birds, and under what circumstances meat, poultry, and other birds are likely to become contaminated to such an extent as to present a definite health risk to the consumer. Increased knowledge will, it is hoped, also in time lead to the introduction of better control measures for dealing with salmonellosis in animals and man.

One serious impediment to the establishment of salmonella-free stock has been the persistent use of contaminated feeding stuffs. The Diseases of Animals (Waste Food) Order, 1973 which replaced the earlier 1957 Order, gives an increased measure of control over waste food intended for feeding to livestock and poultry but does not cover meals containing protein intended for use in animal feeding. Similarly the Meat (Sterilization) Regulations, 1969 provide control only over meat which is unfit or not intended for human consumption, or has originated from knackers' yards.

It is intended to use the powers contained in the Diseases of Animals Act, 1950 to make an order covering the control of protein meals. The purpose of the proposed Protein Processing Order will be to ensure that any material of animal, bird, or fish origin intended to be used or incorporated into a feeding stuff intended for consumption by livestock or poultry is processed at licensed premises. The processing will need to ensure that organisms which can infect livestock and poultry, including salmonellae, are destroyed and that recontamination at the processing premises does not occur.

At present protein meals and feeding stuffs containing them are subject to control under the Fertilizers and Feeding Stuffs Regulations, 1973 as amended 1976 and 1977 (SI 1973 No. 1521; SI 1976 No 840; SI 1977 No. 115). These Regulations cover the sampling and chemical composition of feeding stuffs but at present do not have provisions relating to microbial content which could be applied for checking the effectiveness of any protein processing method. Obviously something of this kind will be required in connection with enforcement of the Protein Processing Order when it passes into legislation.

It has been shown that animals transported long distances suffer stress causing higher rates of salmonella excretion. This is applicable to calves; their welfare is considered in the Transit of Calves Order, 1963 (SI 1963 No. 1228) and the Transit of Animals (Road and Rail) Order, 1975 (SI 1975 No. 1024), both made under the Diseases of Animals Act, 1950, but only as respects protecting the young animals from unnecessary suffering during loading, unloading, and transport. They could still experience stress possibly resulting in an increased rate of salmonella infection with risk also to public health. The hazard of salmonellae in calves is reduced if they are reared for 2 to 3 weeks on the farm where they are born.

The widespread use of antibiotics in animal feeds and for treatment was held responsible for the rapid increase in antibiotic-resistant strains of *Salmonella typhimurium*. The agricultural uses of antibiotics are now controlled by Regulations made under the Therapeutic Substances Act, 1956, and replaced by the Medicines Act, 1968.

So much of the spread of infection is concerned with the transfer of organisms between animals and man via foodstuffs that the epidemiological investigation not only of outbreaks but of the spread of salmonellae in general involves the combined efforts of medical, veterinary, and public health workers together with food technologists.

Local authorities have for many years been required by the Meat Inspection Regulations to inspect all meat for human consumption from slaughterhouses. Meat for export to countries of the European Economic Community comes from slaughterhouses and cutting premises which conform with the requirements of the EEC Council Directives on health problems connected with intra-Community trade in fresh meat. There are standards for structure, layout, equipment, hygiene, meat inspection, and refrigeration; the meat must be accompanied by a health certificate signed by a veterinary officer. In the past poultry has not been subject to compulsory inspection, whereas it is now required for export to countries of the EEC. In 1979, the inspection of poultry from slaughterhouses and intended for home consumption will be compulsory also.

Where it is not feasible to use high temperatures for the disinfection of equipment, the use of chemical agents could be useful. This would apply, for instance, to the treatment of large surfaces where heat is readily lost, certain refrigerated apparatus, and other equipment where the material of construction or the lubrication of bearings may be affected by excessive heat. The approval scheme for disinfectants used for dairy purposes could perhaps be extended to cover the use of these chemical agents in food premises generally.

Certain foods such as bulked liquid or frozen whole egg which are especially liable to be contaminated at source are already required to receive a form of heat treatment to render them safe, but it may well be thought that such protective measures should be prescribed for all bulked egg products. It has been proposed that liquid egg white should undergo a heat treatment of 57·2 °C (135 °F) for 2½ minutes and thereafter be cooled. However, in this case it is not possible to use the alpha-amylase test, as for liquid whole egg, as a check on heat treatment because there is little of the enzyme present in the white.

Although the bulk of milk supplies are pasteurized, raw milk may still be sold for manufacturing purposes, including the making of cheese, and retailed under the designation 'Untreated'. A Government Code of Hygienic Practice for the Manufacture of Cheese, 1963, recommends that milk intended for cheese making should be heat treated for 15 seconds at 71·7 °C (161 °F) or as a minimum for 15 seconds at 67·8 °C (154 °F). Both cheese and raw milk have in the past been associated with outbreaks of food poisoning. The original purpose of pasteurization, as a measure against tuberculosis, has lapsed with the achievement of tubercle-free herds but the process continues to be of immense public health value since milk is liable to infection at source from brucella organisms, staphylococci, salmonellae, and numerous other organisms. The brucellosis eradication scheme is now advanced to a stage where sales of untreated milk are restricted to the produce of brucellosis-accredited herds. It is also the Government's intention that in 1980 the sale of untreated milk for liquid consumption will be prohibited except in areas where an alternative supply of heat-treated milk is not readily available.

A number of useful Food Hygiene Codes of Practice are available. They are produced by the Department of Health and Social Security, Ministry of Agriculture, Fisheries and Food, and Welsh Office; they are *not* covered by legislation. Some of these need updating and others could be introduced; for example, the provision of meals in public houses, storage facilities for keeping foods hot and cold, facilities for cleaning, disinfection and storage of equipment including materials and tools used for cleaning.

Further information

The full texts of Orders and Regulations are obtainable from branches of Her Majesty's Stationery Office; they should be read in association with any amending legislation as indicated in the text. When ordering, the year and statutory instrument number should be quoted.

19

Education

The prevention of food poisoning should be the concern of all those who provide foodstuffs not only for human consumption but for animal consumption also. The engineers who design equipment and the architects responsible for planning kitchens, manufacturing establishments, slaughterhouses, markets, and farms also have an important part to play in controlling the spread of infection.

All groups concerned with food, therefore, from the architects, farmers, and plant engineers to professional caterers and every individual food handler working in manufacture, retail trade, or kitchen should receive information on the causes of food poisoning and on the sources of the various bacterial agents and means of control. In this respect the word 'control' covers protection of both man and animal against invasion by disease-bearing groups of bacteria, prevention of their transmission to foodstuffs by living agents and equipment, and prevention of their multiplication in foodstuffs.

The necessity for this teaching may be justified by a summary of the latest annual figures for food poisoning and salmonella infections in England and Wales, an analysis of reports to the Public Health Laboratory Service (PHLS) compiled by the Epidemiological Research Laboratory, and more recently by the Communicable Disease Surveillance Centre. For the three years 1973 to 1975 some 17 000 incidents involving 29 000 cases were reported; these figures include general and family outbreaks and sporadic cases where the causal organism was identified; there were more incidents in which the agent of infection was not recognized and undoubtedly there were many more unreported cases. In many episodes of food poisoning either no specimens were sent for laboratory examination or, where they were sent, an aetiological agent was not found. Although there is legislation to ensure that outbreaks and cases of food poisoning are notified to the Department of Health and Social Security (DHSS), many incidents, and this means thousands of cases, are not reported to the doctor and thus information will not reach the PHLS or the DHSS. Sometimes a large number of single incidents, regarded as sporadic cases, may be part of one large outbreak from a contaminated foodstuff distributed widely over the country, but unrecognized as a source of danger.

There is no evidence to suggest that food poisoning is on the decline in England and Wales. Indeed the reverse is true — in 1975 there was a 50 per cent increase in the number of reported cases.

The outbreaks most commonly notified are those which occur in specific locations feeding large numbers of people such as hospitals, schools, factories, old people's homes, hostels, halls of residence, nurseries, and children's homes where faults in the daily feeding of the same groups of people cannot fail to be observed. The same faults causing illness in persons making chance visits to hotels, cafés, and restaurants, or in travellers may pass unnoticed.

Meat and poultry in their various forms are the foods most commonly implicated and they are responsible yearly for about 70 per cent of the notified general and family outbreaks. Organisms of the salmonella group are the predominant causal agents.

An appreciable reduction in the incidence of salmonella food poisoning may be achieved ultimately by eliminating or at least controlling the animal sources. To control staphylococcal food poisoning there must be strict attention to techniques used for the manipulation and storage of cooked foods such as meat and poultry, and prepared sweets such as custards, trifles, and cream products. *Clostridium perfringens* food poisoning could be prevented with more care in rapid cooling and cold storage of bulks of meat and poultry. In all instances, conscientious cold storage of cooked food is important in prevention as well as environmental design and cleanliness. Provision of good conditions is the responsibility of management, in whom, as well as in food handlers, rests the safety of the food they provide and sell.

Widespread and persistent instruction is needed to implant the necessity for correct methods to avoid hazards of food contamination in the minds of responsible people. Groups receptive to information about the causes of food-borne disease and its prevention may vary from girls and boys in schools to adults, including managers and supervisors as well as employees, of the catering and food industries. Medical officers of environmental health and environmental health officers require the latest knowledge for teaching purposes. There will be many different levels of perception, experience, and purpose and a speaker must select information fitted to the needs of each audience; it is probably better to give too many facts rather than to underestimate the lively interest of non-technical groups.

Suggested lecture headings for various groups of people are given in Appendix A to this chapter.

Schools

Children may be taught how infection spreads and they are usually interested in the subject.

Hygienic habits are not instinctive; they need to be implanted early to persist in later life. The instruction necessary for their acquisition may not always be given in the home; the responsibility, therefore, falls partly on the school. In those schools teaching domestic science as a routine part of the curriculum, elementary bacteriology and its application to the prevention of food contamination can be conveniently taught and demonstrated practically during cookery lessons. Useful supplementary education can be given to schools by the local public health departments. This is already carried out in some towns by the environmental health and health education officers. Many local authorities have their own qualified advisory staff for the Education Catering Service.

Practical demonstrations can be given with petri dish cultures of the growth of bacteria from the hands, nose, throat, and bowel showing the vastly increased bacterial flora on the hands after touching raw meat and poultry and other foods. The effect of washing the hands can be shown. Cultures from damp swabs rubbed over various surfaces, utensils, and equipment will illustrate the differences in bacterial cleanliness between surfaces of wood and the more impervious materials, and also the differences in efficacy of cleaning methods. Foodstuffs can be cultured as purchased and after storage in the kitchen and in the refrigerator in order to demonstrate the effect of different temperatures on the numbers of bacteria in foods.

When food hygiene demonstrations are available, parties from schools should be taken round the various exhibits with an explanatory running commentary. Competitions may be held between schools on the composition of a picture showing some particular aspect of food hygiene and the winning picture displayed at the exhibition. The interest aroused by such competitions is likely to be widespread, not only within the particular school, but in the community as a whole.

The school meals service has grown from the days of soup, bread, and cake to a thriving business which provides millions of children each day with varied meals. Many schools have introduced a cafeteria service with a wide choice of food, hot and cold. This midday meal is partly subsidized and in certain instances is provided free of charge. In a large kitchen the staff include a caterer, cooks, and general kitchen assistants. Catering advisers are employed throughout the country for the over-all supervision of the school catering service; they are responsible for a number of schools within an area. All new schools are provided with their own kitchen, and new kitchens are being built for existing schools as far as possible. A central kitchen may produce more than 1000 meals a day for several schools; it may also provide meals for old people in the area.

Members of the staff for the school meals service are generally trained to a high degree of efficiency. In the county of North Yorkshire they attend in-service training courses on hygiene and nutrition at their residential College for Further Education. In addition, staff are encouraged to study for the City and Guilds qualifications at the colleges of further education or to attend locally arranged courses which could include certificate courses on the hygienic handling of food.

Lectures on food hygiene to groups of organizers and cooks are most rewarding and the results may be seen in the desire for improved methods and equipment. Domestic science teachers in schools and hospitals also request talks, sometimes after the usual teaching hours and as part of weekend training courses.

Hospitals

Each regional board has an officer responsible for all training schemes; they arrange courses for various classes of hospital officers within their region, either at their own centre or in conjunction with local technical colleges. Several regions give supervisory courses for catering personnel; the subject of food safety and quality is sometimes included. The teaching of hygiene in hospitals is considered in the Department of Health Circular HM (64) 34.

The Catering and Dietetic Branch of the DHSS produce the Health Service Catering Manual which includes a series of publications issued in the interest of good food in hospitals and similar establishments. It calls on the experience of people working in the field and the assistance of experts from both within and outside the Health Service. In 1974 a booklet entitled *Hygiene* was published; it was first produced under the auspices of the Birmingham Regional Hospital Board as a code of practice for that Region and the interest shown led to its publication by DHSS.

Restaurants, hotels, and factories and food handlers in retail shops

Special courses reaching degree level are available for students wanting responsible work in the catering industry as well as in hospitals. University and independent colleges also give training in domestic science which includes food hygiene. There are correspondence courses available also. The Hotel Catering and Institutional Management Association examinations held yearly give papers on food hygiene and nutrition.

There are two methods used separately or in conjunction with each other for the teaching of food handlers in commercial eating establishments and shops. The first seeks to gather together the managers, supervisors, and other key personnel for a series of lectures. Three or four talks may be given at weekly or shorter intervals. The provision of comprehensive lecture notes helps to disseminate information to employees; better still a similar course can be given to all kitchen staff. For large catering establishments and multiple stores this method can be used within the shop or store. For school kitchens it may be convenient to arrange a meeting at one particular centre, under the control of the local authority. The owners and assistants of small establishments including shops, cafés, snack-bars and portable food vans may be attracted to these meetings, otherwise, special courses of lectures should be given for them. Public lecture demonstrations and exhibitions with films may attract a wider audience, discussions should be encouraged and free literature should be made available.

The second method is to go out to people rather than to invite them to a centre. This may be arranged fairly readily in large or small establishments by the local environmental health officers or other suitably qualified persons. Demonstration material may be taken to various departments and talks given on the spot to small groups of staff within the kitchen or shop. Public talks and exhibitions should be followed by visits and further discussions.

The Catering Trade Working Party, in the Report published in 1951, stated that 'no large scale and lasting improvement in the hygienic conditions of catering establishments can be brought about unless informed public opinion demands it. We would stress the word "informed" because many people, while appreciating generally the value of cleanliness, have little knowledge of the real risks attendant on particularly faulty practices. The dissemination of knowledge of the principles underlying food hygiene should, therefore, be carried out by practical means.' There has been much improvement in the standard of kitchens since that was written, but the hazards leading to food poisoning are still not always fully understood by responsible persons who must avoid them.

Provision of information

Information on food hygiene is available from many sources, but much of the responsibility for assimilating facts is assumed nationally by the environmental health officers, medical officers of environmental health, health education officers, and other public health workers. In many European countries and in the USA the veterinary officer takes a prominent part also. The environmental health officer is the link between the medical officer of environmental health and the food trader, restaurant and canteen supervisor, and other food handlers in his area; his district work keeps him constantly in touch with a wide variety of food workers. The success of any drive to establish and maintain better conditions and techniques amongst food handlers will depend largely on his or her efforts. Environmental health officers trained by local authorities are sometimes employed by the food and catering industries to help both in the education of food handlers and in the maintenance of high standards of hygiene in food production and preparation.

In 1972, a committee of experienced environmental health officers reported that lack of administrative action in certain areas resulted in malpractice. They recommended the registration of all catering premises and stressed the need for inspection by local authorities of kitchens in establishments, such as hospitals and other 'Crown Property', now exempt from local authority care.

Administrative experts of the Department of Health and Social Security are available for advice and lectures on legislation and Codes of Practice on a number of subjects related to food hygiene (see Appendix D). The Ministry of Agriculture, Fisheries and Food provides a similar service for the veterinary profession and industry.

The Public Health Laboratory Service in England and Wales is active in the field of education on matters relating to the prevention of bacterial and viral diseases. Amongst the many functions of these laboratories, scattered throughout the country, are the examination of foodstuffs associated with outbreaks of food poisoning and the investigation of the sources and means of spread of the bacterial agents responsible.

Regular samples of home-produced and imported food, as well as milk, water and ice-cream are submitted for bacteriological examination. Surveillance studies and research are carried out on foods known to be public health hazards and suspected to spread bacterial agents in manufacturing establishments, shops, and kitchens. The zoonotic illnesses due to bacteria shared between men and animals and which cause both to suffer are investigated jointly with the veterinary profession.

The results of epidemiological studies on outbreaks of food poisoning and the conclusions reached on the spread of food-poisoning organisms from human, animal, and food sources in relation to the prevention of food-borne disease are communicated to others in lectures, discussion groups, papers, and reviews.

Agricultural Research Council Laboratories, such as those of the Meat Research Institute, Food Research Institute, and Poultry Research Station, the food research laboratories of the manufacturing and baking industries and other independent laboratories are continually checking and investigating means of preventing food spoilage, as well as the contamination and build-up of pathogenic organisms in food.

Independent organizations active in the field of food hygiene education include the Health Education Council, St. John Ambulance, the Red Cross, Women's Institutes, and Women's Royal Voluntary Service.

Short courses on food hygiene are given by the Royal Society of Health, the Institute of Public Health and Hygiene, and members of the Environmental Health Officers Association. The St. John Ambulance Association in conjunction with the Environmental Health Officers Association have introduced a joint course in basic food hygiene.

For many years the King Edward's Hospital Fund for London supported an excellent Hospital Catering Advisory Service providing a centre with model kitchens and equipment and facilities for lectures. This service instituted trials of new feeding systems for hospitals — for example, the use of frozen cooked meals and frozen prepared single items issued from central kitchens or food manufacturers, and methods to thaw and reheat including hot air circulation and microwave ovens. Reports on these projects are still available on loan from the King's Fund Centre, 126 Albert Street, London, NW1.

The Central Office of Information, various industries, and overseas teaching laboratories such as the Center for Disease Control, Atlanta, and universities in the USA produce films, slides, and bulletins. Many commercial firms engaged in the manufacture of foods, equipment, and detergents willingly provide exhibits for educational purposes.

Television and broadcast programmes for both adults and schools have a wide appeal. Newspaper reports of outbreaks of food poisoning should be as accurate as possible. Thus the press should be given full information including sponsored notes on the faults and reasons which lead to outbreaks, the method of spread of infection, and how it can be prevented.

Aids to teaching food hygiene

Audiovisual aids such as films, film strips, overhead projection, and 35 mm transparencies are valuable assets for talks to all types of audience. Charts and tables may be used to show the rise in any particular type of food poisoning, the increase in food poisoning during the summer months, and the predominance of meats and poultry as food vehicles in gastroenteritis. Amateur photography can be used to illustrate good and bad practices in the kitchen. Environmental factors such as design of surface structure, equipment, storage, washing-up procedures, and garbage disposal may show clearly in picture form facts that may be difficult to express in words. Large charts and posters may be photographed and shown on the screen when travelling makes transportation of equipment difficult.

Films also illustrate in a lifelike manner points which may be unconvincing by the spoken word. They should be preceded by an explanatory talk on the sources of food-poisoning organisms, methods of spread, conditions which encourage multiplication in foods, and methods of prevention.

Films can be borrowed or hired from the Central Office of Information, the British Gas Library, Diversey Ltd. (Northampton), the National Audiovisual Library (London), the Health Education Council, the Rentokil Film Unit (Liverpool), and Unilever Ltd. (London). Two particularly good films have been produced in the USA — *An outbreak of* Salmonella *infection*, and *Epidemiology of Salmonellosis* available from the National Audiovisual Center, Washington, DC 20409.

Simple pictorial stories in colour of actual outbreaks of food poisoning with short explanatory headings have proved to be popular both for use in lecture demonstrations and for exhibitions; they can be photographed for slides. Examples of these story charts are given in Chapter 6. A poster may serve to illustrate a single fact in a straightforward serious manner, or factual evidence may be presented in a humorous way.

Bacterial cultures on various agar media in petri dishes may be shown by means of an illuminated viewing box. Such plate cultures can be used to demonstrate bacterial colonies from fingers rubbed lightly on the surface of the media. Comparative culture plates will show the effect of touching food and the efficacy or otherwise of washing the hands, the growth from clean and dirty handkerchiefs, kitchen cloths, towels, and surfaces. Hairs and flies may be placed on agar plates also. Colonies of bacteria may be grown from imperfectly washed utensils. Portions of food may be cultured in agar media to illustrate bacteriologically clean and dirty food, and the effect of refrigeration on the prevention of bacterial growth.

The flannelgraph (Fig. 68) is another useful method to focus attention on headings, important facts, pictorial diagrams, and coloured sketches emphasizing points from a lecture. Once pre-

Fig. 68 Flannelgraph showing chain of infection

pared, the printed and pictorial messages can be used many times and save the labour of blackboard work before and during a talk. A flannelgraph board can be improvized with a large piece of flannel, felt, or lint pinned on to a blackboard.

Investigations into the causes of bacterial food poisoning continually reveal new facts and the information should be passed on to food handlers so that they can be taught to play their part in breaking the chains of infection which give rise to one outbreak after another. Education about food poisoning and its prevention is essential if this intestinal disease is to be brought under control. The subject interests most people because it affects everyone.

Teaching requires a knowledge of the statistical facts about food poisoning and also familiarity with the sources and habits and general behaviour in food of the various organisms responsible for food-borne illness.

A set of rules to control one organism may do little to stop the activities of another. For example, emphasis on personal hygiene alone may reduce the incidence of staphylococcal food poisoning but it will do little to prevent salmonellosis and nothing to stop *Clostridium perfringens* food poisoning. Even the strictest rules of personal hygiene will not prevent outbreaks when large quantities of contaminated raw foods are handled by people unaware of the presence of salmonellae in the food, and in their immediate environmental surroundings. The onus of producing salmonella-free foods goes far back in the chain of production and it should not be the responsibility of those who handle food after distribution at the retail and consumer end. Recommendations to help the retail and consumer trade are essential but, by right, they should expect to be given safe food.

All the usual precautions against *C. perfringens* and *B. cereus* food poisoning will fail unless it is understood that the spores of these organisms can survive cooking and must be prevented from growing out into vegetative cells by rapid cooling and cold storage of meat and poultry dishes (*C. perfringens*) and rice (*B. cereus*) if the foods are not to be eaten freshly cooked and hot. Perhaps the greatest of all the measures against food poisoning is the prevention of bacterial growth in foods after cooking by attention to cooling times and cold storage.

It is possible to teach the general principles which govern the prevention of food poisoning without reference to the organisms known to be causal agents (and considered in Table 21); but information will be more comprehensive if preventive measures are related at least to the main groups of organisms and their characteristics.

The control of temperature during manufacture, storage, preparation, and service in the factory, canteen, and home is essential to keep bacterial numbers low.

Appendix A gives suggested outlines for lectures to various groups of people; e.g. Schedule 1 is intended for domestic audiences, Schedule 2 for non-technical professional food handlers. Appendix B is intended to help travellers and campers with their choice of food, so that they remain free from gastroenteritis. Appendix C is a simple questionnaire for the investigation of food poisoning outbreaks. Appendix D is a list of useful references to supplement the information given in this book.

Table 21   Sources and control of food poisoning bacteria

Source	Public Health control	Laboratory control
	Salmonella	
Animal		
stool, coat, hooves, paws	Rearing methods Feeding stuffs Farm hygiene Slaughterhouse hygiene	Diagnostic media for stool samples, swabs, and food Bacteriological counts on foods and feeds Biochemical tests Serological and bacteriophage typing
Foodstuffs (animal origin) meat and poultry feeding stuffs for animals, egg products, raw milk	Hygiene of production Treatment to render safe Storage	
Environment of food preparation	Cleanliness of equipment, utensils and surfaces	
Water for drinking and preparation of food	Treatment by filtration and chlorination	
Human stool, hand	Care in handling foods Avoidance of cross-contamination from raw to cooked food Personal hygiene	
	Staphylococcus aureus	
Human nose, throat, hand, skin, and lesions	Care in handling foods Storage of cooked foods Personal hygiene and habits	Diagnostic media for swabs and food Bacteriological counts on food
Animal cow, goat	Care of mastitis	Coagulase test Bacteriophage and serological typing
Foodstuffs (dairy) milk, cheese, cream	Hygiene of milk production Heat treatment of milk intended for drinking and for cream and cheese	Enterotoxin detection by gel diffusion techniques
	Clostridium perfringens	
Foodstuff meat and poultry, dehydrated foods	Cooking and cooling techniques Storage of cooked food	Diagnostic media for stool samples and food Bacteriological counts on food

Table 21 (cont.)   Sources and control of food poisoning bacteria

Source	Public Health control	Laboratory control
	Clostridium perfringens (cont.)	
Environment of food preparation (food and dust) Human stool Animal stools and dust	Cleanliness of equipment and surfaces	*C. perfringens* counts on stools Serological typing
	Clostridium botulinum	
Soil and mud Fish Foodstuff fish, meat, and vegetables	Processing and cooking	Toxin identification (neutralization tests in mice) Diagnostic media
	Bacillus cereus	
Foodstuff (cereals) dust, soil	Storage after cooking Cleanliness of environment	Diagnostic media Bacteriological counts on food Serological typing
	Vibrio parahaemolyticus	
Seafoods	Warning against eating raw fish and other seafoods Avoidance of cross-contamination from raw to cooked seafood	Diagnostic media Bacteriological counts on food Serological typing
	Other organisms, e.g. streptococci	
Human Animal Foodstuff	General care of food and storage	Diagnostic media Bacteriological counts on food Serological typing

(Modified from Herschdoerfer, S. M., 1967, *Quality Control in the Food Industry*, Vol. 1. Academic Press, New York and London.)

Appendix A

Suggested lecture material

The following notes and headings for talks on food hygiene have been useful for various groups studying the safety and keeping quality of foodstuffs.

Schedule 1 may be used for one or two lectures with demonstrations and pictorial charts of outbreaks of food poisoning. Schedule 2 includes a course of ten talks with suggestions for charts, compiled by the late Miss I. J. Martin, and Miss C. F. Scott.

Schedule 1

Introduction

The term food poisoning describes a state in which the victim suffers an acute attack of abdominal pain and diarrhoea sometimes accompanied by vomiting and lasting usually 1–2 days, but sometimes a week or more. The onset is usually sudden and may start as early as 2 hours and up to 40 or more hours after eating the contaminated food.

Safe food will not cause food poisoning. Food may be harmful because it has taken up toxic metals such as zinc, copper, or antimony; it may be poisonous itself, for example some fish, plants, and fungi or it may induce allergic manifestations, but most food poisoning is caused by minute living organisms. These micro-organisms are invisible except when viewed through a microscope. Their presence in food may be demonstrated either by food poisoning symptoms when the food looks, smells, and tastes normal, or by spoilage when it looks, tastes, and smells bad. At least seven different bacterial agents are concerned in food poisoning, and the symptoms and incubation periods vary from group to group. In general, the organisms must grow in the food to produce sufficient numbers to invade the body (infection) or to produce toxic substances either in the foodstuff or within the intestine. However, food may act as a vehicle for small numbers of bacterial agents causing more serious infections such as dysentery, typhoid, and paratyphoid fevers or even for viral agents such as those causing infectious hepatitis, poliomyelitis, and gastroenteritis.

Sources of food poisoning bacteria

(1) Foods or food ingredients both imported and home-produced, as purchased or brought into the kitchen such as raw meat and poultry, rice and other cereals, other dehydrated food and sea foods.

(2) Food handlers concerned with the manufacture and retail sale of food, those in catering and domestic kitchens; nose, throat, and skin carriers of staphylococci and faecal excreters of salmonella and shigella organisms.

(3) Food animals, poultry, pigs, and other living creatures which infect the foods arising from them and intended both for human and for animal consumption. Domestic pets, vermin and flies which may be symptomless excreters in the environment of food preparation.

(4) The factory, shop, and kitchen which can harbour bacteria from all sources in benches, tables, cloths, boards, slicers, can openers and other equipment. Such contamination may be picked up by foods during preparation and after cooking.

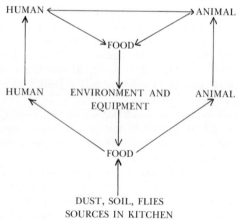

DUST, SOIL, FLIES
SOURCES IN KITCHEN
Food handlers and other living things
Foodstuffs, e.g. meat, poultry and sea foods
Surfaces and equipment

Chart   Cycle of infection and contamination

Bacterial agents of food poisoning

Salmonella enters the kitchen on foods which are of animal origin such as meats, poultry, and raw egg products, as well as from human excreters. Fertilizers and pet meats, which may be handled in the kitchen, are also sources of salmonellae. They are the commonest food poisoning agents and the most serious. There is usually a 6 to 36 hour incubation period, the symptoms resemble gastric flu, and the illness lasts for 1 to 7 days.

Staphylococcus aureus comes mainly from human carriers. The nose, throat, hand, or skin lesion may harbour staphylococci able to cause food poisoning if the organisms are allowed to grow in foodstuffs, particularly those handled after cooking. While growing some staphylococci produce a toxin; the amount of toxin present will be proportional to the amount of bacterial growth, which depends on the length of time and the temperature at which the food has been stored. Staphylococci are frequently present in the milk of cows and goats; if the milk is not pasteurized the organisms may develop and produce toxin in the milk and it can be carried over into cream and cheese. Staphylococcal food poisoning has a 2 to 6 hour incubation period, the symptoms resemble acute sea-sickness, and the illness lasts for about 1 day.

Clostridium perfringens produces hardy structures called spores which survive for a long time in dust, soil, and excreta from both human and animal sources. The surfaces of raw meat and poultry are frequently contaminated with *C. perfringens*. Some spores remain alive after boiling and other methods of cooking and grow readily in the cooked meat when it is cooled slowly and stored in a warm place. *C. perfringens* will not grow in the presence of air; thus freshly cooked food is more able to support its growth, for the oxygen has been driven off during cooking. Furthermore, the spores may require heat to initiate germination and this is provided by cooking. Rolled joints are particularly dangerous because the spores are folded inside where conditions are suitable for anaerobic growth and the penetration of heat may be poor. The disease has an 8 to 22 hours incubation period, and the characteristic symptoms are abdominal pain and diarrhoea lasting 1 to 2 days. Toxin is produced in the intestine.

Clostridium botulinum poisoning (botulism) is rare in the United Kingdom. The spores are very heat resistant and the organism grows only in the absence of air. The contamination of canned and bottled foods, uncured and smoked fish (stored unfrozen), and preserved vegetables imperfectly prepared have given rise to outbreaks in the past. Incidents are reported from other countries.

Bacillus cereus is commonly found in foodstuffs and in the environment; it produces spores which can survive cooking and grow out in slowly cooling food. Toxin is formed in the food in proportion to the growth of the organism. The incubation period may be 1–6 hours, when the main symptom is vomiting, up to 16 hours (see p. 29).

Vibrio parahaemolyticus occurs in warm coastal waters and various sea foods and it may pass from raw to cooked foods. It is a common cause of food poisoning in Japan and is reported from other countries also. The incubation period is approximately 15 hours and the illness includes profuse diarrhoea and vomiting which may last five or more days.

Escherichia coli is known to cause diarrhoea in adults as well as in infants and the number of types found to be enteropathogenic is increasing.

Other organisms, such as certain streptococci, *Proteus* and those in the Providence group are sometimes suspected to cause food poisoning when reaching abnormal numbers in food.

Prevention

(a) Education and care of food handlers.
(b) Animal care.
(c) Vigilance: (i) imported food, (ii) home-produced food. Farming, slaughtering, manufacture, catering.
(d) Care of equipment and cleanliness.

Conditions

Micro-organisms causing food poisoning must be able to grow in the food, which is known as the vehicle of infection; the prevention of growth is an important control measure. Bacteria increase by doubling in number every 10 to 30 minutes in ideal conditions. Most bacteria will grow at varying rates within the temperature range of 5 °C (41 °F) to 50 °C (122 °F). The most favourable temperature is about 37 °C (98·6 °F) — the temperature of the human body. Much of the food eaten by man is favourable for growth, for example, meat and meat products, poultry, eggs and egg products, milk and milk products.

Factors which encourage growth are high moisture, low salt (although staphylococci can tolerate more salt than other pathogenic bacteria), low acid, low fat, and moderate sugar. Growth is repressed by heat, cold and dehydration, and by high concentrations of salt, sugar, acid and fat.

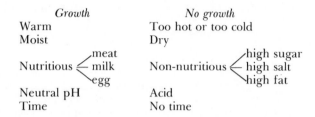

Growth	*No growth*
Warm	Too hot or too cold
Moist	Dry
Nutritious ⟨ meat, milk, egg	Non-nutritious ⟨ high sugar, high salt, high fat
Neutral pH	Acid
Time	No time

Foods which do and do not encourage bacterial growth

The type of food is significant because some organisms will live and multiply readily in one type of food and others in another. For example, staphylococci grow in high salt concentrations, whereas salmonellae and *C. perfringens* do not; thus staphylococcal food poisoning is frequently caused by semi-preserved salted meats.

C. perfringens grows rapidly in boiled fresh meat which is cooled slowly. Certain foods will not allow growth of food-poisoning organisms, for example those which are acid such as sauces, pickles and some soft drinks. Foods with a high sugar content, jams, syrups, and honey, and foods with a high fat content discourage growth of bacteria, although they may survive. In dried or frozen foods organisms cannot multiply but a proportion of those already present before freezing or dehydration will survive.

Measures to control bacterial growth

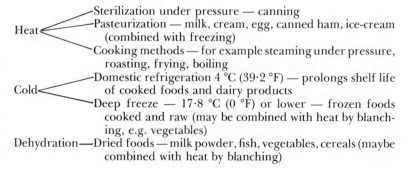

Heat ⟨
Sterilization under pressure — canning
Pasteurization — milk, cream, egg, canned ham, ice-cream (combined with freezing)
Cooking methods — for example steaming under pressure, roasting, frying, boiling

Cold ⟨
Domestic refrigeration 4 °C (39·2 °F) — prolongs shelf life of cooked foods and dairy products
Deep freeze — 17·8 °C (0 °F) or lower — frozen foods cooked and raw (may be combined with heat by blanching, e.g. vegetables)

Dehydration—Dried foods — milk powder, fish, vegetables, cereals (maybe combined with heat by blanching)

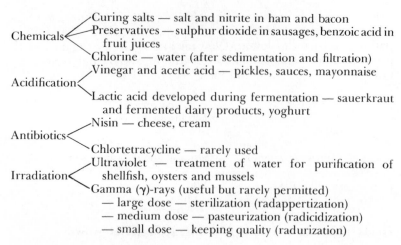

Chemicals
- Curing salts — salt and nitrite in ham and bacon
- Preservatives — sulphur dioxide in sausages, benzoic acid in fruit juices
- Chlorine — water (after sedimentation and filtration)

Acidification
- Vinegar and acetic acid — pickles, sauces, mayonnaise
- Lactic acid developed during fermentation — sauerkraut and fermented dairy products, yoghurt

Antibiotics
- Nisin — cheese, cream
- Chlortetracycline — rarely used

Irradiation
- Ultraviolet — treatment of water for purification of shellfish, oysters and mussels
- Gamma (γ)-rays (useful but rarely permitted)
  - — large dose — sterilization (radappertization)
  - — medium dose — pasteurization (radicidization)
  - — small dose — keeping quality (radurization)

Thus milk is made safe by pasteurization, ultra heat treatment, or sterilization; ice-cream by pasteurization, quick cooling, and freezing; bulked egg by pasteurization; and water by filtration and chlorination.

The hygiene of food including purchase and preparation

Purchasing and shops. More food should not be purchased than the amount which can be stored in the available deep freeze cabinet or domestic refrigerator (4 °C, 39·2 °F).

Storage. Deep freeze storage keeps food safe for many months and even years, but domestic refrigeration can keep food palatable for a limited number of days only.

Shops. The shop or supermarket should have chill cabinets (4 °C, 39·2 °F) for susceptible foods such as cold cooked meats and raw meat or poultry; the raw products should be well separated from cooked meatstuffs.

Sliced meats. Susceptible foods such as semi-preserved cooked meats and pies should not be handled nor shown in the shop window; sliced and weighed quantities prepared under specially hygienic conditions should be wrapped in cellophane and kept chilled before sale. In fact there should be no opportunity of cross-contamination between raw and cooked materials.

Sausages. Sausages should not be on sale alongside cooked products, and they should be kept cold.

Fish. Fish should be bought from enclosed shops with chilled cabinets or chilled window displays.

Cans. Canned goods should be in good condition; when the containers are rusted or damaged they should not be on sale. It must be emphasized that large cans of ham and similar products which are not sterile should be refrigerated; the canner's instruction to 'keep cold' implies that the pack is perishable.

Cream cakes. Imitation cream cakes should be kept under chilled storage for a limited period of sale (1 day). Fresh cream should be chilled unless long storage is assured by in-bottle pasteurization. There should be ample cold and cool storage space both for raw and cooked products in the kitchen.

The food handler

Personal hygiene. The nose, mouth, and skin can be sources of staphylococci which produce toxin in foods; thus cooked foods able to support growth should not be touched by hand. Salmonellae, dysentery bacilli and *Clostridium perfringens* may be excreted in stools so hands should be washed after using the WC.

Hands. Hands should be washed well after, as well as before, handling foods because food-poisoning organisms can be picked up from many raw foodstuffs and transferred to cooked and other foods. Hands should be dried on paper towels or the continuous roller towel. Lesions must be covered and persons with septic lesions should not handle food.

Habits. Habits should be good — no smoking while handling food, no tasting of food by sampling with the fingers; spoons used for tasting should be immediately washed in hot water.

Handkerchiefs. Paper handkerchiefs should be available and after use disposed of in a box or cellophane bag kept in a convenient place.

Nails and clothes. Nails should be short and clean and clothing clean; personal clothes should not be washed in the kitchen.

No-touch techniques. There should be little or no actual man-handling of susceptible foods, particularly after recent lesions on the hands.

Soaps and hand creams. Bactericidal soaps and hand creams are useful, because the hands must be kept in good condition. Cracks, blemishes, and broken nails will all harbour bacteria, and a good hand cream containing a bactericidal substance should be used after washing.

Toilet facilities. Pedal-operated flushes and taps, and easily cleaned metal fittings should be used wherever possible.

Environment of the kitchen

Layout. Work benches, cooking and hand-washing facilities as well as the sink unit should be conveniently placed and well lit. So far as possible there should be separate work areas for raw and cooked food; for large-scale catering this is essential and should include separate equipment and personnel in the different areas.

Surfaces. Smooth and impermeable surfaces are easy to clean and thus the number of bacteria in the environment will be reduced; stainless steel and Formica, even good enamel, are preferable to all other types of material. Boards should be made from one piece of hardwood for ease of cleaning and disinfection; Formica, rubber, or other materials should be used in place of wood for cutting boards.

Hot water. There should be a plentiful supply of hot water.

Storage. A cold room or refrigeration and deep freeze facilities are required, also a well-ventilated, cool cupboard or larder. There should be provision for the rapid cooling of bulks of meat, poultry, and other foods to be refrigerated, such as a special chill room with extraction fans or a fan in the larder. An internal cupboard may be used for canned and bottled foods. There should be ample space for cleaning materials and also for storing vegetables, preferably outside the main kitchen, in a cool place away from direct sunlight. Food required to be served hot should be maintained at a temperature above 65 °C.

Equipment. Equipment should be bought with a view to easy cleaning, and sited for ease of cleaning and accessibility; it should be easily taken apart and reassembled and maintained in good repair.

Cleaning equipment. All parts should be freed from food debris (if necessary using a brush) with hot soapy or detergent water and rinsed with very hot water. Hypochlorites and other suitable chemical agents, or steam, may be used; adequate time for contact should be allowed.

Nail brushes. Nail brushes should not be harsh; Nylon and plastic are recommended so that they can be disinfected. They should be stood so that the water drains from them and they are not resting in pools of water. They should be disinfected in hot water and stored dry overnight; but not all plastics will withstand hot water disinfection.

Paper. The use of disposable paper instead of cloths for mopping up is important to prevent spreading contamination from place to place by a moist much-handled cloth.

Washing-up. There should be three stages; pre-cleaning, a good cleaning detergent, and a really hot water rinse; where it is impossible to obtain hot water a bactericidal detergent should be considered, or a final rinse in hypochlorite solution.

Garbage. Garbage can be discarded by burning in the boiler or by wrapping and placing in pedal-operated bins or dustbins; cans should be washed free from remains of food. Garbage receptacles should be kept dry and clean; when they are damp bacteria can multiply in the waste, thus creating spoilage smells. They should be covered and placed in the shade.

Paper sacks are useful and popular, also the waste disposal system attached to the sink, although there are limitations to its use, as cans and clothing materials cannot be disposed of in this way.

Flies. Flies should be denied access to dustbins otherwise eggs will be laid and the grubs will hatch in suitable refuse; flies must be kept out of the kitchens also.

Cooking and preparation

Poultry. Poultry may harbour food-poisoning organisms on the skin, in offal, and inside the carcass. Thus care should be taken where and how birds are prepared, surfaces and utensils should be well cleaned after use, and the hands should be washed well after handling the raw materials. Cloths should not be used to wipe carcasses either inside or outside, or to cover poultry or meat. Frozen meat and poultry should be thawed properly before being cooked. If foods are not to be eaten freshly cooked and hot they must be cooled quickly and refrigerated.

Pet meat. Pet meat, raw or in open packs, frequently contains food poisoning organisms; it should not be handled, but utensils should be kept for that purpose only and boiled after use.

Sausages. Sausages, raw scraps, and minced meat may be contaminated with salmonellae. Great care should be taken when preparing sausages for cooking. If they are pricked (now said to be unnecessary) the fork should be washed immediately with very hot water. Sausages should be well cooked.

Egg powders. Dried products such as meringue powder and powdered egg should be handled with care and used only for well-cooked products. Prepared cake mixes should not include egg products such as egg white or whole egg powder.

Shell eggs. Ducks' eggs should not be used unless cooked thoroughly and all receptacles and utensils scalded after use.

Meat pies. Casseroles, cottage and shepherd's pies, steak and kidney puddings and pies, pasties and similar dishes should be prepared freshly from raw meat. If there is likely to be any delay in using cooked meat for pies, steaming under pressure is the best way to ensure the destruction of heat-resistant organisms; it is a safe method of cooking. If left-overs are used 'warmed-up' they must be cooked thoroughly to boiling point to destroy contaminants and toxins which may have been formed. All cooked meats should be hurried from cooker to refrigerator and back again.

Rolled meats. Rolled joints are particularly prone to give rise to *C. perfringens* food poisoning, because spores on the outer surfaces are rolled inside where they are more likely to survive. Such joints should be cooked thoroughly and eaten freshly cooked; they ought not to be allowed to cool slowly and stored at atmospheric temperature.

Cold cooked meats. A very large proportion of food poisoning is caused by cold cooked meats; great care should be taken with their handling and storage.

Tongue and ham. These products and particularly tongue, are subject to contamination by hand after cooking; the skinning of tongues while warm followed by long storage at atmospheric temperature encourages contamination and bacterial multiplication. Tongues should be heated again after skinning and pressing.

Salads and fruits. Salad vegetables including watercress and lettuce, and dessert fruits which cannot be peeled, should be well washed, preferably in water containing hypochlorite.

Sandwiches. Sandwiches should be made as near the time required as possible; if prepared the night before they should be refrigerated in a container overnight.

Cooked rice. Cooked rice should not be stored overnight unless refrigerated. Care must be taken with bulks of rice required in eating places specializing in curries and other dishes both for sitdown and take-away meals.

Seafoods. Oysters, mussels, and other shell-fish should be obtained only from reputable sources. After thawing, frozen cooked prawns and shrimps should be stored cold until required. Care is needed to prevent cross-contamination from raw to cooked food.

Summer. If the weather is hot all precautions should be strengthened and the foodstuffs which are prone to give rise to food poisoning should be excluded from the menu.

Points to remember

(1) All cold cooked meats to be refrigerated and not handled.
(2) Raw foods, such as meats and poultry to be thawed properly, cooked well and eaten hot or cooled quickly and refrigerated.
(3) All equipment to be cleaned well and disinfected preferably by heat.

Schedule 2

Food-borne disease is caused by the consumption of contaminated food and drink (see 'Types of food poisoning' below). Food which smells good, looks good and tastes good can still cause food poisoning.

Types of food poisoning (Session 1)

(1) Food itself may be poisonous; for example, some plants, fungi, and shellfish.
(2) Allergic or sensitivity reactions to certain foods.
(3) Micro-organisms, most commonly bacteria or the poisons they form (called toxins), present in food or drink, some of which survive the heat of cooking.
(4) Chemical contamination may occur during food preparation. Acid foods can dissolve metal from containers or utensils; for example, apples left in a galvanized container can cause zinc poisoning.

(5) Parasites in animals which may be present in meat; for example, trichinella.

Types 1, 2, 4 and 5 occur occasionally, but the third is the commonest cause and can be prevented by care in the production and handling of food.

Bacteria

These organisms are minute living cells, varying in shape and visible only through a microscope. They are present everywhere. Most bacteria are harmless and even useful to man, but a small proportion are dangerous.

Given the right conditions, bacteria will divide into two every 20 to 30 minutes, so that one organism can develop into many millions within 12 hours.

(1) Foods	Plants, fungi, some shellfish	
(2) Allergies		
(3) Micro-organisms		
	BACTERIA	
	Small dose*	Dysentery bacilli
	(spread readily)	
	Large dose†	*Salmonella* spp.
	(usually after growth in food)	*Staph. aureus*
		C. perfringens
		C. botulinum
		B. cereus
		V. parahaemolyticus
		Esch. coli
	VIRUSES	
	Small dose*	
(4) Chemicals		
	Zinc	
	Copper	
	Tin	
	Alkaloids	
	Pesticides	
(5) Parasites		
	Trichinella	
	Taenia	

* Small dose=few organisms only.
† Large dose=thousands to millions of organisms.

Chart   Causes of food poisoning

Characteristics of illness

The symptoms are diarrhoea and abdominal pain, usually but not always accompanied by vomiting, coming on within 1 to 36 hours of eating food.

Conditions which affect the growth of bacteria (Session 2)

(1) *Food.* Much of the protein food eaten by man is favourable for the growth of bacteria; for example, meat and meat products, poultry, eggs, milk and milk products.

(2) *Temperature.* Many bacteria will grow at varying rates within the temperature range of 5 to 50 °C (41 to 122 °F). The most favourable temperature for food poisoning bacteria is 37 °C (98·6 °F), the temperature of the human body; spoilage bacteria grow at lower temperatures.

(3) *Time.* When food and temperature provide favourable conditions for bacterial growth, time is needed for multiplication to take place.

(4) *Moisture.* Moisture is necessary for growth, but most bacteria can survive indefinitely when dry, as in powdered food.

(5) *Atmosphere.* Most bacteria require air to grow actively but some can multiply only in the absence of oxygen.

The danger zone

Optimum temperatures for bacterial growth are 20–45 °C (68–113 °F). Outside these temperature limits the bacteria which infect man and animals grow slowly.

The safety zone

Extreme cold will not kill all bacteria, but most will cease to multiply under refrigerated storage and none will grow in the freezer.

Effect of heat

Bacteria are destroyed by temperatures above 63 °C (145·4 °F) if held for sufficient length of time in cooking processes, due to irreversible protein changes (coagulation of whole egg), and in the pasteurization of milk; spores may not be killed by these treatments.

Toxins

Poisonous substances are produced in food by some bacteria, such as staphylococci, *B. cereus* and *C. botulinum.* Some are destroyed readily by heat (toxins of *C. botulinum*), whereas others (staphylococcal enterotoxin) can withstand boiling.

Spores

Hardy structures are produced by bacteria such as *C. perfringens, C. botulinum* and *B. cereus.* They are not killed by temperatures which kill bacteria; some spores survive boiling. They remain dormant in dust and soil for long periods.

Food poisoning bacteria (Session 3)

There are seven main types of bacteria causing food poisoning today:

(1) *Salmonella* — infection by living bacteria in food.
(2) *Staphylococcus aureus* — toxin from growth of bacteria in food.
(3) *Clostridium perfringens* — toxin released in intestine from living bacteria swallowed in food.
(4) *Clostridium botulinum* — toxin from growth of bacteria in food.
(5) *Bacillus cereus* — toxin from growth of bacteria in food.
(6) *Vibrio parahaemolyticus* — infection by living bacteria in food.
(7) *Escherichia coli* — infection by living bacteria in food.

Salmonella

This is the commonest cause of food poisoning and the most serious.

Source. Carried in the human and animal intestine, and excreted in stools. Likely to come into the kitchen on raw foods of animal origin; for example, meat, poultry, pet meat, sausages, egg products or to be brought in by human and animal excreta and fertilizers. Insects, birds, vermin, and domestic pets may play a part.

Cause of illness. The living bacteria in food.

Illness. Begins 6 to 36 hours after eating contaminated food. Symptoms include fever, headache, abdominal pains, diarrhoea, and vomiting. The illness lasts from 1 to 7 or 8 days and can be fatal in the elderly, very young or sick people.

Kitchen control. (1) Kitchen hygiene:
 (a) separation of raw from cooked foods, particularly meat and poultry, using different surfaces and equipment to prevent cross-contamination by boards, cutting and mincing machines, cloths, and kitchen tools;
 (b) thorough cleaning of all surfaces, equipment and tools.
(2) Care of personal hygiene by washing hands before and after handling food — especially raw meat and poultry.
(3) Cold storage of food to prevent multiplication of bacteria.

Staphylococcus aureus

Staphylococci are a common cause of food poisoning.
Source. Comes mainly from the skin of human carriers and can be found in the nose, on the hands, in the throat, in boils, carbuncles, whitlows, styes, septic lesions, burns, and scratches. Also comes from the raw milk of cows and goats; the organisms and toxin can be carried over to cream and cheese made from raw milk.

Cause of illness. A toxin produced by the bacteria as they grow in food.

Illness. Begins 2 to 6 hours after eating contaminated food. Symptoms include acute vomiting, pain in abdomen, diarrhoea, and sometimes collapse; there is no fever. The illness lasts not more than 24 hours, and is seldom fatal.

Kitchen control. (1) Care of personal hygiene; it is impossible to sterilize the hands, therefore cooked food should not be touched by the hands.
(2) Cold storage of food to prevent multiplication of bacteria.
(3) Kitchen hygiene to prevent bacteria becoming numerous in equipment, boards, cutting and mincing machines, cloths, Savoy bags, and other tools; clean thoroughly after use.

Clostridium perfringens

Clostridium perfringens is also a common cause of food poisoning.

Source. Found in the human and animal intestine, soil, dust, and flies. Raw meat and poultry and some dried products are frequently contaminated with *C. perfringens*; the spores can survive normal cooking temperatures. The organism grows without oxygen.

Cause of illness. Large numbers of bacilli growing in food. The spores remain active after boiling and slow roasting, and grow readily in cooked meat cooled slowly or stored in a warm place. Large numbers of bacilli build up quickly under these conditions. A toxin is produced and released in the intestine.

Illness. Begins 8 to 22 hours after eating contaminated food. Symptoms include abdominal pain and diarrhoea, but rarely vomiting. The illness lasts from 1 to 2 days; it may be fatal in elderly and sick people.

Kitchen control. (1) Consideration of cooking methods and size of joints.
(2) Rapid cooling to prevent multiplication of bacteria.
(3) Cold storage of food to prevent multiplication of bacteria.
(4) Separation of raw from cooked food to prevent cross-contamination.
(5) Kitchen hygiene; thorough cleaning of all surfaces and equipment, boards, cutting machines, cloths, and other tools after use. Regular removal of soil from vegetable store and preparation area and dust from cereals in dry goods store.

Clostridium botulinum

Clostridium botulinum is an uncommon cause of food poisoning.
Source. Found in soil, meat, and fish in some areas; the spores survive cooking and other processes. The organism grows without oxygen.

Cause of illness. A toxin produced by the bacilli as they grow in food.

Illness. Begins 12 to 96 hours after eating contaminated food. There is fatigue, headache, and dizziness. There may be diarrhoea at first but not later. The nervous system is attacked and vision and speech are disturbed. Death often occurs within 8 days, unless antitoxin is given soon after onset of illness.

Kitchen control. (1) Avoid home preservation of meat, poultry, game, and fish except by freezing.
(2) Avoid eating raw and fermented fish.
(3) Discourage smoking and curing of fish in certain areas of the world where the organism is common.
(4) Careful inspection of cans and contents.
(5) Care with curing solutions.

Bacillus cereus

Bacillus cereus may be a common cause of food poisoning.

Source. Found in soil, dust, cereals, spices, vegetables, dairy products, and many other foods; some spores may survive cooking. The organism grows best with oxygen.

Cause of illness. Probably a toxin produced by the bacilli as they grow in food.

Illness. (1) *Vomiting-type.* Begins 1 to 6 hours after eating contaminated food, usually a cooked rice dish. Symptoms include nausea and vomiting, and sometimes diarrhoea a little later. The illness lasts not more than 24 hours.

(2) *Diarrhoeal-type.* Begins 8 to 16 hours after eating contaminated food — a wide variety of foods have been incriminated. Symptoms include diarrhoea and abdominal pain, but rarely vomiting. The illness lasts not more than 24 hours.

Kitchen control. (1) Avoid cooking large bulks of rice and other cereals, and if possible cook in smaller quantities.

(2) After cooking, either keep hot (above 63 °C; 145·4 °F) or cool quickly and refrigerate (4 °C; 39·2 °F).

(3) Kitchen hygiene; thorough cleaning of all surfaces, equipment, and tools. Regular removal of cereal dust from storage and preparation areas.

Vibrio parahaemolyticus

Vibrio parahaemolyticus is a common cause of food poisoning in Japan; occasionally reported from other countries.

Source. Found in sea creatures and coastal waters.

Cause of illness. The living bacteria in raw and cooked sea foods such as fish, prawns, crabs and other shell-fish.

Illness. Begins approximately 15 hours after eating contaminated food. Symptoms include acute diarrhoea, abdominal pain, and vomiting with fever. The illness lasts for 2 to 5 days or more.

Kitchen control. (1) Care that cooking methods destroy the organisms.

(2) Separation of raw and cooked food to prevent cross-contamination from raw to cooked products by hands and other methods.

(3) Rapid cooling to prevent multiplication of vibrios.

(4) Cold storage of food to prevent multiplication.

(5) Kitchen hygiene; thorough cleaning of all surfaces, equipment and tools after use.

Escherichia coli

Escherichia coli may be a common cause of food poisoning (also thought to be associated with traveller's diarrhoea).

Source. Carried in the human and animal intestine and excreted in stools. Likely to come into the kitchen in the human and animal excreter and in raw foods of animal origin; for example, meat, poultry, and pet meat. The part played by insects, birds, vermin, and domestic pets is not yet known.

Cause of illness. The living bacteria in food.

Illness. Begins 18 to 48 hours after eating contaminated food (or drinking polluted water). Symptoms include pain and diarrhoea and sometimes pyrexia and vomiting. The illness lasts from 1 to 5 days.

Kitchen control. (1) Care of personal hygiene by washing hands before and after handling food — especially raw meat and poultry.
(2) Care of water used for washing salad and vegetables.
(3) Separation of raw from cooked food to prevent cross-contamination.
(4) Kitchen hygiene; thorough cleaning of all surfaces, equipment and tools after use.

How bacteria reach food — contamination (Session 4)

Foods which encourage growth of bacteria

Raw and cooked meat and poultry, foods with meat as a base, soups, stocks, gravies, 'made-up' meat dishes; also eggs, milk and milk products, fresh and imitation cream.

Foods and liquids which are safe

Water — filtered, chlorinated, and bottled mineral waters.
Milk — pasteurized, ultra heat treated, or sterilized.
Ice-cream — mix pasteurized, cooled rapidly and kept cold until frozen: manufacture controlled by regulations.
Whole egg mix in bulk — pasteurized.
Most canned foods (large cans of ham are not sterile and must be kept cold), bread, flour, jams and honey, pickles and acid fruits, fats.

How bacteria reach food

Raw foodstuffs. The organisms can be carried in the animal intestine and may be spread on to the carcass. Therefore meat and poultry can come into the kitchen already contaminated with salmonellae and clostridia. Contact between carcasses and between meats will spread bacteria, and food handlers may pick up food-poisoning organisms from the foods they handle.

Food handlers. Careless handling during transport, manufacture, preparation, and service may add and spread bacteria to food. Hands can transfer food-poisoning germs from raw to cooked foods. Personal bacteria from the nose, mouth, skin, stool, and hands can contaminate food.

Environment. (1) Unclean kitchen surfaces and equipment can harbour bacteria and so contaminate other foods; bacteria from raw meat and poultry can be passed to the cooked foods.
(2) Flies, rats, mice, cats, dogs, birds, and other animals and pets can carry bacteria to food.
(3) Dust and soil with dried organisms or excreta can contaminate food.

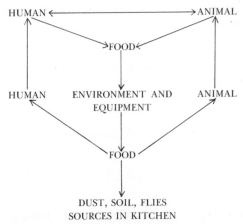

DUST, SOIL, FLIES
SOURCES IN KITCHEN
Food handlers and other living things
Foodstuffs, e.g., meat, poultry and sea foods
Surfaces and equipment

Chart   Cycle of infection and contamination

(1) Prevent spread of contamination in the kitchen:
   (a) separation of raw and cooked food to avoid cross-contamination;
   (b) care on part of food handler;
   (c) cleanliness of kitchen environment.
(2) Prevent bacteria already in food from growing and spreading.
   (a) cold storage facilities must be adequate and efficiently maintained;
   (b) avoid long storage in warmth — close time gaps between preparation and serving;
   (c) provide facilities for rapid cooling.

   } In the retail store and in the kitchen.

(3) Cook to destroy most bacteria (but not spores), with particular attention to:
   (a) careful preparation and adequate cooking. If possible, serve at once. If not:
   (b) keep hot; or
   (c) cool rapidly and store cold;
   (d) avoid recontamination.

Chart   Prevention of food poisoning

Personal hygiene (Session 5)

It is the food handler's responsibility to take scrupulous care that personal bacteria are not added to food. Bacteria from the following sources can be passed to food by the hands:

(1) Secretions from the nose, throat, and skin, dust, and dandruff from the hair.
(2) Excreta from the bowel.
(3) Other people's secretions and excreta.
(4) Liquor from raw meat and poultry and from other foods, powdered foods.
(5) Utensils and equipment.
(6) Cloths — tea towels, dishcloths, meat cloths.

   Personal hygiene can break the chain of infection in the following ways:

Hands

Hands should be kept in good condition, free from roughness:

(1) *Washing.* Thorough washing with hot water and soap is essential after using the WC, immediately before, during and after food preparation, after handling raw meat or poultry, and after using a handkerchief. Hand washing should not be done in kitchen sinks.

Wash-basins should be:

(a) in or adjacent to a toilet

(b) in the kitchen preparation area

they should be supplied with hot and cold water, a soap dispenser, nail brush and an individual method of hand drying. Hand cream with added disinfectant should be available.

Hands are NOT sterile after washing.

(2) *Nails.* Keep short and very clean.

(3) *Cuts and abrasions.* Cover with a non-porous dressing or Newskin and a fingerstall or glove if necessary. Persons with septic lesions should not work with food until the infection is completely healed.

(4) *Fingers.* Do not lick when tasting or serving food or separating sheets of paper.

Good habits

Take care not to touch the nose, hair or face; avoid sneezing and coughing near food; maintain a high standard of bodily cleanliness.

Smoking

Smoking must be prohibited in premises where there is uncovered food.

Handkerchiefs

Handkerchiefs carry infection from nasal secretions. They can contaminate hands and clothing and, indirectly, foods. Paper tissues are useful and easily disposable.

Hair

Hair should be well covered with cloth, net or paper caps.

Clothing

Clean overalls and aprons are essential; changed regularly and frequently.

Health

Illness, particularly diarrhoea, vomiting, throat and skin infections, should be reported. Severe septic conditions should also be reported.

Purchasing and storage (Session 6)

Purchasing

The standards of hygiene maintained by the supplier should be noted, such as cold and chilled storage, separation of raw and cooked foods, handling of unwrapped raw and cooked foods, cleanliness of premises and equipment, and type of equipment.

Perishable foods

Raw and cooked meat and poultry, milk, cream, and fish should be bought in quantities sufficient for one day only unless there is ample refrigerated space. Meat and fish should not be refrigerated for more than three days.

Non-perishable foods

Dry goods, preserves, and canned foods should be bought in reasonable quantities. Avoid overstocking; there is danger from vermin and deterioration where storage facilities are poor. These products should be stored in a dry, well ventilated storeroom.

Storage of perishable foods

The following foods must be refrigerated: raw and cooked meat and poultry, dairy products, fats, fish, jellies, and trifles.

Raw meat and poultry must be refrigerated on delivery. Store raw and cooked meat and poultry separately to prevent cross-contamination.

Refrigerator

The temperature should be 1–4 °C (33·8–39·2 °F), checked with a thermometer. Bacteria are not destroyed but those that are significant to man do not grow readily.
(1) Packing
    (a) do not overcrowd the shelves and prevent circulation of cold air;
    (b) use the coldest part for the most susceptible foods;
    (c) cover food to prevent loss of moisture and transfer of smells;
    (d) ensure that all containers are dry and clean; milk bottles should be wiped.
(2) Food must be cooled before refrigeration, otherwise the humidity and temperature will rise in the refrigerator.
(3) Open the door as little as possible and close it quickly.

(4) Defrost and clean weekly.
(5) Regular servicing is essential.

Storage of non-perishable food — storeroom and larder

(1) Keep cool, well ventilated, and dry.
(2) Proof against vermin and flies.
(3) Surfaces of shelves, walls, and floors should be easy to clean.
(4) Arrange packs in an orderly manner:
　　(a) food 18 inches (450 mm) from floor unless in mobile metal
　　　　bins;
　　(b) stock rotated — dated on delivery.

Deep freeze unit

The temperature, −18 °C (−0·4 °F), is much lower than the refrigerator. Use for long-term storage; food must be well protected. Defrost periodically; regular servicing is essential.
　Read and follow instruction on packs of frozen foods. Thawed food should not be refrozen.

Vegetables

Keep in cool storage, preferably screened from the kitchen to keep soil bacteria away from food preparation and cooking areas.

Rapid cooling larders

Rooms with extractor fans and adequate intake of air through filter pads to give moving air currents should be available. Impervious materials should be used for all surfaces.

Food preparation — cooking and serving (Session 7)

Remember

(1) Conditions which favour growth of bacteria must be avoided, especially the length of time food is left at temperatures suitable for bacterial growth.
(2) Foods which are sources of food-poisoning bacteria and those which encourage growth need special care; for example, raw and cooked meat, foods with meat as a base, made-up meat and fish dishes, sandwiches, raw and cooked poultry, sweets with lightly cooked or raw egg, milk products, and fresh and imitation cream. Keep pet foods out of commercial kitchens; in

the home, store apart from household foods and use separate utensils. Cook well.

(3) Particular care is needed in the summer months (June to October); bacteria grow readily in warm weather.

Kitchen practice

Personal hygiene

Bacteria from all sources can be passed to food by hands. Wash frequently before and during food preparation. In spite of washing, do not handle cooked foods.

Cooking techniques

Heat penetrates slowly and is lost slowly in traditional cooking methods; with microwaves heat penetration is rapid but not necessarily uniform. Infrared rays are used for browning only. Cooking does not always destroy bacterial spores or even bacteria, particularly in rolled and stuffed joints, poultry, large meat pies, and sausages.

(1) Avoid partial cooking.
(2) Cool cooked food rapidly and refrigerate within $1\frac{1}{2}$ hours. Cooling can be speeded up by:
    (a) provision of rapid cooling larders;
    (b) breaking up bulk and placing in shallow containers in a moving current of air;
    (c) limiting the size of joints to not more than 6 lb (2·7 kg).
(3) Avoid reheating food. If it is essential the food must be boiled or recooked thoroughly in all parts.
(4) Keep hot food hot and serve quickly.
(5)

Safe cooking methods	Less safe methods
Pressure cooking	Boiling
Grilling	Stewing
Frying	Braising
Roasting of small or thin joints	Roasting of large bulky and rolled joints

Kitchen equipment

Ease of cleaning is an important factor in selecting all surfaces, equipment, and utensils.

(1) Keep surfaces, equipment and utensils clean and in good repair; they should not be old or worn.

	Hazard	*Action in kitchen*
FOOD DELIVERY	Raw meat and poultry	Immediate cold storage Care in handling
PREPARATION	Hands	Wash thoroughly and frequently
	Surfaces, containers, equipment, kitchen tools, boards, and cloths.	(1) Clean thoroughly with hot water and detergent. (2) Heat and chemical disinfection; e.g. hypochlorite solutions (combined with compatible detergent or after washing)
COOKING PROCESSES	*Less safe methods* Boiling Stewing Braising	*Safer methods* Pressure cooking Roasting Grilling Frying
	Large bulks of food	Divide into small quantities
COOLING AFTER COOKING	Long slow cooling	Rapid cooling within $1\frac{1}{2}$ hours. Refrigerate
SERVING	Long storage in warmth	Serve freshly cooked. Keep hot
	Contamination from hands	Do not handle cooked food
	Contamination from equipment	Suitable equipment kept clean
COOKED MEAT		Serve hot and keep hot, above 63 °C (145·4 °F), or cool quickly, serve cold; keep cold, below 5 °C (41 °F),

KEEP TIME SHORT
(1) Between cooking and eating
(2) Between cooking and cold storage
(3) Between cold storage, serving and cold storage of remainder

Chart Food-borne infection in the kitchen and methods of control

(2) Slicing machines, mincing machines, and can openers require frequent and thorough cleaning; they must be easy to dismantle and reassemble. In-plant cleaning may be necessary for fixed parts of equipment.
(3) Use separate boards for raw meat, cooked meat, and vegetables. Choose appropriate materials for ease of cleaning; for example, synthetic and/or natural rubber hardened with plastic fillers, high molecular weight, medium-density polyethylene, or phenolic fibre laminates

For cleaning use hot water and an anionic or non-ionic detergent combined with or followed by a disinfecting agent such as hypochlorite.

Avoid cloths; use disposable paper instead.

Serving

(1) Avoid exposure of susceptible foods in warm atmosphere. Keep cold food cold, below 5 °C (41 °F).
(2) Avoid warm storage of cooked food. Keep hot food hot, above 63 °C (145·4 °F).
(3) Keep displayed food cold and under cover.
(4) Minimize handling of cooked foods; use suitable kitchen tools.
(5) Use new clean paper for wrapping and covering food.
(6) Keep animals and insects out of the kitchen.

Washing-up (Session 8)

Efficient washing-up is necessary to clean and remove bacteria from all dining room and kitchen equipment. The essential provisions are:

(1) Good layout of washing-up area.
(2) Correct temperature of wash and rinse water.
(3) A good detergent suited to the type of water.
(4) Orderly methods of work in rinsing, stacking, racking, and storage.

Preparation

The aim is to remove as much food waste as possible before washing.

(1) Cutlery should be rinsed.
(2) Tableware should be scraped and rinsed.
(3) Tableware should be stacked according to kind for hand-washing, or racked according to kind for machine washing. Cutlery should be racked with bowls and prongs uppermost.

Methods

Dish-washing machine. The large machines operate automatically and provide:

(1) A pre-rinse to soften and remove food particles. When using small machines this process must be done by hand.
(2) A detergent wash, temperature 60 °C (140 °F); an automatic dispenser can be fitted.
(3) A rinse at a higher temperature 82–87 °C (180–190 °F). Remove clean dry ware from racks and store.

Two- or three-sink method. Suitable for domestic and large-scale use.

(1) Rinse, scrape, or wipe off, with paper, food particles.
(2) Wash in hot water, 46–50 °C (115–122 °F) with measured detergent or detergent/disinfectant.
(3) Rinse in racks in hot water, 77–82 °C (170–180 °F) (maintained). Both wash and rinse waters should be changed as soon as they become soiled or lose temperature.
(4) Rack for drying before storage.

One-sink or bowl method. Inefficient since crockery and cutlery may still be contaminated with bacteria.

Drying

When the hot rinse is at the right temperature, dishes in racks will air-dry in 30 to 40 seconds.

Cloths

Dish cloths and tea towels harbour bacteria and require daily disinfection, preferably by heat. They can contaminate hands, equipment, and cutlery.

Paper

Disposable paper should be used in place of dish cloths and tea towels.

Storage

Covered storage should be provided.

Waste disposal (Session 9)

In kitchen

Food scraps on floors and surfaces encourage bacterial growth and attract vermin.

Waste can be collected:

(1) In pedal-operated bins which can be emptied regularly and washed out.
(2) In paper or plastic bags on pedal-operated stands. Bags can be sealed and put into dustbins, incinerated, or collected by the local council.

Outside kitchen

Provide sufficient waste bins or paper sacks to prevent over-spilling.

Bins with well-fitting lids should be placed in shade on a stand 250 to 300 mm (10 to 12 inches) high above a concrete area with drainage, which can be hosed down. Wet-strength paper or plastic bags with lids should be wall-mounted to give good ground clearance for hosing down.

Paper waste is usually kept separately.

Tins should be rinsed, both ends removed, and beaten flat.

Bins (other than for pig food) should be kept as dry as possible by wrapping wet waste.

Waste disposal unit

The unit is attached to the sink waste pipe. The ground refuse passes into the waste pipe and drain.

Vermin and fly control

Rats, mice, and insects

Rats, mice, flies, cockroaches, and ants are the most common pests.

If premises do not provide food and shelter, infestation is unlikely.

For extermination, seek expert advice from the local authority.

Flies, including bluebottles

Feet and hairs spread bacteria acquired from excreta and other waste.

Control. (1) Do not provide a breeding ground such as uncovered refuse bins. Bins (other than for pig food) should be kept as dry as possible.

(2) Destroy flies by spraying the refuse area in summer to prevent breeding.

(3) Prevent access to kitchen and food by fly-proof windows, doors, and ventilators. Cover food.

Cockroaches

Active at night. Attracted to warm places, such as heating pipes. Seal off crevices which provide hiding places.

Close-fitting lids prevent access to food.

Treat area with suitable insecticide.

Sprays and powders

Care must be taken to prevent pesticides reaching food, preparation surfaces and equipment.

Premises (Session 10)

The layout of a kitchen must be planned with the principles of hygiene in mind, with regard to the sources of food-poisoning bacteria (human, raw foods, environment) and also the importance of hot and cold storage.

Floors

Durable, non-slip surfaces should be impervious to moisture and easy to clean. Equipment preferably is raised or mobile to allow floor to be cleaned underneath.

Walls

Smooth, impervious walls should reduce condensation and be easy to clean. Junctions of wall and floor should be coved for easy cleaning, and equipment should be fixed away from the wall to allow for cleaning.

Ceiling

The surface which encloses the inside of the roof should be smooth, anticondensation, and easy to clean.

Lighting

Illumination must be good, both natural and artificial, particularly over work and preparation areas, sinks, and cooking equipment. Shadows should be avoided.

Ventilation

Good natural and mechanical ventilation is necessary to prevent a rise in temperature and humidity.

Sanitary convenience

Toilets must not open directly into food-preparation rooms. Foot-operated flushes are desirable.
   Wash-basins should be available:

(1) In or adjacent to the toilet.
(2) In kitchen preparation areas. They should be supplied with:
   (a) hot and cold water; foot operation is preferable;
   (b) soap dispenser, which must be kept in an hygienic condition;
   (c) nail brush with plastic or Nylon back and bristle (wood harbours bacteria), although not all plastics will withstand hot water disinfection;
   (d) an individual method of hand drying, such as paper towels, continuous roll towels or hot-air dryers. Roller towels (old type) should not be used because there is danger of cross-infection;
   (e) antiseptic hand cream should be available.

Cloakroom

Outer clothing must not be kept in the kitchen; adequate hanging space for the number of staff employed must be provided in a separate room.

Food preparation surfaces

Wood is unsuitable because it is too difficult to clean. The best materials are stainless steel or a laminate.

Chopping boards

Wood is still used but it constitutes a hazard. In recent years several new cutting surfaces have been developed, and their use in this country has become increasingly popular. The new proprietary boards or pads are usually made of (i) synthetic and/or natural rubber hardened with plastic fillers, (ii) high molecular weight, medium density polyethylene, or (iii) phenolic fibre laminates. Thorough cleaning is necessary after use, followed by a disinfectant or 'sanitizing' agent, such as hypochlorite. Separate 'boards' are required for raw meat, cooked meat, and vegetables.

Sinks

Stainless steel with sink and drainer in one piece is recommended. There should be separate sinks for vegetable preparation.

Refrigerator and/or cold room

Facilities for cold storage are essential for safety and they must be of adequate size. There should be adjustable metal shelves in the cold room.

Fixed equipment

The design must allow easy cleaning, and avoid ledges, nooks, and crannies; fix away from walls.

Facilities

Rapid cooling is most essential.

Summary of preventive care

(1) Do not touch with the hands:
   cooked, prepared food — particularly meats and poultry.
(2) Keep time short between:
   cooking and eating
   cooking and refrigeration
   refrigeration and eating.
(3) Watch environment:
   clean well and disinfect — by heat where possible
   separate raw and cooked foods.

Appendix B

Travelling and camping

Prevention of food poisoning abroad

Most people travelling in Europe, Asia, the Far East, South America, and Africa experience gastroenteritis. Some accept it as inevitable and include in their luggage prophylactic and treatment pills and medicines of various kinds.

It follows meals eaten on intercontinental ships, trains, and planes, in hotels, boarding houses, and private houses, and during camping from food bought in local shops and markets.

The patterns of illness follow those described in the previous chapters and all types of bacterial food poisoning are encountered.

There is much so-called diarrhoea or 'gippy-tummy' which is said to be due to a change of food, overeating, overdrinking, heat, rapid change of temperature, iced drinks, and so on. Unfortunately, the facilities for a full and competent investigation of these illnesses are rarely available. Bacteriological laboratories are not carried routinely, even in the largest and most important shipping lines, nor, of course, on trains.

The traveller on land accepts his predicament knowing that he will soon recover; when medical aid is summoned the doctor recognizes the well known symptoms and seeks to relieve the condition without taking time to study the cause.

While allowing for the fact that loose stools are likely to occur sometimes during a holiday overseas, due to strange foods and cooking habits, and to overdoses of aperients following constipation, the vast majority of incidents are likely to be microbial in origin. The principles underlying the provision of safe food are the same by whatever means one chooses to travel and in whatever country one chooses to be. The countries with hot climates will have greater problems than those in the north; refrigerators are a necessity where it is consistently hot, whereas temperate countries may require

328

refrigeration as a luxury instead of necessity. Particular food habits in certain countries may expose the inhabitants and the travellers to special hazards. For example, the eating of raw fermented fish dishes in the Arctic and Japan has given rise to botulism, and, in Japan, to much food poisoning caused by *Vibrio parahaemolyticus.* The recognition of this type of food poisoning is growing in countries other than Japan and the importance of cross-contamination from raw to cooked seafoods has been reported. On the other hand care in the processing of canned foods, a distaste for raw fish, and general habits of home preservation which include heat treatment of acid fruits but rarely meat, poultry, game, or vegetables have no doubt protected the population of the British Isles from botulism. This fatal food poisoning occurs frequently in countries where housewives cure and heat preserve many foods. The prevalence of *Clostridium perfringens* food poisoning in England and Wales may be related to the habit of precooking and warming meat dishes, a practice which became more prevalent in the war years due to shortage of meat.

Rules for travellers

(1) Avoid drinking or cleaning teeth in cold water unless it has been either personally chlorinated by the addition of proprietary brands of tablets or liquids containing sodium hypochlorite, or pumped through a filter such as the Berkefeld filter. Wines, bottled mineral water, and soft drinks are usually safe.

(2) Avoid using ice in drinks as the ice may be prepared from impure water.

(3) Foods to be avoided unless their safety is guaranteed:

    (a) ice-cream, as few countries outside the United Kingdom have legislation governing the method of production, which can be subject to many faults in hygiene;

    (b) milk, unless pasteurized or boiled, and any form of fermented milk;

    (c) soft and semi-hard cheese, particularly goats' milk cheese. In many Continental countries soft cheeses are prepared from pasteurized or boiled milk and are safe; this may or may not be stated on the packet. In the Middle or Far East such cheese is usually prepared from raw or inadequately heated milk and may be bacteriologically dangerous;

    (d) cooked or semi-preserved cold meats, sausages, and meat sandwiches, which may be subjected to much handling and poor storage in warm countries; with the exception of those products known to have a very high salt content;

    (e) meatballs, which are popular in some countries and may be prepared with meat cooked ahead of requirements and thus be a suitable medium for the growth *C. perfringens*;

(f) curried foods prepared some hours before required and kept warm pending consumption;

(g) shell-fish and other seafoods, particularly from warm countries;

(h) 'bar tasties', particularly those including prawns and other sea foods;

(i) cooked chickens, unless seen to be freshly cooked in a reputable shop;

(j) salads and dessert fruits, unless carefully washed in water containing hypochlorite.

Campers and travellers who buy their own picnic lunches can take care of their own purchases and preparation of food. Meals eaten out at night should be chosen with regard to freshly cooked meat, e.g. grills and fresh roasts.

Those who live in tents, caravans, and cars should take precautions with tea towels and dish cloths which should be washed thoroughly and stored in or wrung out in disinfectant after use. However, preferably disposable paper instead of cloths should be used. A similar precaution applies to flannels. Children are particularly susceptible to gastroenteritis and as a precaution against infection from hands each child should rinse the hands in disinfectant before and after meals. This practice should apply also to adults preparing food.

The floors of caravans should be washed over daily with disinfectant.

A list of names of suitable disinfectants should be available from the local health department.

It may be considered by some that the precautions are unnecessary and troublesome to carry out; the alternative may be at best a short attack of gastroenteritis or at the worst an attack of typhoid or paratyphoid fever or dysentery during the holiday or after returning home. However, holidays are expensive and it is a pity to lose days by illness.

It may be reasoned that similar precautions should be taken in the home country and this is true, but when crowds in holiday countries must be fed quickly and atmospheric temperatures are soaring, the hazards of mass feeding are magnified.

The World Health Organisation acts as the directing and co-ordinating authority on international health work. WHO fosters close working relationships between health administrations, air-lines, shipping companies, and other bodies associated with international traffic to ensure co-ordination for health protection in international traffic. World Health Organization (1974), International Health Regulations (1969), 2nd Annotated Edition, Geneva.

Canvas and hutted camps

Certain aspects of general food hygiene advice need emphasizing in canvas and hutted camps where large numbers of young people are accommodated in often primitive conditions. These notes are especially applicable to camps in the UK.

(1) *Water supply*

In urban areas mains water supplies are taken for granted and can be used with confidence. In the country, where a mains water supply is not available, great care must be taken. In some areas there may be a local piped supply from an artesian well or other source; the advice of the local health department should be taken before it is used for drinking or even for the preparation of food and dish-washing (unless boiled). If there is any doubt all drinking water must be boiled.

(2) *Milk supply*

In towns most milk is pasteurized or otherwise heat treated and therefore safe, unless it is mishandled after delivery. In the country, raw milk is often the only available supply and it may be contaminated with harmful organisms. Every effort should be made to obtain a supply of pasteurized, UHT, or sterilized milk. If none is available, all milk used cold must be boiled, preferably immediately on delivery. If raw milk is used for cooking, it must be regarded as contaminated and kept strictly away from other foods.

(3) *Food storage and preparation*

As refrigeration is seldom available, the separation of raw and cooked foods is very important. Raw meat, sausages, and poultry, in particular, must be kept in a separate place, together with utensils and implements used for handling them. Meat and poultry should be kept raw until just before cooking and served immediately afterwards. Reheating should' be discouraged and unused leftover gravy discarded. Late-comers should be given safe food, such as freshly cooked eggs or bacon, bread and cheese, or a freshly opened canned product. Cold foods such as sliced ham, meat pies or brawn should be obtained from a reliable source and eaten as quickly as possible after purchase.

If it is necessary to serve cold meat the day after it has been cooked, small joints should be used, preferably not more than 5 lb. They should be well roasted and after draining away the gravy, allowed to cool quickly in the open air or in an outside safe as a protection against marauders, and kept covered until sliced just before use. If the gravy is not needed for immediate use it should be discarded.

Custard, blancmange, and similar milk dishes should be prepared immediately before use and not kept afterwards.

(4) *Hand-washing*

Hand-washing is as important in camp as elsewhere. An ample supply of clean water, soap and either disposable towels or clean towels (changed twice daily) should be provided.

(5) *Dish-washing*

Crockery and cutlery should be washed clean, rinsed in hot water, and allowed to drain dry. Utensils and other implements used for raw meat or poultry should be cleaned and scalded with boiling water after use.

(6) *Foods to avoid*

Certain foods are best avoided in camps, such as duck or goose eggs and shellfish including shrimps and prawns.

(7) *Local health contacts*

It is a wise precaution to contact the local health department before camp. Advice can be taken about water and milk supplies and action in the event of food poisoning (or other large-scale illness). Many health authorities advise that samples of all meals should be kept for 24 hours so that if gastroenteritis occurs, relevant food samples are available for examination; specimen containers may also be supplied for samples of faeces or vomit. If there is any suggestion of food poisoning, a local doctor should be informed and he will pass on this information to the health department. On no account should a camp be closed and the campers dispersed without the knowledge of the health department. It is their responsibility not only to report and investigate outbreaks but also to trace and clear contaminated food, and people who may be excreting harmful organisms.

Appendix C

A questionnaire for food poisoning outbreaks

Area and place of outbreak...

Date and time suspected meal eaten ....

Number affected .... Number at risk ....

Incubation period ....

Symptoms..

Occupation and approximate age group...

Details of suspected meal..

....

Foods eaten by affected persons ....

....

Number of meal sittings and times ....

Methods of cooking (particularly meat and poultry) ....

....

Time and temperature of storage after cooking...................................

....

Staff illnesses..

....

General notes on facilities and environment ....

....

....

....

Appendix D

Suggested bibliography for further reading

Austwick, P. K. C. (1975) Mycotoxins. In *Chemicals in Food and Environment. British Medical Bulletin*, **31**, 222–229.

British Association for the Advancement of Science (1978) *Salmonella: The Food Poisoner.* Report by Study Group 1975–1977.

Bryan, F. L. (1972) *Guide for Investigating Foodborne Disease Outbreaks and Analyzing Surveillance Data.* Atlanta, Ga. U.S.A.: Department for Health, Education and Welfare, Center for Disease Control.

Bryan, F. L. (1975) *Diseases Transmitted by Foods (classification and summary),* Atlanta, Ga. U.S.A.: Department for Health, Education and Welfare, Center for Disease Control.

Catering Research Unit, The University, Leeds (1975) *A Manual on Cook-Freeze Catering.* Luton: Local Government Training Board.

Christie, A. B. and Christie, M. C. (1971) *Food Hygiene and Food Hazards.* London: Faber and Faber.

City of Canterbury (1976) *Thought for Food.* Canterbury: Environmental Health Department.

Department of Health and Social Security, Ministry of Agriculture, Fisheries and Food, and Welsh Office. *Food Hygiene Codes of Practice*:
No. 3 (1960) Hygiene in the Retail Fish Trade.
No. 4 (1960) The Hygienic Transport and Handling of Fish.
No. 5 (1961) Poultry Dressing and Packing.
No. 6 (1966) Hygiene in the Bakery Trade and Industry.
No. 7 (1967) Hygiene in the Operation of Coin Operated Food Vending machines.
No. 8 (1969) Hygiene in the Meat Trades.
No. 9 (1972) Hygiene in Microwave Cooking. London: HMSO.

Department of Health and Social Security and Ministry of Agriculture, Fisheries and Food (1969) *Joint Committee on the Use of Antibiotics in Animal Husbandry and Veterinary Medicine: Report.* Cmnd. 4190 London: HMSO.

Department of Health and Social Security, Scottish Home and Health Department, Northern Ireland Ministry of Health and Social Services Welsh Office (1972) *Clean Catering.* London: HMSO.

Department of Health and Social Security (1974) Health Service Catering Manual, Vol. II. *Hygiene in Catering Departments and Food Service Areas.*

Issued by: Catering and Dietetic Branch, DHSS, Alexander Fleming House, London SE1 6BY.

Edel, W. and Kampelmacher, E. H. (1969) *Salmonella* isolation in nine European laboratories using a standardized technique. *Bulletin of World Health Organization,* **41**, 297–306.

Edel, W. and Kampelmacher, E. H. (1974) Comparative studies on *Salmonella* isolations from feeds in ten laboratories. *Bulletin of World Health Organization,* **50**, 421–426.

FAO/WHO Expert Consultation (1975) *Microbiological Specifications for Foods.* GC/Microbiol/75/Report 1. Rome: Food and Agriculture Organization of the United Nations.

FAO/WHO Second Joint Expert Consultation (1977) *Microbiological Specifications for Foods.* EC/Microbiol/77/Report 2. Rome: Food and Agriculture Organization of the United Nations.

Frazier, W. C. (1967) *Food Microbiology.* New York: McGraw-Hill Book Co. Inc.

Graham-Rack, B. and Binsted, R. (1973) *Hygiene in Food Manufacturing and Handling.* London: Food Trade Press Ltd.

Harrigan, W. F. and McCance, M. E. (1976) *Laboratory Methods in Food and Dairy Microbiology.* New York: Academic Press.

Hobbs, B. C. (1976) Microbiological hazards of international trade. In *Microbiology in Agriculture, Fisheries and Food,* ed. Skinner, F. A. and Carr, J. G. Society for Applied Bacteriology Symposium Series No. 4. London: Academic Press.

Hobbs, B. C. and Christian, J. H. B. (1973) Ed. *The Microbiological Safety of Food.* London: Academic Press.

Hobbs, B. C. and Gilbert, R. J. (1975) Food hygiene and sanitation. In *Current Topics in Applied Microbiology,* ed. Tauro, P. and Varghese, T. M. International Bioscience Monographs 2. Hissar, Madras: International Bioscience Publishers.

Hobbs, B. C. and McLintock, J. S. (1973) *Hygienic Food Handling.* London: The St. John Ambulance Association.

International Commission on Microbiological Specifications for Foods (1978) *Microorganisms in Foods,* Vol. I, 2nd Edn. Their significance and methods of enumeration. Canada: University of Toronto Press.

International Commission on Microbiological Specifications for Foods (1974) *Microorganisms in Foods,* Vol. II. Sampling for microbiological analysis: Principles and specific applications. Canada: University of Toronto Press.

International Commission on Microbiological Specifications for Foods (1978) *Microorganisms in Foods,* Vol. III. Microbiol Ecology of Food. Canada: University of Toronto Press.

International Symposium on *Vibrio parahaemolyticus,* Tokyo (1973), ed. Fujino, T., Sakaguchi, G., Sakazaki, R. and Takeda, Y. Tokyo: Saikon Publishing Company.

Lawrie, R. A. (1974) *Meat Science.* Oxford: Pergamon Press Ltd.

Maurer, I. M. (1974) *Hospital Hygiene.* London: Edward Arnold.

Ministry of Agriculture, Fisheries and Food (1971) *Home Preservation of Fruit and Vegetables.* Bulletin 21. London: HMSO.

Parry, T. J. and Pawsey, R. K. (1973) *Principles of Microbiology for Students of Food Technology.* London: Hutchinson Educational, Ltd.

Public Health Laboratory Service Working Group, Skovgaard, N. and Nielsen, B. B. (1972) Salmonellas in pigs and animal feeding stuffs in England and Wales and in Denmark. *Journal of Hygiene, Cambridge,* **70,** 127–140.

Riemann, H. and Bryan, F. L. (1979) *Food-borne Infections and Intoxications,* 2nd Edn. New York: Academic Press.

Scottish Home and Health Department (1964) *The Aberdeen Typhoid Outbreak 1964: Report of the Departmental Committee of Enquiry.* (Chairman: Sir David Milne) Cmnd. 2542 Edinburgh: HMSO.

Society for Applied Bacteriology (1973) *Sampling — Microbiological Monitoring of Environments,* ed. Board, R. G. and Lovelock, D. W. Society for Applied Bacteriology, Technical Series 7. London: Academic Press.

Symposium: British Egg Marketing Board (1971) *Poultry Disease and World Economy,* ed. Gordon, R. F. and Freeman, B. M. Symposium No. 7. Edinburgh: Longmans.

Symposium: Association for the Study of Infectious Disease. Food. Is It Safe? (1974), ed. Medlock, J. M. *Postgraduate Medical Journal,* **50,** No. 588.

Vernon, E. (1977) Food poisoning and *Salmonella* infections in England and Wales, 1973–1975. *Public Health, London,* **91,** 225.

WHO (1977) *Food Hygiene in Catering Establishments, Legislation and Model Regulations.* Offset Publication No. 34. Geneva: World Health Organization.

WHO Expert Committee Convened in Cooperation with FAO (1974) *Fish and Shellfish Hygiene. Technical Report Series,* No. 550. Geneva: World Health Organization.

WHO Expert Committee with the Participation of FAO (1976) *Microbiological Aspects of Food Hygiene. Technical Report Series,* No. 598. Geneva: World Health Organization.

WHO Report on a Working Group (1977) *Aviation Catering.* Copenhagen: World Health Organization.

WHO Study Group on Food-borne Disease (1974) *Methods of Sampling and Examination of Surveillance Programmes. Technical Report Series,* No. 543. Geneva: World Health Organization.

Williams, L. P. and Hobbs, B. C. (1975) Enterobacteriaceae Infections. In *Diseases Transmitted from Animals to Man,* ed. Hubbert, W. T., McCulloch, W. T. and Schnurrenberger, P. R. 6th Edn. Springfield, Illinois: Charles C Thomas, Publisher.

Wilson, G. S. and Miles, A. A. (1975) *Principles of Bacteriology, Virology and Immunity,* 6th Edn., Volumes 1 and 2. London: Edward Arnold.

Wood, P. C. (1976) *Guide to Shellfish Hygiene.* WHO Offset Publication, No. 31. Geneva: World Health Organization.

Index

Abattoir. *See* Slaughterhouse
Acids, effect on bacteria of, 23, 51, 72–3
Aerobic and anaerobic sporing bacilli, 20–1, 27–9
Aeromonas hydrophila, 12, 31
  poisoning, 31
Aerosol sprays, from water closets, 39, 152
Aflatoxin, 32, 184
Agar, properties of, 18
Agricultural Research Council Laboratories, 291
Agriculture (Miscellaneous Provisions) Act 1972, 280
Aircraft, food poisoning on, 93, 117
Albumen, 64
  crystalline, 105
  pan-dried, 105
Alkaloid poisoning, 4
Alpha-amylase
  heat destruction in eggs of, 63–4
  test, for pasteurized egg, 64, 76, 275
Alpha-chloralose, as mouse poison, 256
Ampholyte disinfectants, properties of, 219
Animal reservoirs of infection, 40 *et seq*
Animals
  as salmonella excreters, 95 *et seq*
  calves
    Salmonella typhimurium in, 95–7

Animals — *contd.*
  food poisoning associated with, 95–6
  cats and dogs
    Food Hygiene Regulations for, 48
    salmonellae in, 47–8
  cattle, 131–3
    salmonellae in, 48
    tuberculin testing of, 131
    tuberculosis in, 131
  chickens. *See* Poultry
  ducks. *See* Poultry
  feeding meals for, 10, 11, 41, 46, 62, 96, 97, 162, 281
    antibiotics in, 43, 123, 162, 281–2
    legislation for, 123, 281–2
    salmonellae in, 98, 122
  horses, 43–4
    meat as pet food, 44
  kangaroos, 44
  mice. *See* Animals, rats and mice
  pigs, salmonellae in, 48–9,123
  rats and mice, 142
    baits for, 254–6
    block control of, 251–2
    control of, 252–3, 324
    destruction of, 254–6
    poison containing salmonellae for, 47
    poisons for, 254–6
    resistance to warfarin, 255
    rodent-proofing of buildings, 252–3

337